Basic
Topics in
Mathematics

Prentice-Hall, Inc.   Englewood Cliffs, New Jersey

John Riner

Associate Professor of Mathematics   The Ohio State University

Basic
Topics in
Mathematics

Prentice-Hall Mathematics Series

Dr. Albert A. Bennett, editor

To L.A.R.

PRENTICE-HALL INTERNATIONAL, INC. *London*
PRENTICE-HALL OF AUSTRALIA, PTY., LTD. *Sydney*
PRENTICE-HALL OF CANADA, LTD. *Toronto*
PRENTICE-HALL FRANCE, S.A.R.L. *Paris*
PRENTICE-HALL OF INDIA PRIVATE LIMITED *New Delhi*
PRENTICE-HALL OF JAPAN, INC. *Tokyo*
PRENTICE-HALL DE MEXICO, S.A. *Mexico City*

Preface

Mathematics has long been a traditional subject in various academic programs. In the recent past it had been excluded from academic programs, on both the college and high school levels, where the applications were few or of little interest. However, for various reasons, mathematics is now being required in more programs than ever before. One obvious reason is that many applications of the subject have been discovered in fields that had, a few years ago, little use for mathematics.

Now mathematics itself has changed greatly over recent years and most people, even well-educated people, have little understanding of its nature. If a person is to use the subject as a tool or if a person is required to study it as a cultural course, he should be somewhat aware of its nature. It is unfortunate that an awareness of the nature of mathematics cannot be given quickly to an interested person. It is only by doing mathematics that one can gain insight in mathematics. We set, then, as our primary goal in this text that of imparting to the reader an awareness of the nature of mathematics. We will do this by giving the reader a chance to do a little mathematics.

The high school mathematics programs being implemented now through-out the country are producing students with a non-traditional mathematical background. Programs such as the SMSG program, the Illinois program, and those being developed by many individual school systems must be accom-modated. It is felt that the treatment of topics in this text is not inconsistent with these programs. On the other hand, the treatment is such that the traditionally-trained student is not particularly handicapped.

It should be pointed out that this book is not a survey text. No claim for comprehensiveness is made and no emphasis will be put on the historical development of the subject. The subject matter fits into two major categories, namely, *functions* and *algebra* from an axiomatic point of view. An attempt is made to relate every topic treated, in a reasonable manner, to these central concepts. It is hoped that, by so doing, a unity is given to the diverse subjects presented.

Many persons have been of help in the development of this text and I would like to thank all of them. In particular, Dr. Richard Barnes and Dr. William Coppage, who have taught this material to large groups of students, have helped with their comments and suggestions. Mrs. Jan Willhardt and Mrs. Lois Graber who helped in the preparation of the manu-script merit sincere thanks for their patience and general helpfulness. Professor Frank J. McMackin, who reviewed the manuscript at an early stage, made many valuable suggestions for the improvement of the material.

Prentice-Hall has been extremely cooperative and has made the production of this book as simple as possible. Miss Lois Fox, who has frequently been my contact point with the company, has especially contributed to the simplification of our joint effort.

JOHN RINER

Contents

Algebra 30

2

Graphs 62

3

Vector Spaces 83

4

Linear Programming 121

Matrix Theory 133

Trigonometry 173

Limits   211

8

Applications of the Limit Concept   240

9

Answers to Exercises   252

Index   275

Index of Symbols   279

Basic
Topics in
Mathematics

Sets
and
Functions

Comment. In this chapter we introduce concepts basic to all that we do in this text. In order to illustrate these, it is convenient to use examples from the set of real numbers. Later we shall develop certain elementary properties of the real numbers. Here we assume that the reader is familiar with many of these properties. To be a little more exact, we expect that the reader is aware that real numbers can be represented as points on a line. The reader should know that $0, \pm 1$, ± 2, etc., are called *integers*, that numbers that can be represented as a quotient a/b of two integers (for example, $-97/222$), where $b \neq 0$, are rational numbers, and that there are numbers that are not rational (for example, $\sqrt{2}, \pi$). The reader also should be aware that for any two real numbers a and b, $a < b$, there are "many" numbers between a and b. For example,

$$a < \frac{a+b}{2} < b \quad \text{and} \quad a < \frac{1}{2}\left(\frac{a+b}{2} + b\right) < b.$$

1

Other properties of real numbers that we require to illustrate the basic concepts of this chapter will be assumed when we need them, even though we have not yet developed these properties.

1.1 Preliminary Concepts

In everyday life we frequently use the word "set" or a synonym. For instance, we speak of a set of dishes, a deck of cards, a collection of paintings. Intuitively, set is thought of as a collection of objects. No one has been able to give a definition of set that is free from certain troubles.

Our starting point, then, is the concept of set and that is undefined. The objects making up a set will be called *elements* or *points* of the set. The fact that the concept of set is not defined does not present an unusual situation. For example, when the reader studied geometry, the notion of point was probably undefined although the reader had some intuitive idea of the nature of point. One might note that every definition of a given word is in terms of other words. One could define each of these in other terms, but somewhere the process should stop.

In our study of mathematics we have logic as our basic tool. Primarily we deal with statements of the form: if p then q, where p and q are themselves statements. Theorems that we prove are statements of this form and proving them is the process of establishing their truth.

Time might well be taken to give a formal introduction to logic. It is felt, however, that one can probably gain more by seeing valid proofs than by studying their nature. For that reason we do not treat logic* formally here.

As a matter of notation we will use capital letters $A, B, \ldots, Z$ to denote sets and small letters, $a, b, \ldots, z$ to denote elements of sets. We will frequently have occasion to use the phrase: object x is an element of the set A. (This, again, is an undefined relationship between elements of sets and sets.) The frequency of occurrence of this phrase warrants the introduction of a shorthand way of writing it. So the symbol $x \in A$ will be used to say that x is a point in the set A. To negate the statement that $x \in A$, we write $x \notin A$ and read, "Object x is not an element of set A." We will frequently read the symbol $x \in A$ as "x belongs to A" rather than, "Object x is an element of set A." Similarly we would read $x \notin A$ as "x does not belong to A."

We will want to use the word "set" in a little more exact sense. To do this we make the following definition:

Definition 1.1. A *well-defined set* is a set and a property that allows us to say whether or not any given object is an element of the set. From now on when we use the word "set," we will mean *well-defined set*.

* For a treatment of logic see Chapter 1, J. G. Kemeny, J. L. Snell, and G. L. Thompson, *Introduction to Finite Mathematics* (Englewood Cliffs, N. J.: Prentice-Hall, Inc., 1957).

Let us now look at some examples of sets:

EXAMPLE 1. The collection of all living men who are or have been President of the United States is a (well-defined) set.

EXAMPLE 2. The set of all positive integers less than 12 is also an example of a (well-defined) set.

EXAMPLE 3. The collection of all integers is a set.

EXAMPLE 4. The set of all points on a given circle is a well-defined set.

A set that is not well-defined, and thus not what we will call a set, is the collection of all persons now living who will be President of the United States after 1961. Here we cannot say that any particular person is or is not a member of that set.

Frequently it is awkward to describe a particular set. We have a notation that helps us write an exact description of a set. In brief form, if A is the set of objects x satisfying property p, we write:

$$A = \{x \mid p\} .$$

As indicated, $\{\quad\}$ is read, "the set of," and $\mid$ is read, "such that." For example,

$$A = \{x \mid x \text{ is an integer and } x^2 \geq 16\}$$

means that A is the set of all integers whose squares are greater than or equal to 16. Sometimes when dealing with a finite set we use the braces but enter or indicate the elements by inserting them in the braces. For example $\{1, 2, 3, \ldots, 20\}$ would indicate the set of positive integers less than 21.

The notation just introduced is very convenient in making certain other definitions. Remember that we can do without this notation but we will be able to express sets concisely and precisely with it.

Exercise 1.1

1. Express the following statements in English. Your answers should be complete sentences.

  (a) $x \in A$.

  (b) Either $x \in A$ or $x \in B$.

  (c) $y \in B$.

  (d) $y \in \{x \mid x \text{ is an integer and } x > 0\} .$

  (e) $y \in \{x \mid P\} .$ (Here P is a property that holds for each x.)

2. Translate the following sentences into mathematical notation. Use a symbol instead of a word whenever possible.

   (a) z belongs to C.

   (b)   The element x is a point in the set B.

   (c) y belongs to the set of x such that x is a positive integer. (*Hint:* x is a positive integer means that x is an integer and x is greater than 0.)

3. Let $E = \{1, 2, 4, 5\}$ and let $F = \{2, 3, 5, 6\}$.   Determine whether the following statements are true or false.

   (a) $1 \in E$.   (b) $1 \in F$.

   (c) $3 \in E$.   (d) $3 \in F$.

   (e) $2 \in E$.   (f) $2 \in F$.

   (g)   Every element of E is an element of F.

   (h)   Every element of F is an element of E.

   (i)   Some elements of E are not elements of F.

   (j)   Some elements of F are not elements of E.

4. Write in the above notation the indicated sets:

   (a)   The set of all integers between 1 and 10. (Don't include 1 and 10.)

   (b)   The set of all integers whose squares are less than 16.

   (c)   The set of all integers greater than 9.

   (d)   The set of all integers less than 0.

   (e)   The set of all integers between 0 and 101.

   (f)   The set of all integers which, when added to 4, give a sum of 7.

   (g)   The set of all integers whose squares are greater than 9.

   (h)   The set of all integers whose squares are greater than 9 but less than 50.

   (i)   The set of all integers whose cubes are less than 8 and greater than 125.

   (j)   The set of all teachers in Ohio now.

5. Write some sets of your own in the notation $\{x \mid p\}$.

1.2   More Notation and Definitions

Certain other phrases occur frequently enough to warrant introducing a notation for them. We shall not abbreviate as completely as we might, but we will use some rather standard notation. The phrase "there exists" is written ∃. The phrase "p implies q" or "if p then q," where p and q are statements, is written $p \Rightarrow q$. If the statements p and q are equivalent, that is, if $p \Rightarrow q$ and $q \Rightarrow p$, we write $p \Leftrightarrow q$. We read $p \Leftrightarrow q$ as p if and only if q. When $p \Rightarrow q$ we say that q is a necessary condition for p and that p is a sufficient condition for q. We also say that p only if q. For example, if p is the statement that m is an integer whose square does not exceed 4 (m is an integer and $m^2 \leq 4$) and if q is the statement that m is either $-2, -1, 0, 1$, or 2 then $p \Leftrightarrow q$.

Using this notation, we are ready now to make some definitions.

Definition 1.2. Let A and B be sets. *A is a subset of B* if and only if every element of A is an element of B. To denote that A is a subset of B we write $A \subset B$ or $B \supset A$.

In giving this definition, we made no use of the notation just introduced. In the future, we will use it as a matter of course. In order to see its use we restate Definition 1.2, this time making use of the notation available.

Definition 1.2. $(A \subset B) \Leftrightarrow (x \in A \Rightarrow x \in B)$.

The parentheses are inserted to group the statements properly.

Exercise

Translate into a sentence the restated Definition 1.2.

Remark. Let A be any set. Note that $x \in A \Rightarrow x \in A$. Thus for any set A, $A \subset A$.

Definition 1.3. Let A and B be sets. $A = B$ (A equals B) $\Leftrightarrow A \subset B$ and $B \subset A$.

In words, A equals B if and only if A is a subset of B and B is a subset of A.

Definition 1.4. A is a *proper subset* of $B \Leftrightarrow A \subset B$ but $A \neq B$.

This means of course that every element of A is an element of B but that B has at least one element that is not in A.

Before we go further, let us look at some examples:

EXAMPLE. Let N be the set of positive integers. ($N = \{1, 2, 3, \ldots\}$.) Let $A = \{1, 3, 5, 7\}$. Then $A \subset N$. Let $E = \{2n \mid n \in N\}$. That is, let E be the set of even positive integers. ($E = \{2, 4, 6, \ldots\}$.) Then $E \subset N$. On the other hand let $B = \{-1, 1, 2\}$. Then B is not a subset of N because there is one element in B which is not in N. In this situation, we write $B \not\subset N$.

Exercise 1.2

1. Translate into English:
   (a) $A \subset B$.
   (b) $C \subset D$.
   (c) $x \in A \Rightarrow x \in C$.
   (d) $(A \subset B) \Leftrightarrow (x \in A \Rightarrow x \in B)$.
   (e) $(B \subset C) \Leftrightarrow (x \in B \Rightarrow x \in C)$.

2. Translate into mathematical notation:
   (a) A is a subset of B.
   (b) B is a subset of A.
   (c) x belongs to A implies x belongs to B.
   (d) Every element of A is an element of B.
   (e) B is a subset of C if and only if every element of B is an element of C.

3. Let $E = \{1, 2, 4, 5\}$; $F = \{2, 3, 5, 6\}$; $G = \{2, 5\}$; $H = \{1, 2, 3, 4, 5, 6\}$.
   (a) Is every element of G an element of E?
   (b) Consequently, is G a subset of E?
   (c) Is every element of F an element of G?
   (d) Consequently, is F a subset of G?
   (e) Is E a subset of H? Why?
   (f) Is H a subset of F? Why?

4. (a) Suppose every element of C is an element of D. How are C and D related?
   (b) Suppose some elements (one or more) of C are not elements of D. How are C and D related?
   (c) Suppose C is a subset of D and D is a subset of C. How are C and D related?
   (d) Suppose C is a subset of D and $x \in C$. What other statement can we make about x?
   (e) Suppose C is a subset of D and $y \in D$. Can one necessarily make some other statement about y?

5. (a) Construct 5 examples of sets A and B so that $A \subset B$.
   (b) Let $A = \{1, 2, 3, 4\}$. Construct all subsets of A.

1.3 Cartesian Products

In this section, we turn our attention to a rather simple concept that many readers will have encountered earlier in specialized form. Although it is simple, it gives us a tool for making clear certain concepts that are not so simple. It generalizes the consideration of the euclidean plane as ordered pairs of real numbers. If the reader were asked to plot the point with coordinates (2, 5), he probably could do so. And in fact given any pair (a, b) of real numbers, he could plot the point in a plane which has (a, b) as coordinates. If all such "points" were plotted, the resulting "graph" would be the euclidean plane. It is this sort of thing that is generalized by Definition 1.5:

Definition 1.5. Let A and B be sets. The *Cartesian product of A and B*, denoted by $A \times B$, is defined by:

$$A \times B = \{(x, y) \mid x \in A, y \in B\} .$$

(We usually read the symbol $A \times B$ as "A cross B.")

Here note that the elements in $A \times B$ are pairs, the first entry taken out of A, the second out of B. $A \times B$ is the set of all such pairs. Note too that there is nothing in this definition that precludes the possibility that $A = B$.

EXAMPLE. Let $A = \{a, b, c\}$, $B = \{0, 1, 2, 3\}$. Then

$$A \times B = \{(a, 0), (a, 1), (a, 2), (a, 3), (b, 0), (b, 1), (b, 2),$$
$$(b, 3), (c, 0), (c, 1), (c, 2), (c, 3)\} .$$

$$A \times A = \{(a, a), (a, b), (a, c), (b, a), (b, b),$$
$$(b, c), (c, a), (c, b), (c, c)\} .$$

As an immediate application of this concept, we consider the idea of sets having the "same number of elements." If one were asked whether two sets had the same number of elements, the answer could be obtained by simply counting the elements if the sets were finite. If even one set were finite, by counting this set first and by counting the elements in the second set until the number of elements in the first set was passed by, one could still answer the question. If counting were not possible; i.e., if there were more than a finite number of elements in each of the sets, the answer to our question might not be obtainable.

We introduce the following definition to help us in situations of this sort. Although counting is not possible, what we essentially do is to pair up the elements in one set with those in the other.

Definition 1.6. Let A and B be sets. *A and B are in one-to-one (1–1) correspondence* if and only if ∃ a subset K of $A \times B$ such that every element of A and every element of B appear once and only once as first and second entries respectively in a pair in K.

EXAMPLE 1. Consider A and B in Definition 1.6. We attempt to find a subset K of $A \times B$ with the desired property. We can select $(a, 0)$, $(b, 1)$, $(c, 2)$. We need a pair with 3 in the second position. But if we have such a pair it will be either $(a, 3)$, $(b, 3)$ or $(c, 3)$. If we add any of these, we will have an element in A appearing more than once in pairs in K. We can generalize this to say that it is impossible to find a subset K of $A \times B$ with the property listed in the definition.

EXAMPLE 2. Let N be the set of positive integers and let E be the set of even positive integers. N and E are in 1–1 correspondence because the set $K \subset N \times E$ defined by

$$K = \{(n, 2n) \mid n \in N\}$$

has the desired property.

To see this a bit more clearly, let us write out a number of elements in K.

$$K = \{(1, 2), (2, 4), (3, 6), (4, 8), \ldots\} .$$

Continuing in this way, every element in N appears once and only once as a first entry in a pair in K whereas every number in E appears exactly once as a second entry in a pair in K. This is an example of a proper subset of a set being in 1–1 correspondence with the set. (If the sets involved are finite this cannot happen. The existence of a proper subset with this property in fact characterizes infinite sets.)

We might note at this point that when finite sets are in 1–1 correspondence they have the same (finite) number of elements. In fact, if two finite sets A and B have the same number of elements, it is easy to see they are in 1–1 correspondence. For instance, simply pair the elements counted first in each set, second in each set, etc. This subset of $A \times B$ will have the desired property.

Exercise 1.3

1. Let $A = \{a, b, c, d\}$, $B = \{0, 1\}$. Find $A \times B$, $B \times A$, $A \times A$, and $B \times B$.

2. Let $A = \{a, b, c, d\}$, $B = \{1, 2, 3, 4\}$.

   (a) One can construct a $1-1$ correspondence K' between A and B by the following scheme:

$$A = \{a\ b\ c\ d\}$$
$$\updownarrow\ \updownarrow\ \updownarrow\ \updownarrow$$
$$B = \{1\ 2\ 3\ 4\}$$

   (Here the arrows, $\updownarrow$, indicate that the elements on each end are to be paired with each other.)

   Since $a \leftrightarrow 1$, we will include $(a, 1)$ in the set K', etc. By this scheme, what are the members of K'?

   (b) Now use the scheme

$$A = \{\ a\ b\ c\ d\ \}$$
$$\updownarrow\ \updownarrow\ \updownarrow\ \updownarrow$$
$$B = \{\ 4\ 3\ 2\ 1\ \}$$

   Construct the set K'' which results.

(c)   How many times does a member of A appear as a first entry in K' above? In K''?

How many times does a member of B appear as a second entry of K'? Of K''?

Does K' satisfy the definition for a 1–1 correspondence between A and B? Does K''?

(d)   One can use a similar scheme for infinite sets. Let $N =$ the set of positive integers and let N_E be the set of even positive integers:

$$N = \{ 1 \ 2 \ 3 \ \ldots \ n \ \ldots \}$$
$$\updownarrow \ \updownarrow \ \updownarrow \qquad \updownarrow$$
$$N_E = \{ 2 \ 4 \ 6 \ \ldots 2n \ldots \}$$

The set K_0 resulting from this scheme is $\{(n, \ \underline{?} \ ) \mid n \in N\}$. Show that N and N_E are in 1–1 correspondence by showing that K_0 has the desired properties.

(e)   Let $N_{odd} = \{2n - 1 \mid n \in N\}$ be the set of odd positive integers. Show that N and N_{odd} are in 1–1 correspondence.

3. (a)   Show that $A = \{1, 2, 3, 4\}$ and $B = \{a, b, c, d, e\}$ are not in 1–1 correspondence.

(b)   Show that, if N is the set of positive integers and if

$$M = \{10, 11, 12, \ldots\} = \{n \in N \mid n \geq 10\},$$

then M and N are in 1–1 correspondence.

For the next exercise we need

Definition 1.7.   Let A and B be sets. *A and B are equivalent* if and only if A and B are in 1–1 correspondence.

4. Let $A \sim B$ denote that A is equivalent to B. Prove:

(a) $A \sim A$ for any set A.

(b) $A \sim B \Rightarrow B \sim A$.

(c) $A \sim B,\ B \sim C \Rightarrow A \sim C$.

5. (a)   Let U denote the set of negative integers and N denote (as before) the set of positive integers. Show that $U \sim N$.

(b)   If I denotes the set of integers, show that $N \sim I$.

1.4   Union and Intersection

When we considered sets A and B and formed their Cartesian product $A \times B$, we were, in a way, "combining" A and B to form a new set. The set $A \times B$ has as elements pairs with first entry from A and second entry from B.

In this section, we look at other ways of "combining" sets to get new sets. But this time the new sets will have elements that are not so different.

The idea of taking the elements in each of two sets to form a new set is not unusual; in fact, this is what we do in forming the "union" of two sets.

Definition 1.8. Let A and B be sets. We define the *union* $A \cup B$ *of* A *and* B by

$$A \cup B = \{x \mid \text{either } x \in A \text{ or } x \in B\} \ .$$

(If $x \in A$ and $x \in B$, it is true that $x \in A$ and therefore $x \in A \cup B$.)

The symbol $A \cup B$ is read, "A union B" as well as "the union of A and B."

EXAMPLE 1. Let $A = \{1, 2, 3\}$, $B = \{4, 5, 6\}$. Then

$$A \cup B = \{1, 2, 3, 4, 5, 6\} \ .$$

EXAMPLE 2. Let $A = \{1, 2, 3\}$, $C = \{2, 3, 4, 5\}$. Then

$$A \cup C = \{1, 2, 3, 4, 5\} \ .$$

In this example notice that 2 and 3 are in both sets. By the remark following the definition, both 2 and 3 are in $A \cup C$. Further observe that in indicating the elements of $A \cup C$ we write 2 and 3 only once. We might note that, in indicating the elements of a given set, we could, if we desired, write a given element more than once. Usually this is not done.

EXAMPLE 3. Let

$$K = \{n \mid n \text{ is an integer and } n \geq 9\} \ ,$$

and

$$L = \{n \mid n \text{ is an integer and } n \geq 2\} \ .$$

Then

$$K \cup L = L \ .$$

Can you say why?

In order to consider further examples, we introduce the following notation. Here we use our assumption that the reader has some notion of real numbers. As pointed out, this need not be a solid knowledge; later, we will consider the real numbers more rigorously.

Definition 1.9. Let a and b be real numbers such that $a < b$. We define the *open interval* (a, b) by:

$$(a, b) = \{x \mid x \text{ is a real number and } a < x < b\} \ .$$

(The notation used here is a common one, but it should be noted that (a, b) is also used to denote the coordinates of a point in a plane on which a coordinate system has been introduced. The context will usually indicate the meaning of the symbol (a, b); if there is danger of confusion, the notation will be modified by a phrase explaining it. For example, we would speak of the interval (a, b), or of the point (a, b), if the meaning is not clear from the immediate context.)

We define the *closed interval* $[a, b]$ by

$$[a, b] = \{x \mid x \text{ is a real number and } a \leq x \leq b\} \,.$$

In the same way, the *half-open intervals* or *half-closed intervals* $(a, b]$ and $[a, b)$ are defined by:

$$(a, b] = \{x \mid x \text{ is a real number and } a < x \leq b\} \,,$$

$$[a, b) = \{x \mid x \text{ is a real number and } a \leq x < b\} \,.$$

Recalling that the real numbers can be identified with points on a line, we can represent geometrically the intervals just defined as indicated below. We will indicate the end points of intervals by small circles, ∘, and will fill in the circle if the end point is to be included in the interval.

Thus, as examples, in Fig. 1.1, (a) represents $[2, 4)$ and (b) represents $(-1, 2)$.

Figure 1.1

So, for further examples of unions of two sets consider:

$$[1, 2] \cup [2, 4] = [1, 4] \,, \ [1, 4] \cup [2, 7) = [1, 7) \,.$$

Geometrically we see that $[1, 4] \cup [2, 7) = [1, 7)$ from Fig. 1.2:

Figure 1.2

As further examples, we can consider sets of points (Fig 1.3) in a plane inside and on simple closed curves. Let A and B be sets indicated. We shade $A \cup B$.

Another way of combining two sets to get a new set is by considering the set of elements common to both. It isn't unnatural to call this set the *inter-section* of the two sets.

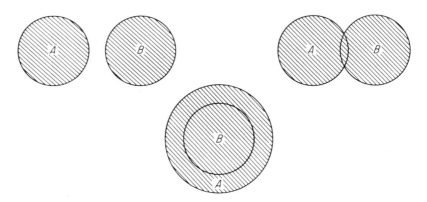

Figure 1.3

Definition 1.10. Let A and B be sets. We define the *intersection* $A \cap B$ of A *and* B by

$$A \cap B = \{x \mid x \in A \quad \text{and} \quad x \in B\} .$$

EXAMPLE 1. Let $A = \{1, 2, 3\}$, $B = \{2, 4, 6\}$.

$$A \cap B = \{2\} .$$

EXAMPLE 2. Let

$$A = \{n \mid n \text{ is an integer and } n \leq 9\} ,$$

and

$$B = \{k \mid k \text{ is an integer and } k \geq 6\} .$$

Then

$$A \cap B = \{6, 7, 8, 9\} .$$

EXAMPLE 3. $[1, 4] \cap [3, 5] = [3, 4]$.

EXAMPLE 4. $[1, 5) \cap [2, 7) = [2, 5)$.

Again, geometrically, we verify that $[1, 5) \cap [2, 7) = [2, 5)$. Consideration of this graph of the intervals (Fig. 1.4) should convince one that the intersection of the two given intervals is indeed $[2, 5)$.

Now we ask, what is $[1, 2] \cap [3, 4]$? Clearly these sets have no points in common. In order to be able to handle this situation we need the following definition.

Figure 1.4

Definition 1.11. Let $\varnothing$ represent the set with no elements. It will be called the *null set* or the *empty set* or the *void set*.

With this device we can now say that

$$[1, 2] \cap [3, 4] = \varnothing .$$

Exercise 1.4

1. (a) Let $A = \{1, 3, 5\}$, $B = \{3, 5, 7, 8\}$. Find $A \cup B$ and $A \cap B$.
   (b) Let $A = \{1, 3, 5\}$, $B = \{2, 4, 6, 8\}$. Find $A \cup B$ and $A \cap B$.
   (c) Find $[1, 3] \cup [2, 5]$, $[1, 3] \cap [2, 5]$.
   (d) Find $[1, 2) \cup [2, 4)$, $[1, 2) \cap [2, 4)$.

2. In Fig. 1.5 shade $A \cap B$.

3. The following implications follow from the definitions of $A \cap B$ and $A \cup B$. Complete
   (a) $x \in (A \cap B) \Rightarrow$
   (b) $(x \in A \quad \text{or} \quad x \in B) \Rightarrow$
   (c) $(x \in A \quad \text{and} \quad x \in B) \Rightarrow$
   (d) $x \in (A \cup B) \Rightarrow$

4. Let
   $$E = \{1, 2, 4, 5\} , F = \{2, 3, 5, 6\} , G = \{4, 5, 6, 7\} .$$
   (a) Find $E \cup F$. How is E related to $E \cup F$?
   (b) Find $E \cap F$. How is $E \cap F$ related to E? to F? to $E \cup F$?
   (c) (1) List $E \cup F$; (2) List G; (3) "Union" the results of (1) and (2) to get $(E \cup F) \cup G$.
   (d) (1) List E; (2) List $F \cup G$; (3) "Union" the results of (1) and (2) to get $E \cup (F \cup G)$. (4) How is $E \cup (F \cup G)$ related to $(E \cup F) \cup G$?
   (e) Find $(1, 2] \cap [2, 4]$, $(1, 2] \cup [2, 4]$.
   (f) Find $(1, 5) \cap (5, 6)$, $(1, 5) \cup [5, 6]$.
   (g) Find $[1, 8] \cap [3, 7]$, $[1, 8] \cap [3, 7]$.

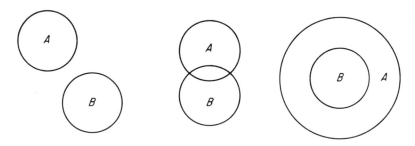

Figure 1.5

1.5   Some Algebra of Sets

The reader might now note that, just as addition of real numbers is a way of combining two real numbers to get another real number, the operations of union and intersection are ways of combining sets in order to get another set. Now we are familiar with certain properties of addition that might well be satisfied by these operations on sets. For example, addition of real numbers has the property that $x + y = y + x$ for every pair x, y of real numbers. We raise the question of whether or not $A \cup B = B \cup A$ and $A \cap B = B \cap A$ for every pair of sets A, B. Rephrasing the question, consider arbitrary sets A and B. Although these are any sets whatsoever, they are now fixed. We now ask, is the set $A \cup B$ a subset of $B \cup A$ and is $B \cup A$ a subset of $A \cup B$? (This makes use of Definition 1.3 of "$=$" as applied to sets.) In the symbols we have introduced, we ask if $A \cup B \subset B \cup A$ and if $B \cup A \subset A \cup B$. Recall that for any sets K, L, $K \subset L \Leftrightarrow x \in K \Rightarrow x \in L$. So, to show that $A \cup B \subset B \cup A$ all we need establish is the implication

$$x \in A \cup B \Rightarrow x \in B \cup A.$$

If $x \in A \cup B$, then either $x \in A$ or $x \in B$. But if either $x \in A$ or $x \in B$, then it is true that either $x \in B$ or $x \in A$. Thus, if $x \in A \cup B$, then $x \in B \cup A$. This establishes the implication

$$x \in A \cup B \Rightarrow x \in B \cup A.$$

So $A \cup B \subset B \cup A$. In exactly the same fashion, we can show $B \cup A \subset A \cup B$. Thus $A \cup B = B \cup A$ for any pair of sets A, B.

Exercise

Show that $A \cap B = B \cap A$ for any two sets A and B.

We can state these two results in the following theorem which we have proved.

Theorem 1.1. For any two sets A and B,

$$A \cup B = B \cup A \quad \text{and} \quad A \cap B = B \cap A.$$

These results follow almost immediately from the definition and the proofs are almost obvious. Certain other results will not be so easy to prove and the reader must not be misled by the simplicity of the foregoing proofs.

We want now to consider the following question: For any three sets A, B, C, is it true that

$$(A \cap B) \cap C = A \cap (B \cap C)?$$

This may seem a bit unnecessary and indeed the proof of the truth of this equality follows quickly from the definition of the symbols involved. However, the property is an important one. This is its meaning: Recall first that $\cap$ is defined for just two sets, and given three sets, we must first combine two of them to get a set to combine with the third. And we have no assurance that the results would be the same no matter how we do it. As an example, consider the subtraction of real numbers. This can be viewed as a rule of combining two real numbers to get a third. If 1, 3, 5 are three real numbers to be "combined" by subtraction, it clearly is important to specify how we want them combined. For if we subtract 5 from $1 - 3$ we get -7. But if we subtract $3 - 5$ from 1 we get 3. So the order of operating indicated by the insertion of parentheses as in $(1 - 3) - 5$ and in $1 - (3 - 5)$ can be significant. Now if $(A \cap B) \cap C = A \cap (B \cap C)$, we need not bother to insert the parentheses, for the result would be the same.

We now state and prove

Theorem 1.2. For any three sets A, B, C,

$$(A \cap B) \cap C = A \cap (B \cap C).$$

Proof. As before we show that

$$(A \cap B) \cap C \subset A \cap (B \cap C)$$

and

$$A \cap (B \cap C) \subset (A \cap B) \cap C.$$

In order to show that

$$(A \cap B) \cap C \subset A \cap (B \cap C),$$

we show

$$x \in (A \cap B) \cap C \Rightarrow x \in A \cap (B \cap C).$$

Now

$$x \in (A \cap B) \cap C \Rightarrow x \in (A \cap B) \quad \text{and} \quad x \in C.$$

This is because of the definition of $\cap$. Again using this definition, $x \in (A \cap B)$ and $x \in C \Rightarrow x \in A$ and $x \in B$ and $x \in C$. But this means that $x \in A$ and $x \in (B \cap C)$. So $x \in A \cap (B \cap C)$. Thus we have shown the desired implication and

$$(A \cap B) \cap C \subset A \cap (B \cap C).$$

In the same fashion,

$$x \in A \cap (B \cap C) \Rightarrow x \in (A \cap B) \cap C$$

and

$$A \cap (B \cap C) \subset (A \cap B) \cap C.$$

So $(A \cap B) \cap C = A \cap (B \cap C)$.

Exercise

Prove the following theorem:

Theorem 1.3. For any three sets A, B, C,
$$(A \cup B) \cup C = A \cup (B \cup C).$$

There are many other results of the same type. Since not many of them merit being called theorems, we incorporate some of them into exercises.

Exercise 1.5

1. Consider Fig. 1.6:

   (a) Shade A.

   (b) Shade B.

   (c) Shade $A \cup B$. How is $A \cup B$ related to A? to B?

   (d) Shade $A \cap B$. How is $A \cap B$ related to A? to B? to $A \cup B$?

   (e) Shade C.

   (f) Shade $(A \cup B) \cup C$.

   (g) Shade A, shade $B \cup C$, then find the union of the resulting sets. This is $A \cup (B \cup C)$. How is it related to $(A \cup B) \cup C$?

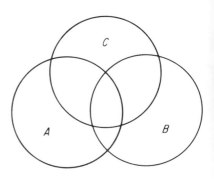

Figure 1.6

   (h) Shade $A \cap B$, shade C, and "intersect" them to get $(A \cap B) \cap C$.

   (i) Shade A, shade $B \cap C$, and "intersect" them to get $A \cap (B \cap C)$. How is this related to $(A \cap B) \cap C$?

   (j) Summarize the relationships you found in 1–9.

2. Prove that for any two sets A and B, $A \subset A \cup B$ and $A \cap B \subset A$.

3. Prove that for any set A, $A \cup \varnothing = A$ and $A \cap \varnothing = \varnothing$ . . . .

4. Prove that for any set A, $A \cup A = A$ and $A \cap A = A$.

1.6 Complements

Frequently, when we deal with sets, we restrict ourselves to dealing with subsets of a given set. Suppose that X is such a set.

Definition 1.12. Let $A \subset X$. The *complement*, A' or $X \setminus A$, of A in X is defined by
$$A' = \{x \in X \mid x \notin A\} .$$

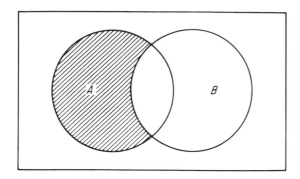

Figure 1.7

EXAMPLE 1. Let $X = \{1, 2, 3, 4, 5,\}$. If $A = \{1, 3\}$, $A' = \{2, 4, 5\}$.

EXAMPLE 2. Let X be the set of all integers. If

$$E = \{2n \mid n \in X\}, E' = \{2n + 1 \mid n \in X\}.$$

EXAMPLE 3. Let X be a set indicated by the rectangle (Fig. 1.7) and let A and B be subsets of X as indicated. The set $A \cap B'$ is shaded. For $x \in A \cap B' \Leftrightarrow x \in A$ and $x \in B' \Leftrightarrow x \in A$ and $x \notin B$. The part of the picture shaded is exactly the set of points in X, in A but *not* in B.

Exercise 1.6

1. Let $E = \{1, 2, 4, 5\}$, $F = \{2, 3, 5, 6\}$, $G = \{4, 5, 6, 7\}$, and $X = \{1, 2, 3, 4, 5, 6, 7, 8\}$.
   (a) Find (1) E', (2) F', (3) G'.
   (b) Find $E' \cap F'$.
   (c) Find $(E \cup F)'$. How is it related to $E' \cap F'$?
   (d) Find $(E \cap F)'$.
   (e) Find $E' \cup F'$. How is it related to $(E \cap F)'$?

2. Prove that if A and B are subsets of X, then $(A \cap B)' = A' \cup B'$ and $(A \cup B)' = A' \cap B'$.

3. As in Example 3, draw a diagram and, assuming A, B, and C are subsets of X, shade the following sets:
   (a) A'.   (b) $(A \cap B)'$.
   (c) $(A \cup B)'$.   (d) $A' \cap B$.
   (e) $A' \cup B'$.   (f) $(A' \cap B') \cap C'$.
   (g) $A' \cap (B' \cap C')$.   (h) $A' \cup (B \cup C)'$.
   (i) $(A \cup B)' \cap (A \cup C)$.

1.7 Functions

Although the notion of set is basic to all that we do, the concept of function is also quite basic and permeates all of mathematics. The reader is certainly familiar with this concept but probably has never bothered to pinpoint it. In fact, it is a simple idea but is frequently complicated with awkward definitions. Probably the reader's hardest job is forgetting the half-learned definitions from his past experience or reconciling the definition given here with the ones he learned earlier.

We would here remark that, in the experience of the reader, functions have something to do with "variables." We are now in a position to define "variable."

Definition 1.13. Let A be a set. If x is a symbol used to represent an arbitrary element of A, we call x *a variable on A*.

Very simply, this means that x is a symbol that can be replaced by any of the elements of the set or, indeed, that stands for any element of the set.

Notice that, if A consists of a single element, b, and if x is a variable on A, then x can represent or be replaced by only one object. We will still allow x to be considered as a variable but at the same time will consider x to be fixed.

The idea of function in most readers' minds has to do with one variable, r, being a function of another variable, t, in the sense that, if t is assigned a specific value, then r is determined. This notion is not too bad, but it uses words rather loosely and uses undefined terms.

We look at some examples of what would probably be recognized as functions by most readers.

EXAMPLE 1. The amount, T, of sales tax paid on a given purchase in Ohio is certainly a function of the price, p, of the thing purchased.

Note that, given the price, p, of an object, there is assigned to p or paired with p an amount of money, T, called the *sales tax*. For example, if $p = \$1.00$, $T = \$.03$; if $p = \$1.99$, $T = \$.06$. Thus the number T is associated with p whenever p is given.

EXAMPLE 2. The area A of a square is clearly a function of the length s of a side of the square.

Again, note that, whenever we have given the length s of the side of a square, there is paired with s the area, $A = s^2$. If $s = 2$ ft, then the area 4 sq ft is associated with 2.

Exercise

Point out three other examples of functions in this sense.

We now give the definition of function. We have established the definitions (or pointed out that they are undefined) of all the terms used in this definition.

Definition 1.14. Let X and Y be sets. A *function f from X into Y* is a subset of $X \times Y$ such that

(1) $x \in X \Rightarrow \exists y \in Y$ such that $(x, y) \in f$.

(2) $(x, y) \in f$ and $(x, z) \in f \Rightarrow y = z$.

Certainly this definition tells us that a function from X into Y is a way of pairing elements of Y with elements of X.

Condition (1) says that every element in X appears at least once as a first entry in a pair in f; condition (2) says that each $x \in X$ appears only once in a pair in f.

In what follows, we include in a single definition other terms and notation used relative to the idea of functions.

Definition 1.15. The symbol "$f : X \rightarrow Y$" is read "f, a function from X into Y." If f is a function and $(x, y) \in f$, we call y the *value of f at x* and write y as $f(x)$, which is read "f of x." The set X is called the *domain* of f. The set Y is called the *image space* of f. The *range of f* is defined to be

$$\{y \in Y \mid (x, y) \in f \text{ for some } x \in X\}.$$

We now look at some examples of functions in the sense of Definition 1.14. Remember that two sets must be given and a subset of their product set, in some order, must be given so that properties (1) and (2) of this definition hold.

EXAMPLE 1. Let the set X be the set of all the people in your classroom at a fixed time. Further, let set Y be the set of all positive integers. Consider the subset f of $X \times Y$ consisting of all pairs (x, w) where x represents a person in the room and w represents his or her weight to the nearest pound. (Round off $\frac{1}{2}$ to the nearest even integer.) Since each person in the room has weight, condition (1) of the definition is satisfied and, because each person has a unique weight at the given time, condition (2) is satisfied. If Joe Blow is in the classroom and weighs 187 pounds, then the pair (Joe Blow, 187) $\in f$. Set X is, of course, the domain of the function f. We would write $187 = f$(Joe Blow) because the pair (Joe Blow, 187) $\in f$.

EXAMPLE 2. Let $U = \{1, 2, 3, 4\}$ and $V = \{a, b, c\}$. Consider now the subset $g \subset U \times V$ given by

$$g = \{(1, a), (2, a), (3, b), (4, c)\}.$$

It is easy to see that (1) and (2) of Definition 1.14 are satisfied and that g is a function from U into V. On the other hand, consider the set:

$$h = \{(1, a), (1, b), (2, c), (3, b), (4, a)\}.$$

This is not a function because the presence of $(1, a)$ and $(1, b)$ violates condition (2) of our definition. Also consider

$$k = \{(1, a), (2, b), (3, b)\}.$$

The fact that $4 \in U$ fails to appear in any of the pairs in k tells us that k is not a function. Observe that in the function g, all the elements in V appear. This would say that the range of g is V. On the other hand, referring back to the function f in the preceding example, it is unlikely that any person weighs 2,000 pounds. Hence 2,000, a number in Y, does not appear in any of the pairs in f. So it is not necessary that the range coincide with the image space of a function.

Definition 1.16. Let $f : X \to Y$ be given. If Y is the range of f, we call f an *"onto" function*.

Exercise

Convince yourself that a function $f : X \to Y$ is an "onto" function if and only if $y \in Y \Rightarrow \exists\, x \in X$ such that $(x, y) \in f$.

As we pointed out earlier, the function g in Example 2 is "onto," but the function f of Example 1 is not an onto function.

Another type of function that is of importance is the so-called one-to-one (1–1) function.

Definition 1.17. Let $f : X \to Y$ be given. Then f is *one-to-one* if and only if

$$(1)\ \text{for } u, v \in X,\, u \neq v \Rightarrow f(u) \neq f(v),$$

or

$$(2)\ \text{for } u, v \in X,\, f(u) = f(v) \Rightarrow u = v.$$

[Conditions (1) and (2) are logically equivalent. In testing whether a given function is 1–1, one may be easier to apply than the other.]

EXAMPLES. Let $X = Y = R^1$, where R^1 is the set of all real numbers. Let

$$f = \{(x, y) \mid y = x + 1\}, \qquad g = \{(x, y) \mid y = x^2\}$$

$$\text{and} \quad h = \left\{(x, y) \mid y = \frac{1}{1 + x^2}\right\}$$

be functions from X into Y. Then f is 1–1. For, if $u \neq v$, then $u + 1 \neq v + 1$, which says that $f(u) \neq f(v)$. (Remember, if $(x, y) \in f$, we write $y = f(x)$.) More than this, f is an "onto" function. For if x is any element of Y (any real number), the pair $(x - 1, x) \in f$. This means that each element of Y is in the range of f or that Y is the range of f. On the other hand, g is not one-to-one. This is true because there are numbers u, $v \in X$ with $u \neq v$ but with $g(u) = g(v)$. For example, $2 \neq (-2)$ but $g(2) = g(-2) = 4$. That is, the same number, 4, is paired with the distinct numbers 2 and -2 in the domain of g.

Remark. The image space of a function always contains the range of the function. Note that, if $f : X \to Y$ is given, we can always consider f as an onto function simply by replacing Y by the range $f(X)$ of f.

Exercise 1.7

Let
$$X = \{1, 2, 3\}, \qquad Y = \{a, b, c\}, \qquad Z = \{a, b, c, d\}.$$
Let
$$f_1 = \{(1, a), (2, a), (3, a)\}, \qquad f_2 = \{1, a), (1, b), (2, b), (3, b)\},$$
$$f_3 = \{(1, a), (2, b), (3, d)\}, \qquad f_4 = \{(1, b), (2, a)\}, \qquad f_5 = \{(1, a), (2, b), (3, c)\} .$$

1. (a) Which of the above are functions from X into Y?

   (b) For those which are, find (1) the domain of each, (2) the range, (3) the image space.

   (c) Which are 1–1? (Consider only those which are functions from X into Y.)

   (d) Which are onto? (Again consider only functions.)

2. (a) Which of the above are functions from X into Z?

   (b) For those which are, find (1) the domain, (2) the range, (3) the image space.

   (c) Which are 1–1?

   (d) Which are onto?

3. In the example preceding these exercises, show that the function h is not 1–1 and not "onto."

4. Let $f : R^1 \to R^1$ be defined by

$$f = \{(x, y) \mid x \in R^1 \quad \text{and} \quad y = 2x + 3\}\,.$$

Show that f is 1–1 and onto.

5. Let $g : R^1 \to R^1$ be defined by

$$g = \{(x, y) \mid y = x^2 + 4\}\,.$$

Find the range of g.

1.8   Domains of Functions

As a matter of convention, when we are given functions, we usually are not given the domain and image space. Some rather general assumptions are made concerning these sets. For example, in this text, if we give a function without mentioning the domain and image space, we assume that these are subsets of the real numbers. (Remember, we use the symbol R^1 to denote the set of real numbers.)

As an example, consider the function

$$f : X \to Y\,, \quad \text{where } X = \{x \mid x \in R^1 \quad \text{and} \quad x \geq 0\}\,,$$
$$Y = R^1\,, \quad \text{where } f = \{(x, y) \mid y = \sqrt{x}\}\,.$$

In order to give you the function we might have said that, for each $x \in X$, let $f(x) = \sqrt{x}$ or let $y = \sqrt{x}$. In practice, we would probably have said, simply, consider the function f defined by $f(x) = \sqrt{x}$. Now we know that if $x < 0$, $f(x)$ is not a real number. So with our assumption that the domain and image space of f are to be subsets of real numbers, we would conclude that the domain of f is no "larger" than $\{x \in R^1 \mid x \geq 0\}$. It will be only when we want to place special emphasis on the domain that we will give it explicitly. Otherwise we assume the domain is the "largest" subset of real numbers allowed by the form of the function.

As a matter of common terminology we call functions that have R^1 or subsets of R^1 as image spaces *real-valued functions*. Again as a matter of common usage, if $f : X \to Y$ is any function so that $f(x) = b$, b a fixed element in Y, we call f a *constant function*. For example, the function f defined by $f(x) = 2$ for all real numbers x, is a constant function. Formally $f : R^1 \to R^1$ is given by $f = \{(x, 2) \mid x \in R^1\}$.

Exercise 1.8

1. Suppose that the following functions all have domains and image spaces that are subsets of R^1. Give the "largest" subset of real numbers that may be the domain of the indicated functions.

    (a) $f(x) = x + 1$.   (b) $h(x) = x^2 + 1$.

(c)　$g(x) = \dfrac{1}{x-1}.$　　　　　　　　　　(d)　$u(x) = \sqrt{\dfrac{1}{x-1}}.$

(e)　$v(x) = x + \sqrt{1-x}.$　　　　　　　　(f)　$w(x) = \dfrac{x}{1-x^2}.$

2. Give the "largest" subset of R^1 that may be the domain of each of the following

(a)　$f(x) = 2x^2 + 3.$　　　　　　　　　　(b)　$f(x) = \dfrac{1}{x}.$

(c)　$f(t) = t - \dfrac{1}{t}.$　　　　　　　　　(d)　$f(z) = 1 + \dfrac{1}{z}.$

(e)　$u(T) = \dfrac{T+1}{T}.$　　　　　　　　(f)　$s(y) = \dfrac{1}{y^2}.$

(g)　$r(x) = x^3 + 1.$　　　　　　　　　　(h)　$w(h) = \dfrac{1}{h} + \dfrac{h}{3}.$

3. Which of the functions in 1 and 2 are 1–1? Why?

4. Find the range of f, g, h, u in 1.

1.9　Functions and Equations

We would like to point out, again, that to describe a function we must have two sets and a subset of the Cartesian product of these sets satisfying the conditions of Definition 1.14. In fact, this subset assigns to, or pairs with, each element of the domain an element of the image space. It is possible to give a definition of functions along the lines of this comment but the definition given is considered a bit more satisfactory.

Functions, as we pointed out earlier, are frequently given by equations. For example, consider the function defined by the equation $y = x + 1$. Probably we would speak simply of the function $y = x + 1$. By this we would understand the function $g : R^1 \to R^1$ defined by

$$g = \{(x, y) \mid x \in R^1 \quad \text{and} \quad y = x + 1\}.$$

Now, in fact, the function $x = y - 1$ or $\{(t, t - 1) \mid t \in R^1\}$ comes from the same equation simply by solving for x instead of y. For this reason, we should understand a little better the nature of an equation.

An *equation*, in fact, may be considered as a statement involving variables on a set, constants in the set, and an equality sign. Of course, this statement might well entail symbols indicating algebraic operations in the set involved. For certain values assigned the variables, the statement might be true; for other values assigned the variables, the statement might be false. We might also note that occasionally the statement makes no sense when we assign values to the variables.

We turn now to some examples to see more clearly just what an equation is and to see what we will mean by the solution set of an equation.

EXAMPLE 1. Consider the equation $x - 2 = 1$. Now, in fact, if we consider the set on which x is a variable to be the set of real numbers, the statement $x - 2 = 1$ is false when $x = 2$, $x = 3.1$, $x = 10^{10}$, and for all $x \in R^1$ except for $x = 3$.

In the remaining examples, we assume that the variables are all variables on the set R^1. We will call these *real variables*.

EXAMPLE 2. Consider $x + y = 2$. Now if $x = 3$ and $y = 4$, clearly the statement $x + y = 2$ is false. Similarly the equation is false for the pairs $(1, 2)$, $(2, 3)$, and $(-2, -4)$. Of course there are many more pairs for which the statement is false. On the other hand, $(1, 1)$, $(0.9, 1.1)$, $(3, -1)$, $(10, -8)$ and many others are pairs for which the equation is a true statement. In fact for all pairs in the set: $\{(x, y) \mid y = 2 - x, \text{ where } x \in R^1\}$, the equation is a true statement.

EXAMPLE 3. Consider

$$\frac{1}{x} + \frac{1}{y} = 1 \,.$$

Here we encounter an equation that is meaningless when either $x = 0$ or $y = 0$. On the other hand, there are values for x and y (for example, $x = 2$, $y = 2$) for which the statement is true and other values (for example, $x = 1$, $y = 3$) for which the statement is false.

Definition 1.18. Suppose that k is an equation in two real variables x and y. The *solution set* for k is

$$\{(u, v) \mid k \text{ is true when } u \text{ replaces } x \text{ and } v \text{ replaces } y\} \,.$$

For our purposes, we will, for awhile, restrict ourselves to equations in two variables. This definition can be generalized to more variables.

A little later we will return to the preceding ideas, but as of now we would point out that functions can be defined by equations. In fact, if two variables are involved, two functions might be defined. But, on the other hand, no functions might be defined. For example, consider the equation $y^2 - x^2 = 1$. Now if we solve this for y, we get $y = \pm \sqrt{1 + x^2}$. So if we use $x = 0$ we get both 1 and -1 as values for y. This means that for $x = 0$ we would have both $(0, 1)$ and $(0, -1)$ in the function defined by $y^2 - x^2 = 1$. But this contradicts (2) of Definition 1.14. So no function is defined when we solve this equation for y. (In a sense this procedure defines two functions, one $y = +\sqrt{1 + x^2}$, and the other, $y = -\sqrt{1 + x^2}$.) The solution set $\{(x, y) \mid y = +\sqrt{1 + x^2} \text{ or } y = -\sqrt{1 + x^2}\}$ of $y^2 - x^2 = 1$ is, of course, a set of ordered pairs but *not* a function, as we noted.

Exercise 1.9

1. Find the solution sets of the following equations:

   (a) $x + y = 1.$ (b) $y = \dfrac{1}{x}.$

   (c) $x^2 = 1 + y.$ (d) $\dfrac{1}{x} + \dfrac{1}{y} = 1.$

   (e) $\dfrac{1}{y} = \dfrac{1}{x}.$ (f) $3 - \dfrac{1}{x} = \dfrac{1}{y^2}.$

   (g) $3x = 1.$ (h) $y^2 = x^2.$

   (i) $y = 3x + 2y.$ (j) $y = 4x^2 + x + 1.$

   (k) $xy = -1.$ (l) $y - x = 2.$

2. Find the solution sets of the following equations:

   (a) $x + y = 3y - 2x.$ (b) $x^2 - y = 3.$

   (c) $(x - 2)^2 = 4.$ (d) $x - 1 = y^2.$

   (e) $\dfrac{1}{x} + \dfrac{1}{y} = 0.$ (f) $\dfrac{1}{x^2} - \dfrac{1}{y^2} = 0.$

   (g) $xy^2 = 1.$ (h) $x^2y^2 = 4.$

   (i) $xy - 3y = 1.$ (j) $x(y - 1) = 2.$

3. Considering the solution set of a given equation as a set of ordered pairs, (u, v), where the first entry u replaces x, say why the solution sets for the following equations are *not* functions on R^1.

   (a) $y^2 + x - 1 = 0.$ (b) $y^2 = -|x|.$

   (c) $y^2 = 4.$ (d) $\dfrac{1}{x^2} = \dfrac{1}{y^2}.$

1.10   Relations

A more general concept than that of function is that of relation.

Definition 1.19. Let X and Y be sets. A *relation* U from X into Y is a subset of $X \times Y$. If $(x, y) \in$ U, we say that x is U-related to y and we usually write $x \,U\, y$. To negate this we usually write $x \,\cancel{U}\, y$ and say that x is not U-related to y.

Much of our work with relations will be concerned with relations from a set X into itself. Such a relation is called a *relation on the set X*.

There are many commonplace examples of relations that fit our definition. As an instance of the general concept, let X be the set of all male human beings and let Y be the set of all female human beings (both sets considered at a fixed time). Then consider

$$U = \{(x, y) \mid x \in X, y \in Y \quad \text{and} \quad x \text{ is married to } y\} \,.$$

So $x \, U \, y \Leftrightarrow x$ is married to y. Thus Jack Kennedy U Jacqueline Kennedy but Bob Kennedy $\cancel{U}$ Mamie Eisenhower.

Another relation, V, from this same set X into the same set Y is given by

$$V = \{(x, y) \mid x \text{ is older than } y\} \,.$$

Thus, given $y_0 \in Y$, $x \, V \, y_0 \Leftrightarrow x$ is older than y_0. This example shows that many x's can be "paired with" the same y_0 in a given relation.

We have encountered many examples of relations on a set in our earlier mathematical training as well as in everyday life. We will look at several such examples.

Consider the set X of all triangles in a plane. We have a relation U on X defined by

$$U = \{(x, y) \mid x, y \in X \quad \text{and} \quad x \text{ is similar to } y\} \,.$$

Thus $x \, U \, y \Leftrightarrow x \sim y$. Here we encounter a bit of awkwardness in notation. For $x \sim y$ says to most of us that triangle x is similar to triangle y and we have introduced a new notation, $x \, U \, y$, to say the same thing. We shall avoid this by using the common symbol to denote the set that is the relation and frequently will make no mention of the set.

As a further example, consider R^1, the set of all real numbers. Then $<$ is a relation on R^1. Of course, for $x, y \in R^1$, $x < y$ means that x is less than y. Clearly there are many more examples that could be considered that are already familiar to us.

Certain properties are satisfied by relations that help us characterize them. The three properties that are of the most interest to us are contained in the following definition:

Definition 1.20. Let X be a set and let U be a relation on X.

(1) U is a *reflexive relation* $\Leftrightarrow x \, U \, x$ for each $x \in X$.

(2) U is a *symmetric relation* $\Leftrightarrow$ for $x, y \in X$, $x \, U \, y \Rightarrow y \, U \, x$.

(3) U is a *transitive relation* $\Leftrightarrow$ for $x, y, z \in X$, $x \, U \, y$, $y \, U \, z \Rightarrow x \, U \, z$.

If all three properties are satisfied by a given relation U, it is called an *equivalence relation*.

EXAMPLE 1. If we consider the set X of all triangles in a plane and take the relation $\sim$ on X we can easily verify that $\sim$ is an equivalence relation if we agree that every triangle is similar to itself.

EXAMPLE 2. Looking at the relation $<$ on R^1, we see that, while $<$ is a transitive relation, it is neither reflexive nor symmetric because $1 \not< 1$ (1 is not less than 1), and $2 < 3 \not\Rightarrow 3 < 2$ (2 less than 3 does not imply 3 less than 2). If we consider $\leq$ on R^1, we have a reflexive and transitive but a nonsymmetric relation.

Thus we see that there are relations that satisfy one, two and three of the properties listed in the definition. A question that should be asked is, do there exist relations satisfying each one of the properties but not the other two and do there exist relations satisfying each pair of properties but not the third? The answer to these questions is that such relations exist.

Exercise 1.10

Which properties do the following relations satisfy?

	Set	*Relation*
(a)	Triangles in a plane	congruence.
(b)	Lines in a plane	perpendicularity.
(c)	Lines in a plane	parallelism, $\|$ (a line is not $\|$ to itself).
(d)	Subsets of a given set	$\subset$.
(e)	Subsets of a given set	$A \sim B \Leftrightarrow A \cap B \neq \varnothing$.
(f)	Subsets of a given set	$A \sim B \Leftrightarrow A \cap B = \varnothing$.
(g)	All male humans	$x \sim y \Leftrightarrow x$ knows the name of y.
(h)	All male humans	$x \sim y \Leftrightarrow x$ and y have at least one common parent.
(i)	All integers	$x \equiv y (\mathrm{mod}\ 2) \Leftrightarrow x - y$ is divisible by 2.
(j)	All integers	$x \equiv y (\mathrm{mod}\ 3) \Leftrightarrow x - y$ is divisible by 3.

1.11 A Property of Equivalence Relations

Suppose X is a set on which an equivalence relation $\sim$ is defined. For a fixed element a of X let $[a]$ denote the set of all elements equivalent to a. That is, let

$$[a] = \{x \in X \mid x \sim a\} .$$

We will call $[a]$ the equivalence class determined by a. First observe that

$a \in [a]$ because $a \sim a$. This tells us that every element in X is in at least one $[x]$, since if nothing else, $x \in [x]$ for each $x \in X$.

We observe further that, if $t \in [a]$, then $[t] = [a]$. This means that all the elements in an equivalence class determine that equivalence class. To see this, consider the following argument:

$$t \in [a] \Rightarrow t \sim a .$$

Let $x \in [t]$, then $x \sim t$. But, $x \sim t$ and $t \sim a \Rightarrow x \sim a$ or $x \in [a]$. Thus we have demonstrated that $[t] \subset [a]$. Recalling that $t \sim a \Rightarrow a \sim t$ we can show that $[a] \subset [t]$. For, if $x \in [a]$, $x \sim a$. Then, if $a \sim t$, $x \sim t$ or $x \in [t]$. We conclude that

$$t \in [a] \Rightarrow [t] = [a] .$$

Another observation concerns the intersection of two equivalence classes. Suppose $t \in [x] \cap [y]$. Then $t \in [x]$ and $t \in [y]$. By what we have just seen,

$$[x] = [t] = [y] .$$

This tells us that if two equivalence classes have a common element they are identical.

From the preceding arguments we see that the following theorem holds.

Theorem 1.4. Let $\sim$ be an equivalence relation on a set X and let

$$F = \{[a] \mid a \in X\} .$$

Every element in X is contained in one and only one set in F.

In this sense, an equivalence relation on X partitions the set X into disjoint classes which cover X, i.e., which contain every element of X. To illustrate this, consider the case where X is the set, I, of all integers and where $\sim$ is $\equiv$ (mod 3) as in an earlier exercise. Then $a \sim b \Leftrightarrow a - b = 3k$ for some integer k. We know this to be an equivalence relation and, by the above theorem, we know the equivalence classes cover I and are disjoint. We now look at these classes.

$$[0] = \{a \mid a - 0 = 3k \text{ for some integer } k\} .$$

Indeed, then,

$$[0] = \{\ldots, -9, -6, -3, 0, 3, 6, 9, \ldots\} .$$

Now

$$[1] = \{a \mid a - 1 = 3k \text{ for some integer } k\}$$

$$= \{a \mid a = 3k + 1 \text{ for some integer } k\} .$$

So

$$[1] = \{\ldots, -5, -2, 1, 4, 7, 10, \ldots\} .$$

In the same fashion,

$$[2] = \{\ldots, -4, -1, 2, 5, 8, 11, \ldots\} .$$

We need go no further, because every integer is in one of these classes and, by our theorem, if $[n]$ contains a, $[n] = [a]$.

Exercise 1.11

1. Let $X = \{(a, b) \mid a, b \in I\}$. We define a relation $\sim$ on X by

$$(a, b) \sim (c, d) \Leftrightarrow b - d = a - c .$$

   (a) Show that $\sim$ is an equivalence relation on X.
   (b) Characterize the equivalence classes.

2. The relation $\sim$ on the same set X as in I is defined by

$$(a, b) \sim (c, d) \Leftrightarrow a - c = d - b .$$

   (a) Show that $\sim$ is an equivalence relation on X.
   (b) Characterize the equivalence classes.

3. Let $K = \{(a, b) \mid a, b \in I, b \neq 0\}$. We define a relation $\sim$ on K by

$$(a, b) \sim (c, d) \Leftrightarrow ad = bc .$$

   (a) Prove that $\sim$ is an equivalence relation.
   (b) Characterize the equivalence classes.

4. For the set I of integers, let $a \sim b \Leftrightarrow a - b = 7k$ for some integer k. Show that $\sim$ is an equivalence relation and determine the equivalence classes.

   Remark. We have been using the symbol "$=$" frequently. In the case of equality of sets we have defined it. More commonly, when we see $x = y$ we interpret "$=$" to mean "is the same as." It usually appears between symbols representing elements of the same set and, indeed, defines a relation on the set in question. This relation is an equivalence relation on the set and the equivalence class $[x]$ is the set consisting of x alone; that is, $[x] = \{x\}$.

Exercise

Let X be any set. Prove that $=$ is an equivalence relation on X.

To this point, we have considered many definitions and have not put them to use. Now we have the basic language we need as we proceed. From now on, we freely use the terms defined heretofore, and most of the new concepts introduced will be defined in these terms.

Algebra

Comment. In this chapter, we want to take a look at elementary algebra. This time, however, we want to try to understand why we perform certain operations and in general what kinds of problems algebra handles. We restrict ourselves for the time being to dealing with real numbers. Our starting point, then, is the set R^1 of real numbers. In the set of real numbers we have ways of combining real numbers to get real numbers. For example, the sum of two real numbers is a real number. Thus, addition is one of these ways of combining real numbers. We are now in a position to say exactly what these ways of combining elements are.

2.1 Binary Operations

2

Before introducing the formal concept of binary operation let us first take a look at a particular type of function. The domains of these functions will be subsets of $R^1 \times R^1$. The image space for all these functions will be R^1. Consider, then, the function $g : R^1 \times R^1 \rightarrow R^1$ defined by

$$g = \{((x, y), z) \mid z = x\} .$$

Observe that the first entry in a pair in g is an element of $R^1 \times R^1$ and is, of course, a pair of real numbers. Then $((1, 2), 1)$ is in the function but $((1, 2), 4)$ is not. We extend the functional notation introduced earlier to take care of this kind of function. In the present case, in keeping with our earlier notation, we would write $z = g((x, y))$. We commonly simplify this and write $z = g(x, y)$. We note that for any pair $(x, y) \in R^1 \times R^1$, $g(x, y)$ is defined. So $R^1 \times R^1$ is the domain of g. On the other hand, since $g(x, y) = x$, only one z is associated with each pair (x, y) of real numbers. Thus g is indeed a function.

Another example of the kind of function under consideration would be $d(x, y) = x/y$. The domain of this function would be

$$K = \{(x, y) \in R^1 \times R^1 \mid y \neq 0\} .$$

Formally, then, $d : K \rightarrow R^1$ would be defined by

$$d = \left\{((x, y), z) \mid z = \frac{x}{y}\right\} .$$

It is not difficult to verify that d is a function. Is it?

Observe that the familiar rules of combining *real numbers* (such as adding real numbers) to get real numbers are ways of *assigning real numbers to ordered pairs of real* numbers. Thus, these rules of combination are functions of the foregoing type. We call these rules *binary operations* on the set of real numbers and define them formally as follows:

Definition 2.1. Let X be a set. A *binary operation on X* is a function from $X \times X$ into X.

Note that the domain of a binary operation on a set is the (complete) Cartesian product $X \times X$. In this sense, division of real numbers (see the function d above) is not a binary operation on R^1, because $R^1 \times R^1$ is not the domain of this function.

We pay particular attention to addition and multiplication of real numbers. These *are* binary operations on R^1 and relative to these operations certain familiar rules hold. For example, let $f : R^1 \times R^1 \rightarrow R^1$ be the function defining addition of real numbers. From our early experience with arithmetic, we believe that, if we add 2 and 3, or if we add 3 and 2, we get the same sum. In fact, a basic assumption (or possibly a theorem if we make other basic assumptions) concerning real numbers is that $f(x, y) = f(y, x)$ for any pair x, y of real numbers. This is nothing more than the familiar statement that for any pair of real numbers, x and y, $x + y = y + x$. As another example, for this same function f and real numbers x, y, z,

$$f(f(x, y), z) = f(x, f(y, z)) .$$

Rewriting this slightly we get

$$f(x + y, z) = f(x, y + z) .$$

Finally, on rewriting, we get that, for any real numbers x, y, z,

$$(x + y) + z = x + (y + z) .$$

This, of course, is a familiar property (the associative law for addition) of real numbers.

Now it should be clear that not every binary operation on a set, even the set of real numbers, has these nice properties. For example, consider the function

$$g : R^1 \times R^1 \rightarrow R^1 \quad \text{defined by} \quad g(x, y) = x - y$$

for every pair, x, y of real numbers. Certainly,

$$g(2, 5) \neq g(5, 2) ,$$

that is, $3 \neq -3$, and certainly

$$g(g(5, 3), 1) = (5 - 3) - 1 = 1$$

is not equal to

$$g(5, g(3, 1)) = 5 - (3 - 1) = 3 .$$

Exercise 2.1

1. Which of the following define binary operation on the set I of all integers? (Let $x, y \in I$.)

   (a) $x \circ y = x^2 + y^2$.   (b) $x \circ y = x + y$.

   (c) $x \circ y = \dfrac{x}{y}$.   (d) $x \circ y = xy$.

   (e) $x \circ y = 2x + y$.   (f) $x \circ y = x + y - xy$.

   (g) $x \circ y = x$.

2. Which of the rules in Exercise 1 define binary operations on the set of rational numbers? (Let x, y be rational numbers.)

3. Which of the following define binary operations on the set of integers?

   (a) $x \circ y = x^2 - y^2$.   (b) $x \circ y = x + \dfrac{y}{x}$.

   (c) $x \circ y = x - y^2$.   (d) $x \circ y = 1$.

   (e) $x \circ y = 2x + 2y$.   (f) $x \circ y = \dfrac{x}{2} - \dfrac{2}{y}$.

   (g) $x \circ y = x^y$.

In all mathematics we study sets. Now in studying that field of mathematics called *algebra* we study sets on which binary operations are defined. There are many ways in which binary operations might be defined on a given set. Not all of them are interesting and the "algebraic structure" determined by them might not be worth studying. We might look briefly at some rather "wild" binary operations on sets.

Let $S = \{a, b, c, d\}$. Let X be the set of all "words" obtained by using these letters a finite number of times. By this is meant only formal words. For example, *abbacadab* $\in X$. Now, if u and v are arbitrary words in X, we form a new word $u \cdot v$ by writing u and v together in that order. To see a sample of this, suppose that u is the word *abba* and that v is the word *dabba*. Then $u \cdot v$ is the word *abbadabba*. Without worrying too much about a formal proof, it is realized that, if u, v, and w are elements in X, $(u \cdot v) \cdot w = u \cdot (v \cdot w)$. If $W : X \times X \to X$ is defined by $W(u, v) = u \cdot v$ for all $u, v \in X$, this property is one of those mentioned relative to f above, namely,

$$W(W(u, v), w) = W(u, W(v, w))$$

for all $u, v, w \in X$.

From now on, when we talk about a binary operation on a set, we will use a more common notation. Usually this will be a symbol inserted between the objects to be combined. This is nothing but a variation on the functional notation used before.

To see how this works, consider a set Z. Let us define a binary operation, using the symbol $\circ$, on Z by $a \circ b = a$ for any $a, b, \in Z$. We could have defined this binary operation as the function $\circ : Z \times Z \to Z$ defined by: $\circ(a, b) = a$ for all $a, b \in Z$. It might be noted that

$$(a \circ b) \circ c = a \circ (b \circ c)$$

for

$$(a \circ b) \circ c = a \circ c = a \quad \text{and} \quad a \circ (b \circ c) = a \circ b = a$$

for all $a, b, c \in Z$. Of course, in this case, $a \circ b \neq b \circ a$, in general.

Now it probably should be pointed out that binary operations are defined in a way that assigns to each ordered pair of elements in a set a unique third element of the set. Our preoccupation with the question of whether or not $(a \circ b) \circ c = a \circ (b \circ c)$ stems from this fact. For, given three elements, we are allowed to combine only two at a time, and as we have seen by example, the way we combine elements *can* make a difference in the number we ultimately get. If this property holds, that is, $a \circ (b \circ c) = (a \circ b) \circ c$, for a binary operation $\circ$ on a set, then we don't worry about the order of combining them. Certainly, if we wanted to add 87, 99, and 1, we would choose to add 87 to $99 + 1$ and because real numbers have this property we can do it the "easy way."

Exercise 2.2

1. Let X be a fixed set and let $P(X)$ denote the set of all subsets of X. Are $\cup$ and $\cap$ binary operations on $P(X)$? Convince yourself that they are. Write down as many properties (for example, $A \cup B = B \cup A$) of these operations as you can. Find sets K and $L \in P(X)$ such that $A \cup K = A$ for all $A \in P(X)$ and such that $A \cap L = A$ for all $A \in P(X)$. Given A, find $B \in P(X)$ such that $A \cup B = L$. Show that $\varnothing \cap A = \varnothing$ for every $A \in P(X)$.

2. Let $X = \{a, b, c\}$.
   (a) List all the subsets of X.
   (b) Write the "multiplication tables" for $\cup$ and $\cap$.
   (c) From these tables, note the properties alluded to in 1.

Definition 2.2. Let $\circ$ denote a binary operation on a set X. If $a \circ b = b \circ a$ for all $a, b, \in X$, we say that $\circ$ satisfies the *commutative law* or that $\circ$ is a *commutative operation*. If $a \circ (b \circ c) = (a \circ b) \circ c$ for all $a, b, c \in X$, we say that $\circ$ satisfies the *associative law* or that $\circ$ is an *associative operation*.

We have seen several examples of binary operations on sets. In the exercises listed below we define a number of binary operations on R^1 in terms of familiar operations on R^1. We ask, then, that the reader discover whether or not the associative and commutative laws hold and to prove his answer.

By way of example, we consider the binary operation, $\circ$, on R^1 defined by:

$$x \circ y = x + y - xy; \qquad x, y \in R^1.$$

Notice what this means by considering several products:

$$1 \circ 3 = 1 + 3 - 1 \cdot 3 = 4 - 3 = 1.$$
$$4 \circ 1 = 4 + 1 - 4 \cdot 1 = 5 - 4 = 1.$$
$$7 \circ (-2) = 7 + (-2) - 7(-2) = 5 + 14 = 19.$$
$$(-2) \circ (7) = (-2) + 7 - (-2)(7) = 5 + 14 = 19.$$

To verify the commutative law, we consider arbitrary real numbers a and b. Now: $a \circ b = a + b - ab$ and $b \circ a = b + a - ba$. But these are equal by familiar properties of real numbers. So $\circ$ is a commutative operation.

The associative law is a bit more complicated to handle. First let us consider an example.

$$(2 \circ 3) \circ 4 = (2 + 3 - 2 \cdot 3) \circ 4 = (-1) \circ 4$$
$$= (-1) + 4 - (-1) \cdot 4 = 3 + 4 = 7.$$

However,

$$2 \circ (3 \circ 4) = 2 \circ (3 + 4 - 3 \cdot 4) = 2 \circ (-5)$$
$$= 2 + (-5) - 2(-5) = -3 + 10 = 7.$$

If the computation of these "products" had resulted in different answers, we could have immediately said that the associative law does not hold. Because, if an operation is associative, it must be so for every set of numbers. The existence of one triple of numbers, a, b, c, for which the "products" differ is enough to assure that the operation is not associative. Now we are in a position where we have to decide whether we should try to prove that $(x \circ y) \circ z = x \circ (y \circ z)$ for all $x, y, z \in R^1$, or whether we should try another example, hoping that we will get different answers. Being lazy, we should probably try another example and hope for the worst. Consider $(-2), 2, 5$. Now

$$(-2 \circ 2) \circ 5 = (-2 + 2 - (-2) \cdot (2)) \circ 5 = 4 \circ 5 = 9 - 20 = -11$$

and

$$-2 \circ (2 \circ 5) = 2 \circ (7 - 10) = -2 \cdot -3 = -5 - (-2)(-3) = -11 .$$

Here we again got the same answers.

At this stage we probably should try to see why these turned out the same and should consider a general situation. So let a, b, c represent arbitrary real numbers.

$$(a \circ b) \circ c = (a + b - ab) \circ c = (a + b - ab + c) - (a + b - ab)c$$

$$= a + b - ab + c - ac - bc + abc$$

$$= a + b + c - ab - ac - bc + abc .$$

$$a \circ (b \circ c) = a \cdot (b + c - bc) = (a + b + c - bc) - a(b + c - bc)$$

$$= a + b + c - bc - ab - ac + abc$$

$$= a + b + c - ab - ac - bc + abc.$$

But here we see that, for any triple of real numbers, the "products" are the same. So indeed the associative law holds.

Remark. The computation in the above paragraph constitutes a proof that the binary operation under consideration is associative. For we proved that, for any three real numbers, the "products" $(a \circ b) \circ c$ and $a \circ (b \circ c)$ are, indeed, the same real number. We repeat that to prove a binary operation commutative or associative we *must* deal with arbitrary elements. To show that the operations do *not* satisfy these properties, it is sufficient to exhibit a particular set of elements for which the properties fail to hold.

Exercise 2.3

1. For each of the following binary operations on R^1, say whether or not the operations are commutative and associative. Prove your answers. Assume x and y

are arbitrary real numbers and that you know the usual operations for real numbers.

(a) $x \circ y = x + y$.   (b) $x \circ y = x \cdot y$.

(c) $x \circ y = x$.   (d) $x \circ y = x - y$.

(e) $x \circ y = x + 2y$.   (f) $x \circ y = \dfrac{x + y}{2}$.

(g) $x \circ y = x^2 + y^2$.   (h) $x \circ y = x + \dfrac{x + y}{2}$.

2. Do the same for the following:

(a) $x \circ y = y$.   (b) $x \circ y = y - 1$.

(c) $x \circ y = (x + 1) + (y - 1)$.   (d) $x \circ y = x(y + 1)$.

(e) $x \circ y = 2xy$.   (f) $x \circ y = 2x^2 y^2$.

(g) $x \circ y = \dfrac{1}{xy}$.   (h) $x \circ y = 1 - \dfrac{x + y}{2}$.

3. Create five binary operations on R^1 and prove that the associative and commutative laws do (or do not) hold.

2.2 Real Numbers

With this introduction, we now turn our attention to the real number system. There are many ways to approach a study of this system. We shall not be extremely formal, but we shall assume that the real numbers satisfy certain axioms and show how some of the very familiar properties are derived from the axioms we assume. Those things we assume are among the more familiar properties, and the reader will probably not be disturbed by assuming these properties.

In treating the system of real numbers, we encounter an instance of using "$=$" to mean "is the same number as." (See Sec. 1.11) For example, $11 = (5 - 3)$ means that 11 is the same number as $(5 - 3)$. (This is a false statement.) So "$=$" is a relation on the set R^1 of real numbers and is, in fact, an equivalence relation and, therefore, reflexive, symmetric, and transitive.

In dealing with binary operations we have a sort of substitution principle. If $\circ$ is a binary operation on R^1, $\circ (x, y)$ is a unique real number. So if $x = u$, $\circ (x, y) = \circ (u, y)$. In particular, if $x = u$, then $x + y = u + y$ and $x \cdot y = u \cdot y$.

If we use any of the above properties we will give as justification the nature of equality.

Remembering that this is *not a definition of real numbers*, we assume that the real numbers are a nonempty set R^1 on which two binary operations, addition $(+)$ and multiplication $(\cdot)$, are defined satisfying the following conditions:

(C) $a, b \in R^1 \Rightarrow a + b \in R^1, a \cdot b \in R^1$.

(A1) $a, b \in R^1 \Rightarrow a + b = b + a.$

(A2) $a, b, c \in R^1 \Rightarrow (a + b) + c = a + (b + c).$

(A3)   ∃ one and only one real number, denoted by 0, such that $a + 0 = a$ for every $a \in R^1$.

(A4) $a \in R^1 \Rightarrow$ ∃ a unique element $(-a) \in R^1$ such that $a + (-a) = 0.$

(M1) $a, b \in R^1 \Rightarrow a \cdot b = b \cdot a.$

(M2) $a, b, c \in R^1 \Rightarrow (a \cdot b) \cdot c = a \cdot (b \cdot c).$

(M3)   ∃ a unique real number 1, $1 \neq 0$, such that $a \cdot 1 = a$ for all $a \in R^1$.

(M4) $a \in R^1, a \neq 0 \Rightarrow$ ∃ a unique element $a^{-1} \in R^1$ such that $a \cdot a^{-1} = 1.$

(D) $a, b, c \in R^1 \Rightarrow a \cdot (b + c) = a \cdot b + a \cdot c.$

These axioms (postulates, assumptions) are commonly referred to in certain terms and we should note these here. (C) is referred to as the *closure axiom*. (A1) and (M1) are called the *commutative laws* for *addition* and *multiplication*, respectively; (A2) and (M2) are called the *associative laws*. (A3) is called the *zero axiom* or the *axiom of the additive identity*. (M3) is referred to as the *unity axiom* or the *axiom of the multiplicative identity*. (A4) and (M4) are called the *additive* and *multiplicative inverse axioms*, respectively, and (D) is referred to as the *left distributive law*.

We note that (C) is included as an axiom merely for convenience and that it is implied by the fact that $+$ and $\cdot$ are binary operations on R^1.

2.3   Some Algebra of the Real Numbers

On the basis of these axioms we can prove many properties of real numbers that you have probably assumed before this. We will state some of these as theorems and prove them. The proofs of some of the theorems we list are left as exercises.

Theorem 2.1. Let a and b be real numbers. There exists one and only one real number x such that $a + x = b$.

Proof. Consider the number $-a + b$. Then

$$a + (-a + b) = (a + (-a)) + b, \text{ by (A2)}.$$

$$(a + (-a)) + b = 0 + b, \text{ by (A4)}.$$

$$0 + b = b + 0, \text{ by (A1)}.$$

$$b + 0 = b, \text{ by (A3)}.$$

By the transitivity of equality we see that $a + (-a + b) = b$. Hence, there exists a number with the desired property.

Suppose that x and y are real numbers so that $a + x = b$ and $a + y = b$. Then $a + x = a + y$ and, by (A1), $x + a = y + a$. Then $-a$ exists and

$$(x + a) + (-a) = (y + a) + (-a).$$

By (A2), $x + (a + (-a)) = y + (a + (-a))$ and by (A4), $x + 0 = y + 0$. Finally, by (A3), $x = y$. Thus, only one number x exists with the property that $a + x = b$.

This theorem says that for any pair of real numbers, a and b, there is exactly one number x with the property that $a + x = b$. We use this fact frequently in the following way: Suppose that we know that $a + 3 = 6$. Further suppose that we show that y is a number so that $a + y = 6$. By Theorem 2.1, we conclude that $y = 3$.

In most of the following theorems, the reasons for the steps taken are omitted. The reader will be expected to furnish the reasons as exercises in many instances.

Theorem 2.2. For any $a \in R^1$, $0 + a = a$.

Proof.
$$0 + a = a + 0.$$

$$a + 0 = a.$$

So, by transitivity of equality, $0 + a = a$.

Theorem 2.3. For any $a \in R^1$, $a \cdot 0 = 0$.

Proof.
$$a \cdot 0 = a \cdot 0 + 0.$$

$$a \cdot 0 = a \cdot 0 + (a + (-a)).$$

$$a \cdot 0 + (a + (-a)) = (a \cdot 0 + a) + (-a).$$

$$(a \cdot 0 + a) + (-a) = (a \cdot 0 + a \cdot 1) + (-a).$$

$$(a \cdot 0 + a \cdot 1) + (-a) = a \cdot (0 + 1) + (-a).$$

$$a \cdot (0 + 1) + (-a) = a \cdot 1 + (-a).$$

$$a \cdot 1 + (-a) = a + (-a).$$

$$a + (-a) = 0.$$

Using the transitivity of equality, we have that $a \cdot 0 = 0$ for every $a \in R^1$. This completes the theorem.

Exercise

Give the reason for each "$=$" in Theorem 2.3.

This theorem assures us that the correct products of $3 \cdot 0$, $-2 \cdot 0$, $\pi \cdot 0$, $\frac{5}{2} \cdot 0$ are all 0.

Theorem 2.4. For any $a \in R^1$, $(-1) \cdot a = -a$.

Proof. Note that

$$a + (-1)a = a \cdot 1 + (-1)a = a \cdot 1 + a \cdot (-1)$$
$$= a(1 + (-1)) = a \cdot 0 = 0 .$$

Since $(-a)$ is the only element with the property that

$$a + (-a) = 0, \text{ then } (-a) = (-1) \cdot a .$$

In this proof, rather than writing out separate equalities, we have strung them together. This has one merit: it saves paper and ink. Since it has no real disadvantage, we continue to do it.

Exercise

State the reasons why each equality holds.

Theorem 2.5. For all $a, b, c \in R^1$,

$$(a + b)c = a \cdot c + b \cdot c .$$

Proof. Exercise.

Theorem 2.4 tells us that we may rewrite -2 as $-1 \cdot 2$ or $-2/3$ as $-1 \cdot (2/3)$. Theorem 2.5 is known as the *right distributive law* and, for example, allows us to rewrite the number $(4 + 5) \cdot 3$ as $4 \cdot 3 + 5 \cdot 3$.

Theorem 2.6. For $a, b, \in R^1$, $(-a) \cdot b = -(a \cdot b)$.

Proof. $(-a) \cdot b = ((-1) \cdot a) \cdot b = (-1) \cdot (a \cdot b) = -(ab)$.

This is, of course, the old law that tells us that $(-10)(2) = -20$ and, in general, that "a minus times a plus is a minus."

Theorem 2.7. For any $a, b \in R^1$, $a \cdot (-b) = -(a \cdot b)$.

Proof. Exercise.

Theorem 2.8. For any $a \in R^1$, $-(-a) = a$.

Proof. $(-a) + (-(-a)) = 0$ and $-a + a = 0$. So by the uniqueness of $-(-a)$, $-(-a) = a$.

Here again we have used the method of proof, using Theorem 2.1., that was stated after Theorem 2.1.

Theorem 2.9. For $a, b \in R^1$, $(-a) \cdot (-b) = a \cdot b$.

Proof. $(-a) \cdot (-b) = -(a \cdot (-b)) = -(-(ab)) = ab$.

Here is the familiar, mystifying law that assures us that the product of two negative numbers is positive. For example, $(-2) \cdot (-3) = 2 \cdot 3 = 6$.

Theorem 2.10. Let a and $b \in R^1$, $a \neq 0$. Then there exists one and only one real number x so that $ax = b$.

Proof. Since $a \neq 0$, a^{-1} exists and $a^{-1}b$ is a real number. But $a(a^{-1}b) = (aa^{-1})b = 1 \cdot b = b \cdot 1 = b$. So there is a number x with the desired property. Suppose x and y are both real numbers such that $ax = b$ and $ay = b$. Then $ax = ay$. From this, $a^{-1} \cdot ax = a^{-1} \cdot ay$ or $x = y$. Thus there is only one number with this property.

Theorem 2.11. For $a, b \in R^1$, $a \neq 0$, $b \neq 0$, $a^{-1}b^{-1} = (ab)^{-1}$.

Proof.

$$(ab)(a^{-1}b^{-1}) = a(ba^{-1})b^{-1} = a(a^{-1}b)b^{-1} = (aa^{-1})(bb^{-1}) = 1 \cdot 1 = 1 .$$

So, by M4,

$$(ab)^{-1} = a^{-1}b^{-1} .$$

We might note here that it is the uniqueness of the solution expressed in Theorem 2.10 that we used. For we know $(ab)^{-1}$ is a solution to $(ab)x = 1$. Since $a^{-1}b^{-1}$ is also a solution, we know it must be, by uniqueness, $(ab)^{-1}$.

Theorem 2.12. Let $a, b, x \in R^1$.

$$a + x = b + x \Rightarrow a = b .$$

Proof. Exercise.

Theorem 2.13. Let $a, b, x \in R^1$. If $x \neq 0$ and if $ax = bx$, then $a = b$.

Proof. $x \neq 0 \Rightarrow x^{-1}$ exists. Then

$$ax = bx \Rightarrow (ax)x^{-1} = (bx)x^{-1} \Rightarrow a = b .$$

The preceding two theorems are known as the *cancellation laws* for addition and multiplication. The way they are stated makes them right (on the right) cancellation laws. Since A1 and M1 hold, it should be clear that we can cancel on the left as well.

Theorem 2.14. Let $a, b \in R^1$. Then $a \cdot b = 0$ if and only if either $a = 0$ or $b = 0$.

Proof. If $a = 0$ or $b = 0$ then $a \cdot b = 0$ by Theorem 2.3. Suppose that $a \cdot b = 0$ and that $a \neq 0$. Then $a \neq 0 \Rightarrow a^{-1}$ exists.

Then
$$a \cdot b = 0 \Rightarrow a^{-1} \cdot a \cdot b = a^{-1} \cdot 0 = 0.$$
Thus
$$1 \cdot b = b = 0.$$

This is an important theorem insofar as it is the key to what we think of as the solution of certain equations by factoring. The theorem tells us that, whenever the product of two numbers is 0, at least one of the factors is 0.

2.4 Applications

We could now prove many other theorems of the foregoing type, but instead let us look at some problems in algebra in the light of what we have been doing.

Suppose that we are asked to solve the linear equation $2x + 4 = 4x + 10$. We are asked, then, to find the real numbers x for which the equation is a true statement. Suppose that x_0 is a number for which $2x_0 + 4 = 4x_0 + 10$. Then $(2x_0 + 4) + (-4x_0 - 4) = (4x_0 + 10) + (-4x_0 - 4)$ or $-4x_0 + 2x_0 = 10 + (-4)$ by the substitution principle, and the use of the foregoing results. By Theorem 2.5,

$$(-4 + 2)x_0 = 10 + (-4)$$

and using arithmetic (adding signed numbers), we get $-2x_0 = 6$. Finally, $(-\frac{1}{2})(-2x_0) = -\frac{1}{2} \cdot 6$. From this, we get $x_0 = -3$. So, if x_0 is a solution for our equation, we have $x_0 = -3$. In fact, we are not done because we do not know that -3 is a solution. To conclude, we note that $2(-3) + 4 = 4(-3) + 10$ because $-2 = -2$.

Earlier, we defined what we meant by the solution set of an equation in two real variables. In dealing with an equation q in one variable x, we will define the solution set as

$$\{x \mid q \text{ is a true statement}\} .$$

In light of this definition, the solution set for the equation $2x + 4 = 4x + 10$ in the given example is $\{-3\}$.

In the preceding problem, everything went well. But other things might have happened. For example, consider the equation $2x + 4 = 2x + 3$. Suppose that x_0 is a solution for this equation. So we assume that x_0 is a number so that $2x_0 + 4 = 2x_0 + 3$. On investigation, it is easy to see that this implies that $4 = 3$, which we know to be untrue. The situation, then, is one where the assumption that there existed a solution x_0 led us to a false statement. So our assumption must have been wrong. In fact, for every real x, it is false that $2x + 4 = 2x + 3$. The solution set for this equation is, then, $\emptyset$.

Suppose that we want to solve the following quadratic equation in one variable:

$$x^2 + 3x + 2 = 0 .$$

Suppose that x_0 is a solution. Then it is true that $x_0^2 + 3x_0 + 2 = 0$. Factoring, we see that it is also true that $(x_0 + 2)(x_0 + 1) = 0$. By Theorem 2.14, if x_0 is a solution, then either $x_0 + 2 = 0$ or $x_0 + 1 = 0$. This means, of course, that either $x_0 = -2$ or $x_0 = -1$. As we indicated before, we are not done but have merely shown that, if x_0 is a solution, then x_0 is either -2 or -1. But $(-1)^2 + 3 \cdot (-1) + 2 = 1 - 3 + 2 = 0$ and $(-2)^2 + 3(-2) + 2 = 4 - 6 + 2 = 0$. So the solution set is $\{-2, -1\}$.

Exercise 2.4

1. For the following equations, find the solution sets in R^1.

   (a) $3x - 4 = 6x + 5$.   (b) $9x + 2 = 9x - 4$.

   (c) $(x - 2)^2 = 0$.   (d) $(x - 2)^2 = 4$.

   (e) $(x - 2)(x + 1) = 0$.   (f) $6x^2 - 19x - 7 = 0$.

   (g) $8x^2 = x$.   (h) $x^3 - 8 = 0$.

   (i) $x^3 + 5x + 4 = -2$.   (j) $\dfrac{1}{x} + 3 = 6$.

   (k) $x - \dfrac{1}{x} = 0$.   (l) $\dfrac{x+2}{2} - \dfrac{8}{x} = 1$.

   (m) $(x + 2)^2 = x + 2$.

2. Prove the following:

   $a, b, c \in R^1$, $a \cdot b \cdot c = 0 \Leftrightarrow$ either $a = 0$ or $b = 0$ or $c = 0$.

3. Prove that $2(x - 3) = 0 \Rightarrow x = 3$.

4. Prove that

   $$\frac{1}{x^2 + 2}(x - 4)(x + 2) = 0 \Rightarrow \text{either } x = 4 \quad \text{or} \quad x = -2 .$$

5. Prove that $a \cdot (b - c) = 0$; $a, b, c \in R^1 \Rightarrow b = c$.

6. Prove that $2(x^2 - y^2) = 0 \Rightarrow$ either $x = y$ or $x = -y$.

2.5   Subtraction and Division

By this time the reader might have wondered what has happened to "subtraction" and "division." To take care of this we now add the following definition.

Definition 2.3. Let a and $b \in R^1$. We define $a - b$ to be $a + (-b)$ and a/b to be $a \cdot b^{-1}$, if $b \neq 0$.

Using these definitions, we arrive at familiar results such as the following:

Theorem 2.15. For all $a, b, c \in R^1$,

$$a(b - c) = ab - ac.$$

Proof.

$$a(b - c) = a(b + (-c)) = ab + a(-c) = ab + (-(ac))$$
$$= ab - ac.$$

Theorem 2.16. Let $a, b, c, d \in R^1$ and suppose $b \neq 0 \neq d$. Then

$$\frac{a}{b} + \frac{c}{d} = \frac{ad + bc}{bd}.$$

Proof.

$$\frac{a}{b} + \frac{c}{d} = ab^{-1} + cd^{-1}$$

$$= (ab^{-1})(dd^{-1}) + (cd^{-1})(bb^{-1})$$
$$= (ad)(b^{-1}d^{-1}) + (bc)(b^{-1}d^{-1})$$
$$= (ad + bc)(b^{-1}d^{-1})$$
$$= (ad + bc)(bd)^{-1} = \frac{ad + bc}{bd}.$$

Exercise 2.5

Perform the indicated operations.

(a) $\dfrac{2}{3} + \dfrac{3}{5}.$

(b) $\dfrac{1}{7} + \dfrac{1}{8}.$

(c) $\dfrac{1}{3} + \dfrac{1}{4}.$

(d) $\dfrac{1}{6} + \dfrac{1}{5}.$

(e) $\dfrac{1}{x} + \dfrac{y}{3}.$

(f) $\dfrac{1}{x} - \dfrac{1}{x + 1}.$

(g) $\dfrac{1}{x+2} + \dfrac{1}{x-2}$.

(h) $\dfrac{1}{x} - \dfrac{1}{x-1}$.

(i) $\dfrac{x}{2} + \dfrac{2}{x}$.

(j) $\dfrac{1}{x} + \dfrac{x}{2}$.

(k) $\left(\dfrac{1}{x} - \dfrac{x}{2}\right)\left(\dfrac{x}{3} - \dfrac{1}{x}\right)$.

(l) $\dfrac{2}{x} - \dfrac{x}{2}$.

(m) $\dfrac{x+2}{2} - \dfrac{2}{x+2}$.

(n) $\dfrac{1-x}{x} + \dfrac{x}{1+x}$.

(o) $\dfrac{1}{x} + \dfrac{1}{y} + \dfrac{1}{z}$.

(p) $\dfrac{x}{y} + \dfrac{y}{z} + \dfrac{z}{x}$.

For completeness and to allow us to write equations in their usual form, we make the following definition:

Definition 2.4. $x^1 = x$ for every $x \in R^1$. $x^n = x^{n-1} \cdot x^1$ for every $x \in R^1$ and any positive integer n. $x^{-n} = (x^{-1})^n$ for every $x \in R^1$, $x \neq 0$, and every positive integer n. $x^0 = 1$ for every $x \neq 0$, $x \in R^1$.

Using this definition, it is possible to prove the usual rules of operating with exponents. A formal proof for these rules will not be presented here. In a later section, we will look at a few of these proofs.

As a reminder, the rules of interest are

$$a^m b^m = (ab)^m, \qquad a^m a^n = a^{m+n}, \qquad \frac{a^m}{b^m} = \left(\frac{a}{b}\right)^m,$$

$$\frac{a^m}{a^n} = a^{m-n}, \qquad \text{and} \qquad (a^m)^n = a^{mn}.$$

There are many properties of real numbers concerned with the operations of subtraction and multiplication that could be listed. Some of these are included in Exercise 2.6.

As a sample of the type of property we might consider, we have

$$\left(\frac{a}{b}\right)^{-1} = \frac{b}{a} \quad \text{if} \quad a \neq 0 \neq b \; ;$$

since

$$\frac{a}{b} \cdot \frac{b}{a} = 1.$$

Also,

$$\left(\frac{a/b}{c/d}\right) = \frac{ad}{bc}$$

because

$$\left(\frac{a/b}{c/d}\right) = \frac{a}{b} \cdot \left(\frac{c}{d}\right)^{-1} = \left(\frac{a}{b} \cdot \frac{d}{c}\right) = \left(\frac{ad}{bc}\right).$$

Exercise 2.6

1. Give reasons for each equality in Theorems 2.15 and 2.16.

2. Show that:

(a) $\dfrac{a}{b} \cdot \dfrac{c}{d} = \dfrac{ac}{bd}$.

(b) $(a^{-1})^{-1} = a$ if $a \neq 0$.

(c) $(a + b)(c + d) = ac + ad + bc + bd$.

(d) $(a - b)(a + b) = a^2 - b^2$.

(e) $\dfrac{a}{b} = \dfrac{c}{d} \Leftrightarrow ad = bc$ $(b \neq 0 \neq d)$.

(f) $(a + b)^2 = a^2 + 2ab + b^2$.

(g) $(a + b)^3 = a^3 + 3a^2b + 3ab^2 + b^3$.

(h) $a^2 = b^2 \Leftrightarrow$ either $a = b$ or $a = -b$.

(i) $a - b = -(b - a)$.

(j) $(a - b)^2(a + b) = a^3 - ab^2 - ba^2 + b^3$.

2.6 Integers and Rational Numbers

We now turn our attention to a particular subset of R^1 called the set of *positive integers* or *natural numbers*. Rather intuitively, we think of these as the numbers obtained by adding 1 to itself a finite (including 1 by itself) number of times. This, however, leaves us with no sound basis for dealing with them. Consider, then, the following definition.

Definition 2.5. The set N of natural numbers is a subset of R^1 satisfying the following properties:

1. $1 \in N$

2. $k \in N \Rightarrow k + 1 \in N$

3. If $S \subset N$, and if S satisfies (1) and (2), then $S = N$.

Now (1) and (2) satisfy our intuition, saying that 1, and all finite sums of 1 with itself, are in N. Property (3) tells us that N is the "smallest" set with these properties. Property (3) also is the basis for a very powerful mathematical tool, called *mathematical induction*, that we will discuss later.

With no more than this definition, we can proceed rather well. For example, we can prove the following theorem:

Theorem 2.17. Let $m \in N$. Then for every $n \in N$, $m + n \in N$.

This theorem means that the sum of every two natural numbers is a natural number. Another way of saying this is that the set N is closed under the addition of R^1.

Proof. Let $K = \{x \in N \mid m + x \in N\}$. Note first that, since $m \in N$, $m + 1 \in N$ (property 2 of our definition). Thus $1 \in K$. Now assume $n \in K$. This means that $m + n \in N$. But (again by property (2) of our definition) $m + n \in N$ implies $(m + n) + 1 \in N$. But

$$(m + n) + 1 = m + (n + 1)$$

because $N \subset R^1$ and R^1 satisfies axiom A2. Thus, if $n \in K$, $n + 1 \in K$. So $K \subset N$ and K satisfies properties (1) and (2) of Definition 2.5. Thus, by property (3) of our definition, $K = N$. This means that every sum $m + n$, $n \in N$ is a number in N, which is what we set out to prove.

Another theorem of this same type, the proof of which is left as an exercise is

Theorem 2.18. Let $m \in N$. Then for every $n \in N$, the product $m \cdot n \in N$.

Proof. Exercise.

The meaning of this theorem is simply that the product of any pair of elements in N is an element in N.

From here on, we will use the usual names and symbols for the natural numbers; that is, $1 + 1$ is 2, $2 + 1$ is 3, etc.

We can extend our present concept to get the set I of integers. From the deep past we know we need to "add" 0 and the numbers $-1, -2, -3, \ldots$ to N to get the set I. We do this by the following definition:

Definition 2.6. The set I of integers is defined by

$$I = \{x \in R^1 \mid x = m - n \text{ for some } m, n \in N\}.$$

This definition, of course, allows many representations for the same integer. For example, -2 is either $1 - 3$, or $2 - 4$, or $100 - 102$. None the less, every integer can be expressed as the difference of two natural numbers and such differences yield only integers.

Observe that the integers include $-x$ for every positive integer x. For, if x is a positive integer, $x + 1$ is a positive integer and $1 - (x + 1)$ is an integer. Of course 0 is an integer, because $0 = x - x$ for any positive integer x.

Notice that we are not attempting to prove that these are integers but simply agreeing that they are. It is undoubtedly true that the reader has some notion of integers that precedes the notion he now has of real numbers. We are not going to try to justify the identification we have just made, but we will assume that the set of integers, as we have defined them, is the set of integers familiar to the reader.

With this in mind, if $m \in I \subset R^1$, $m \neq 0$, then $1/m \in R^1$. Further, if $n \in I$, then $n \cdot 1/m = n/m \in R^1$. We can now define the so-called rational numbers.

Definition 2.7. The set Ra of rational numbers is defined by

$$Ra = \left\{ x \in R^1 \mid x = \frac{n}{m} \text{ for some } m, n \in I, m \neq 0 \right\}.$$

Consider the sets I, Ra, R^1. We have the following inclusions: $I \subset Ra \subset R^1$. It is true that for $x, y \in I$, $x + y \in R^1$ and $x \cdot y \in R^1$. It is also true that if $x, y \in Ra$, $x + y \in R^1$ and $x \cdot y \in R^1$. We can, however, say more than this.

This definition tells us that those numbers, and only those numbers, that can be represented as the quotient of two integers (of course the denominator must not be zero) are rational numbers.

Note that every integer is a rational number. We have the fact that $1 \in I$ and that $1^{-1} = 1$. Thus, for $x \in I$, $x = x \cdot 1 = x \cdot 1^{-1} = x/1$. So every integer x has a representation, namely $x/1$, as a quotient of two integers.

Theorem 2.19. Let $x, y \in I$. Then $x + y \in I$ and $x \cdot y \in I$.

Proof. First recall (Theorem 2.17), for any two positive integers u, v, $u + v$ is a positive integer. Also recall (Theorem 2.18) that, if u, v are positive integers, then $u \cdot v$ is a positive integer.

Now if $x, y \in I$, $x = m - n$ and $y = u - v$, where m, n, u, v are positive integers. Then

$$x + y = (m - n) + (u - v) = (m + u) - (n + v).$$

By the preceding remarks, $x + y \in I$.

Also $x \cdot y = (m - n)(u - v) = (mu + nv) - (nu + mv)$. Since mu, nv, nu, mv are all positive integers, $x \cdot y \in I$.

Theorem 2.20. Let $x, y \in Ra$. Then $x + y$ and $x \cdot y \in Ra$.

Proof. If $x = m/n$, $y = r/s$, where $m, n, r, s \in I$, $n \neq 0 \neq x$, then the proof is clear because

$$x \cdot y = \frac{mr}{ns} \quad \text{and} \quad x + y = \frac{ms + nr}{ns}.$$

and Theorem 2.19.

These two theorems say that I and Ra are closed under the operations of addition and multiplication. In fact, they are of interest themselves, studied relative to these operations. It is not difficult to see that Ra satisfies *all* the axioms we have listed for real numbers.

Exercise

Verify that Ra under $+$ and $\cdot$ satisfy these axioms. Also verify that I satisfies some of these axioms but not others. For example, M4 is not satisfied. Why? (Give a counterexample.)

As we have pointed out, it is true that $I \subset Ra \subset R^1$. In each case, however, the inclusions denote proper subsets. That is, there are real numbers that are not in Ra and elements in Ra that are not in I.

In the past, in solving equations we sought real number solutions. We could have restricted ourselves to finding only the integral solutions — that is, only the solutions in the set I — or the rational number solutions.

EXAMPLE. Consider the equation $x - 2 = 0$. This has only one solution, the number 2; 2 is an element of I, Ra and R^1. But the equation $2x - 1 = 0$ has only the solution $x = \frac{1}{2}$. So the solution set in I is $\varnothing$, but in Ra and R^1 it is $\frac{1}{2}$. The equation $x^2 - 2 = 0$ has solution set $\{-\sqrt{2}, \sqrt{2}\}$. But this means that it has no solutions in I and RA.

Exercise 2.7

1. Solve the following equations in the set of integers.

   (a) $x + 2 = 2x - 1$.   (b) $x + 2 = x + 3$.

   (c) $x^2 + 4x + 4 = 0$.   (d) $x^2 - 6x + 8 = 0$.

   (e) $\dfrac{1}{x} + 3 = \dfrac{1}{2}$.   (f) $2x + 1 = 4$.

   (g) $x^2 - 4 = 0$.   (h) $x^2 + 2 = 0$.

2. (a) Solve the preceding equations in the set of rational numbers.

   (b) Solve the foregoing equations in the set of real numbers.

2.7   Order Axiom

We turn our attention now to another property of the real numbers. Earlier we defined the concept of "relation." We recall and review this now. A relation on a set X is simply a subset L of $X \times X$. So it is a way of pairing elements of X. If $(x, y) \in L$; $x, y \in X$; we will say that x is related to y by L. As a matter of notation we usually write $x L y$ to indicate that $(x, y) \in L$. Frequently we use a symbol different than a letter to denote a relation. Now the reader is familiar with certain relations both from everyday life and from his earlier study of mathematics. For example, let X be the set of all people. Consider the subset L of $X \times X$ defined by

$$L = \{(x, y) \mid x, y \in X \text{ and } x \text{ knows } y\} \,.$$

We would write $x L y$ if the person x knows the person y.

As another example, let Y be the set of all triangles in a plane. Consider the subset K of $Y \times Y$ defined by:

$$K = \{(\alpha, \beta) \mid \alpha \text{ is similar to } \beta; \alpha, \beta \in Y\} \,.$$

If triangle α is similar to β we would then write $(\alpha, \beta) \in K$ or $\alpha K \beta$. As a matter of fact, we have a common symbol to denote this relation, namely $\sim$.

We might also mention again that, if X is any set, " $=$ " is a relation. More explicitly, " $=$ " is defined to be the set

$$\{(x, y) \mid x \text{ is the same element of } X \text{ as is } y\} \,.$$

We pointed out earlier that " $=$ " is an equivalence relation, i.e., a reflexive, symmetric, and transitive relation.

Now in dealing with real numbers there is another property or axiom that we should introduce. This is referred to, commonly, as *the ordering axiom* or *the axiom of order*. It is as follows:

(O) There is a relation, denoted by $<$, on R^1 which satisfies the following properties:

(O1) For any pair, a, b, of elements of R^1, one and only one of $a = b$, $a < b$, $b < a$ holds.

(O2) $a < b, b < c \Rightarrow a < c$; $a, b, c \in R^1$.

(O3) $a < b \Rightarrow a + c < b + c$; $a, b, c \in R^1$.

(O4) $a < b, 0 < c \Rightarrow ac < bc$; $a, b, c \in R^1$.

Remark. We read $a < b$, for $a, b \in R^1$, as "a is less than b." We frequently write $b > a$ to denote $a < b$. In what we do, we will not hesitate to use either notation. Here we read $b > a$ as, "b is greater than a." Axiom (O1) is usually referred to as the *Trichotomy law* and requires that, for any pair of real numbers, one and only one of the three alternatives holds. Axiom (O2) is, in our terminology, developed for relations, the requirement that $<$ is a transitive relation. Axioms (O3) and (O4) are basic properties, familiar to the reader, that we assume in order to prove other properties of this relation.

We can now prove some of these familiar properties of real numbers. First, to agree with everyday usage, we make the definition:

Definition 2.8. If $a > 0$, we call a *positive*, and if $a < 0$, we call a *negative*.

Two basic theorems follow:

Theorem 2.21. Let $a, b, \in R^1$. If $a < b$ then $-b < -a$.

Proof. $a < b \Rightarrow a + (-a) + (-b) < b + (-a) + (-b)$ by Axiom (O3). But

$$a + (-a) + (-b) = -b \quad \text{and} \quad b + (-a) + (-b) = -a.$$

Thus

$$-b < -a.$$

This theorem tells us that changing the signs of the numbers in an inequality reverses the direction of the inequality. Thus, since $3 < 5$, $-3 > -5$.

Theorem 2.22. Let $a, b, c, d \in R^1$. $a < b$ and $c < d \Rightarrow a + c < b + d$.

Proof. $a < b \Rightarrow a + c < b + c$ by Axiom (O3). $c < d \Rightarrow b + c < b + d$ by Axiom (O3) and (A1). Then, by Axiom (O2), we have $a + c < b + d$.

This is the result that adding inequalities maintains the direction of the inequality. For example, $2 < 3$ and $4 < 7$ allows us to conclude that $6 < 10$. A result that we now expect is

Theorem 2.23. Let $a, b, c \in R^1$. $a < b, c < 0 \Rightarrow ac > bc$.

Proof. $c < 0 \Rightarrow 0 < -c$, by Theorem 2.21. By Axiom (O4) we have $a(-c) < b(-c)$ or that $-(ac) < -(bc)$. By Theorem 2.21,

$$-(ac) < -(bc) \Rightarrow -(-(ac)) > -(-(bc)) \text{ or } ac > bc.$$

The following theorem proves a fact that in the past we have assumed. We have postulated that 1 is not 0. Now we are in a position to prove 1 positive. This proof makes rather strong use of the Trichotomy law, Axiom (O1).

Theorem 2.24. 1 is positive.

Proof. Suppose $1 < 0$. By Theorem 2.20, $0 < -1$. Using Axiom (O4), we get that $0 \cdot (-1) < (-1)(-1) = 1$. But, if both $1 < 0$ and $0 < 1$ hold, Axiom (O1) is contradicted. So it is false that $1 < 0$. On the other hand, by Axiom (M3), $1 \neq 0$. So by Axiom (O1), we have $0 < 1$.

Below are proved several theorems that are useful in work dealing with inequalities.

Theorem 2.25. Let $a \in R^1$, $a \neq 0$. Then $a^2 > 0$.

Proof. If $a > 0$, by Axiom (O4), $a \cdot a = a^2 > a \cdot 0 = 0$. If $a < 0$, $(-a) > 0$, and by Axiom (O4), $(-a)(-a) > 0 \cdot (-a)$. Thus $a^2 > 0$.

An obvious consequence of this theorem is that the square root of a negative number is not a real number. For, if $x = \sqrt{u}$, where $u < 0$, then $x^2 = u < 0$. This, of course, contradicts Theorem 2.25.

Theorem 2.26. Let $a, b, c, d \in R^1$. If all are positive, then $a < b$, $c < d \Rightarrow ac < bd$.

Proof. Since $b > 0$, $c > 0$ we have that $a < b$, $c < d \Rightarrow ac < bc$, $bc < bd$, by Axiom (O4). But by Axiom (O2), $ac < bc$, $bc < bd \Rightarrow ac < bd$.

Theorem 2.27. $a > 0 \Rightarrow 1/a > 0$, and $a < 0 \Rightarrow 1/a < 0$ for any $a \in R^1$.

Proof. Suppose $a > 0$ but suppose $1/a < 0$. Then $0 < -(1/a)$. By Axiom (O4), $0 < (-1/a) \cdot a = -1$. By Theorem 2.21, this gives us $1 < 0$, contrary to Theorem 2.24. (Finish the proof as an exercise.)

Theorem 2.28. Let $a, b \in R^1$.

(1) If $a > 0$, $b > 0$, then $a \cdot b > 0$.

(2) If $a < 0$, $b < 0$, then $a \cdot b > 0$.

(3) If $a > 0$, $b < 0$, then $a \cdot b < 0$.

Proof. (1) $0 < a$, $0 < b \Rightarrow 0 \cdot b < a \cdot b \Rightarrow 0 < ab$.

(2) $a < 0$, $b < 0 \Rightarrow -a > 0$, $-b > 0 \Rightarrow (-a)(-b) > 0 \Rightarrow ab > 0$.

(3) $a > 0$, $b < 0 \Rightarrow a \cdot b < a \cdot 0 \Rightarrow ab < 0$.

Exercise 2.8

1. Give the reason for each step in Theorem 2.28.

2. Prove that $a > 0$ implies $a^{-1} > 0$.

3. Prove that $a < 0$ implies $a^{-1} < 0$.

4. Prove that $a > b > 0 \Rightarrow a^{-1} < b^{-1}$.

5. Prove that $a > b > 0 \Rightarrow a^2 > b^2$.

2.8 Applications

We now look at some problems involving $<$. First let us note that, when we "solve" an inequality, q, in one real variable, we are again looking for a solution set. As before, this set would be $\{x \mid q$ is a true statement$\}$. Following convention, we will "solve some inequalities." Usually one is asked to solve an inequality like $2x + 4 < 0$. By this we mean that one should find the set of real numbers, x, for which it is true that $2x + 4 < 0$. Our approach to this problem is pretty much the same as our approach to solving linear equations. Suppose that x_0 is a solution. Then x_0 is a number for which it is true that $2x_0 + 4 < 0$. By Axiom (O3) we can add -4 on both sides. Finally, since $\frac{1}{2} > 0$, we can multiply both sides by $\frac{1}{2}$ to get that $x_0 < -2$. We now have that, if x_0 is a solution, $x_0 < -2$. Suppose that y is any number so that $y < -2$. Then $2y < -4$ and $2y + 4 < 0$. So we see that the solution set is $\{x \mid x \in R^1$ and $x < -2\}$. (Graph this solution set on a line.)

A slightly more complicated problem is the following: Solve $(x - 2)(x + 1) < 0$. As before, we mean find the set of all real numbers, x, for which it is true that $(x - 2)(x + 1) < 0$. Suppose that x_0 is a solution. By Theorem 2.28, we see that it is necessary that the factors $(x_0 - 2)$ and $(x_0 + 1)$ be such that, either $x_0 - 2 < 0$ and $x_0 + 1 > 0$, or $x_0 - 2 > 0$ and $x_0 + 1 < 0$. For, if both were positive or both were negative, the product would be positive. If $x_0 - 2 < 0$, or $x_0 < 2$, then $x_0 + 1 > 0$ or $x_0 > -1$. So, if x_0 is a solution and if $x_0 < 2$, it must be true, also, that $x_0 > -1$. On the other hand, if $x_0 - 2 > 0$, or $x_0 > 2$, then $x_0 + 1 < 0$ or $x_0 < -1$. So, if x_0 is a solution and if $x_0 > 2$, x_0 also satisfies the condition that $x_0 < -1$. But this situation cannot happen, for, if x_0 satisfies both of $2 < x_0$ and $x_0 < -1$, then $2 < -1$, which is not true. We also note that x_0 cannot be 2, for, if $x_0 = 2$,

$$(x_0 - 2)(x_0 + 1) = 0 .$$

So, if x_0 is a solution, it must satisfy $x_0 < 2$ and $x_0 > -1$. Suppose, now that y is any number in the interval $(-1, 2)$. Then $(y + 1) > 0$ and $(y - 2) < 0$. Thus $(y - 2)(y + 1) < 0$. So the solution set is $(-1, 2)$. For, if x_0 is a solution, we have shown $x_0 \in (-1, 2)$ and, if $y \in (-1, 2)$, then y is a solution to our inequality.

Exercise 2.9

1. Find the solution sets in R^1 for the following inequalities. Give a reason for each step of the solution.

(a) $x + 4 < 0$.

(b) $x + 2 < 7$.

(c) $2x + 4 < 8$.

(d) $3x + 6 < -15$.

(e) $3x - 21 < 4x + 1$.

(f) $2x + 6 < 7x + 2$.

(g) $\dfrac{1}{2x + 1} > 0.$

(h) $\dfrac{2}{x + 1} > 0.$

(i) $\dfrac{x}{1 - x} > 0.$

(j) $\dfrac{3x}{x} + 2 > 0.$

(k) $(x - 1)(x - 2) > 0.$

(l) $(x - 1)(x + 2) < 0.$

(m) $x^2 - 4 > 0.$

(n) $x^2 + 4 > 0.$

(o) $x^2 + 4x + 4 < 0.$

(p) $(x^2 + 6x + 9) < 0.$

(q) $5 - 4x > 0.$

(r) $\dfrac{x^2}{x} + 2 < 0.$

(s) $x + 4 > 7 + 3x.$

(t) $x^2(x + 1)^2 < 0.$

(u) $3x - 5 < 3x - 4.$

(v) $x^2(x^2 - 1) < 0.$

(w) $x^2 + 2x > 0.$

(x) $x^2 + 2x < 4.$

2. Consider the relation $\leq$ on R^1 defined by $a, b \in R^1$, $a \leq b \Leftrightarrow$ either $a < b$ or $a = b$.

(a) Which of the properties, reflexivity, symmetry, transitivity, of relations are satisfied by the relation $\leq$?

(b) Which of Axioms (O1), (O2), (O3), and (O4) still hold when $<$ is replaced by $\leq$?

3. In question 1 replace $<$ by $\leq$ and $>$ by $\geq$ and find the solution sets in these new "inequalities."

2.9 Absolute Value

A useful concept is that of absolute value of real numbers. We will have occasion to use it notationally and to examine its meaning in other contexts as we proceed. Because its applications are usually concerned with the order relation, we introduce it here.

Definition 2.9. Let $a \in R^1$. The *absolute value of a*, denoted by $|a|$, is defined by

$$|a| = \begin{cases} a & \text{if } a \geq 0 \\ -a & \text{if } a < 0 \end{cases}$$

Remark. The absolute value is simply a function $\alpha: R^1 \to R^1$ defined by

$$\alpha(x) = \begin{cases} x & \text{if } x \geq 0 \\ -x & \text{if } x < 0. \end{cases}$$

We denote $\alpha(x)$ by $|x|$ instead of keeping the functional notation $\alpha(x)$.

From our definition, we see, for example, $|0| = 0$, $|2| = 2$, $|-3| = 3$, $|-2| = 2$, $|-1001| = 1001$. In effect, we simply ignore the sign on a number.

Probably the greatest confusion arises when we make a statement in letters, like $|x| = -x$. The statement is, of course, true if $x < 0$. For example, if $x = -4$, it is true that $|x| = -x$ because $|-4| = -(-4) = 4$. What is confusing is that $-x$ looks negative and one is inclined to forget that a variable, x, might well take on negative values in which case $-x$ is positive. Remember that our definition takes care of all the problems and is more reliable than intuition.

We now list certain properties of absolute value that we will find useful, but we do not state them as theorems. We will, however, prove certain of these properties.

Properties of absolute values.

(i) $|a|^2 = a^2 = (-a)^2$ for all $a \in R^1$

(ii) $|a| = \sqrt{a^2}$ for $a \in R^1$. (Here $\sqrt{}$ denotes the positive square root.)

(iii) $|x - y| = |y - x|$ for $x, y \in R^1$.

(iv) $|a - b| = |a| \cdot |b|$ for $a, b \in R^1$.

(v) $|a| \geq a$ for all $a \in R^1$.

(vi) $|a + b| \leq |a| + |b|$ for $a, b \in R^1$.

As indicated earlier, we now prove some of these and leave the remainder for the reader to prove as exercises.

(i) If $a \geq 0$, then $|a| = a$ and $|a|^2 = a^2$. If $a < 0$, then $(-a) > 0$ and $(-a)^2 = |a|^2$. But for all $a \in R^1$, $(-a)^2 = a^2$. So for any real number a, $|a|^2 = a^2 = (-a)^2$.

(iii) For any real number x, $|x| = |-x|$. Why? Since $y - x = -(x - y)$, we have

$$|y - x| = |x - y| .$$

(iv) If a and b are both positive,

$$|ab| = ab = |a| \cdot |b| .$$

If a and b are both negative

$$|ab| = ab = (-a)(-b) = |a| \cdot |b| .$$

If one of a and b is positive and the other negative, say $a > 0$, $b < 0$,

$$|ab| = -(ab) = a(-b) = |a| \cdot |b| .$$

We now want to look at some problems. We first consider the equation $|x| = 4$. Clearly, if $x = 4$ or if $x = -4$ we have true statements. Moreover, no other values for x make this a true statement. So the solution set of this equation is $\{4, -4\}$.

A bit more complicated problem is that of solving the inequality, $|x| < 4$. First, suppose x_0 is a solution and that $x_0 > 0$. Then

$$|x_0| = x_0 \quad \text{and} \quad x_0 < 4.$$

So a positive solution x_0 must satisfy the condition that $x_0 < 4$. If $x_0 = 0$, $|x_0| = 0 < 4$. If $x_0 < 0$, then $|x_0| = -x_0$ and, if x_0 is a solution, $-x_0 < 4$ or $x_0 > -4$. So, if x_0 is a solution, then $-4 < x_0 < 4$. On the other hand, if

$$x \in \{x \mid -4 < x < 4\}, \qquad |x| < 4.$$

Thus the solution set is

$$\{x \mid -4 < x < 4\} = (-4, 4).$$

Remark. As a matter of convenience it might be noted that for any real number $k > 0$, $|y| < k$, if and only if, $-k < y < k$.

Using this remark we can solve certain inequalities a bit more simply. For example, consider the inequality $|x - 4| < 3$ and let x_0 be a solution. Then $x_0 - 4$ is a real number and $|x_0 - 4| < 3$. But, by the preceding remark,

$$|x_0 - 4| < 3 \Leftrightarrow -3 < x_0 - 4 < 3.$$

and

$$-3 < x_0 - 4 < 3 \Leftrightarrow 1 < x_0 < 7.$$

Thus x_0 is a solution for $|x - 4| < 3$ if and only if $x_0 \in (1, 7)$. So the solution set for this equation is the open interval $(1, 7)$.

Another example which gives a rather surprising solution is the following:

$$|x - 1| + |x + 1| = 2.$$

For convenience, we will consider, separately, solutions x_0 satisfying $x_0 \geq 1$, $-1 < x_0 < 1$, and $x_0 \leq -1$. If $x_0 \geq 1$, then $x_0 - 1 \geq 0$ and $x_0 + 1 \geq 0$. Thus our equation, with x_0 replacing x, becomes

$$x_0 - 1 + x_0 + 1 = 2,$$

and $x_0 = 1$. If $x_0 \leq -1$, then $x_0 - 1 \leq 0$ and $x_0 + 1 \leq 0$, and we get

$$-(x_0 - 1) + (-(x_0 + 1)) = 2$$

and $x_0 = -1$. Finally, suppose that x_0 is a solution and that $-1 \leq x_0 \leq 1$. On replacing x by x_0, we get that

$$|x_0 - 1| + |x_0 + 1| = 2.$$

But $x_0 - 1 \leq 0$ and $x_0 + 1 \geq 0$. Thus we have

$$(-x_0 + 1) + (x_0 + 1) = 2.$$

But for all $x_0 \in R^1$ this is true. We see, then, that the solution set for this equation is $[-1, 1]$.

Exercise 2.10

1. Prove that if k is any real number, $k > 0$, $|y| < k \Leftrightarrow -k < y < k$.

2. Prove the properties of absolute value listed, but not proved, after Definition 2.9.

3. Solve the following:

   (a) $|x - 3| < 7$.   (b) $|x - 3| = 7$.

   (c) $|x - 3| > 7$.   (d) $|2x + 3| = 1$.

   (e) $|2x + 3| < 1$.   (f) $|x - 3| + |x + 3| = 6$.

   (g) $|x - 3| + |x + 3| = 4$.   (h) $|x - 3| + |x + 3| < 8$.

   (i) $|x| + |x - 3| \leq 4$.   (j) $|x|^2 + 2|x| + 1 \leq 4$.

4. Solve the following:

   (a) $|x + 1| = -1$.   (b) $|x + 1| + |x - 1| = 5$.

   (c) $|4x + 5| + |3x - 1| < 7$.   (d) $|2x| = 7$.

   (e) $|x| + x < 10$.   (f) $|5x| > 5x$.

   (g) $|x| \geq -2$.   (h) $|2x| + |x| = 4$.

   (i) $|x| < 0$.   (j) $\dfrac{|x + 1|}{x} > 0$.

2.10   The Quadratic Formula

A useful tool for the solution of quadratic equations is the so-called quadratic formula. We prove it here as another example of the type of results deriving from our axioms.

Theorem 2.29. Let $ax^2 + bx + c = 0$, $a \neq 0$, be a quadratic equation in the real variable x. Further suppose that $b^2 - 4ac \geq 0$. Then the solution set in R^1 for this equation is:

$$\left\{ \frac{-b + \sqrt{b^2 - 4ac}}{2a}, \frac{-b - \sqrt{b^2 - 4ac}}{2a} \right\}.$$

Proof. We will need in this proof the fact that for real numbers a and b, $a^2 = b^2$ implies either that $a = b$ or $a = -b$. (This result is Exercise 2.5(n).)

Let x_0 be a solution. Then it is true that

$$ax_0^2 + bx_0 + c = 0,$$

or that

$$ax_0^2 + bx_0 = -c.$$

If we multiply both sides by $4a$ (distributing on the left) and then add b^2 to both sides, we have

$$4a^2x_0^2 + 4abx_0 + b^2 = b^2 - 4ac .$$

Observe that

$$4a^2x_0^2 + 4abx_0 + b^2 = (2ax_0 + b)^2 .$$

Thus, if x_0 is a solution,

$$(2ax_0 + b)^2 = b^2 - 4ac ,$$

or

$$2ax_0 + b = \pm \sqrt{b^2 - 4ac} ,$$

then

$$x_0 = \frac{-b + \sqrt{b^2 - 4ac}}{2a} ,$$

or

$$x_0 = \frac{-b - \sqrt{b^2 - 4ac}}{2a} .$$

These two numbers, then, are the only possible solutions to our equations.

To verify that they are, indeed, solutions, the reader should, as an exercise, substitute these into the equation under consideration.

We might note that, since $b^2 - 4ac$ is not negative, $\sqrt{b^2 - 4ac}$ is a real number. If $b^2 - 4ac = 0$, then the solution set contains but one element, $-b/2a$.

The applications of this theorem are well known from high school mathematics.

EXAMPLE. Solve, using Theorem 2.29, the equation $4x^2 - 5x - 6 = 0$. If we apply this theorem with $a = 4$, $b = -5$, and $c = -6$, we get the solutions

$$\frac{5 + \sqrt{5^2 - 4 \cdot 4 \cdot (-6)}}{2 \cdot 4} = \frac{5 + 11}{8} = 2 ,$$

and

$$\frac{5 - \sqrt{121}}{8} = \frac{5 - 11}{8} = -\frac{3}{4} .$$

Exercise 2.11

Solve the following quadratic equations:

(a) $x^2 - 2x - 3 = 0$.

(b) $x^2 + 2x - 6 = 0$.

(c) $x^2 + 2x - 3 = 0$.

(d) $x^2 - x + 45 = 0$.

(e) $x^2 - 4x + 4 = 0$.

(f) $x^2 - 4 = 0$.

(g) $3x^2 + 6x + 1 = 0$.   (h) $(x + 1)^2 + 2(x + 1) + 1 = 0$.

(i) $5x^2 + \pi x - \dfrac{1}{\pi} = 0$.   (j) $(x + 1)^2 + 2(x + 1) - 8 = 0$.

2.11 Mathematical Induction

An important tool in mathematics is based on property 3 in the definition of the natural numbers (Definition 2.5). This property tells us that, if S is any set of natural numbers which contains 1 and which contains $k + 1$ whenever it contains k, then S is the entire set of natural numbers. The tool referred to here is called *mathematical induction*.

To introduce this topic, consider the statement that the sum of the "first" n natural numbers is $[n(n + 1)]/2$. More formally, the statement is that

$$1 + 2 + 3 + \cdots + n = \frac{n(n + 1)}{2}.$$

(Here the dots indicate that we keep adding until we come to the number n). Observe that this is not a single statement but a family of statements, one for each natural number. When $n = 1$, the statement is that

$$1 = \frac{1 \cdot (1 + 1)}{2}.$$

When $n = 4$, the statement is that

$$1 + 2 + 3 + 4 = \frac{4 \cdot 5}{2}.$$

When we deal with statements of this sort we will label each one with a notation, $P(n)$, to indicate that the statement depends on n. Thus, if $P(n)$ is the statement

$$1 + 2 + \cdots + n = \frac{n(n + 1)}{2},$$

we would say that $P(3)$ is the statement

$$1 + 2 + 3 = \frac{3 \cdot 4}{2}.$$

Actually we have, in situations of this sort, statement-valued functions defined on the set, N, of natural numbers.

We frequently would like to prove that $P(n)$ is a true statement for each $n \in N$. In our example, we can easily see that $P(1)$, $P(3)$ and $P(4)$ are true statements. If one had several hours to spend, one could check out the truth (or falseness) of several hundred of these statements. But it is impossible to check out $P(n)$ for each n. (There are too many natural numbers.) We do have a tool that allows us to show the truth of $P(n)$ for each $n \in N$, where P is a statement-valued function defined on N.

Theorem 2.30. Let P be a function defined on N such that, for each $n \in N$, $P(n)$ is a statement. If

(1) $P(1)$ is true,

and

(2) $P(k)$ true $\Rightarrow P(k + 1)$ true,

then $P(n)$ is true for every $n \in N$.

Proof. Let S be the set of natural numbers, x, for which $P(x)$ is true. By (1), $1 \in S$. By (2), if $k \in S$, then $k + 1 \in S$. From property (3) of Definition 2.5, $S = N$. That is, $P(n)$ is true for every $n \in N$.

Let us now consider $P(n)$, where $P(n)$ is the statement

$$1 + 2 + \cdots + n = \frac{n(n + 1)}{2}.$$

$P(1)$ is true because $1 = (1 \cdot 2)/2$. Now let us assume $P(k)$ is true. Then the number $1 + 2 + \ldots + k$ is the number $[k(k + 1)]/2$. If we add $k + 1$ to each of these numbers, we have that

$$1 + 2 + \cdots + k + (k + 1) = \frac{k(k + 1)}{2} + (k + 1).$$

But

$$\frac{k(k + 1)}{2} + (k + 1) = \frac{(k + 1)(k + 2)}{2}.$$

So, if $P(k)$ is true,

$$1 + 2 + \cdots + k + (k + 1) = \frac{(k + 1)(k + 2)}{2}.$$

This says that $P(k + 1)$ is true. We have verified that $P(1)$ is true and that $P(k)$ true implies $P(k + 1)$ true. By our theorem, then, $P(n)$ is true for every $n \in N$.

As another example, consider the statement that for $a, b \in R^1$, $(a \cdot b)^n = a^n \cdot b^n$ for every $n \in N$. This is a familiar law of exponents and one which was probably never proved for the reader. Before we proceed, recall that for $x \in R^1$, $x^1 = x$, and $x^{k+1} = x^k \cdot x$ for $k \in n$. (This is the way we defined x^n for $n \in N$.) In this instance, let $P(n)$ be the statement that $(ab)^n = a^n \cdot b^n$.

First note that $P(1)$ is $(ab)^1 = a^1 \cdot b^1$. But, by definition,

$$(ab)^1 = ab = a^1b^1 .$$

Now assume $P(k)$ is true. Then $(ab)^k = a^k b^k$. We would like to show, on the basis of this assumption, that

$$(ab)^{k+1} = a^{k+1} \cdot b^{k+1} .$$

that is, that $P(k + 1)$ is true. We see that

$$(ab)^{k+1} = (ab)^k(ab) ,$$

by definition. By our assumption, $(ab)^k = a^k b^k$. So

$$(ab)^{k+1} = (ab)^k \cdot (ab) = a^k b^k ab .$$

Using our commutative and associative laws, we can write the right member of these equalities as $(a^k a)(b^k b)$. But, by definition, $a^k a = a^{k+1}$ and $b^k b = b^{k+1}$. Thus

$$(ab)^{k+1} = a^{k+1}b^{k+1} .$$

We have shown that $P(1)$ is true and that $P(k)$ true implies $P(k + 1)$ true. By our theorem, $P(n)$ is true for each $n \in N$.

Exercise 2.12

1. (a)   Prove that $\left(\dfrac{a}{b}\right)^n = \dfrac{a^n}{b^n}$ for $a, b \in R^1, b \neq 0$, and $n \in N$.

   (b)   Prove that for $a \in R^1, m, n \in N, a^m \cdot a^n = a^{m+n}$.

2. Prove that $(a^m)^n = a^{mn}$ for every pair n and m of natural numbers   (*Hint:* Let m be fixed and let $P(n)$ be the statement $(a^m)^n = a^{mn}$)

3. Prove the following by induction ($n \in N$):

   (a) $2 + 4 + 6 + \cdots + 2n = n(n + 1)$.

   (b) $3 + 6 + 9 + \cdots + 3n = \dfrac{3}{2}n(n + 1)$.

   (c) $1 + 3 + 5 + \cdots + (2n - 1) = n^2$.

   (d) $1^2 + 2^2 + \cdots + n^2 = \dfrac{n(n + 1)(2n + 1)}{6}$.

   (e) $\dfrac{1}{1 \cdot 2} + \dfrac{1}{2 \cdot 3} + \cdots + \dfrac{1}{n(n + 1)} = \dfrac{n}{n + 1}$.

4. Prove $2^n > n$ for every $n \in N$.

5. Prove that for every $x \in R^1, x > -1$, and for every $n \in N$,

$$(1 + x)^n > 1 + nx.$$

Remarks. Thus far we have assumed that the real numbers are a set on which two binary operations are defined and on which a relation is defined satisfying certain axioms. In fact there is just one axiom for the real numbers remaining. This remaining axiom is a bit more complicated and we will not introduce it here. There is, however, one more property of real numbers that we would point out.

Theorem 2.31. Let $a, b \in R^1$, $a < b$. Then,

$$a < \frac{a+b}{2} < b.$$

(That is, $a < \dfrac{a+b}{2}$ and $\dfrac{a+b}{2} < b$.)

Proof.

$$a < b \Rightarrow a + a < a + b \Rightarrow 2a < a + b \Rightarrow a < \frac{a+b}{2} \, ;$$

and

$$a < b \Rightarrow a + b < b + b = 2b \Rightarrow \frac{a+b}{2} < b.$$

This theorem is useful because it tells us, for example, that there is no smallest number greater than 0. For, if x is any number so that $0 < x$, $x/2 = (x + 0)/2$ satisfies $0 < x/2 < x$. Indeed, it tells us that for any two distinct real numbers, no matter how close together, there is a real number between them.

Graphs

Comment. In our past work we have assumed an identification of real numbers with points on a line. We now want to make this identification more explicit and to extend it somewhat. First we explicitly want to establish a one-to-one correspondence between the set of all points on a line and the set R^1.

3.1 Introducing Coordinate Systems

Let k be a line and let 0 be a point on the line. Choose any point E on k different from 0. We assume that we have a way of measuring distances on this line. If P and Q are any points on the line, we will let $d(P, Q)$ denote the distance from P to Q. Let P be any point on k. We associate with P a number, $\alpha(P)$, called the *coordinate* of P, as follows:

$$\alpha(P) = \pm \left(\frac{d(0, P)}{d(0, E)} \right)$$

3

where the positive number is used if P is on the same side of 0 as is E and where the negative value is used if P is on the side of 0 away from E. It should be clear that $\alpha(0) = 0$ and that $\alpha(E) = 1$.

If P and Q are distinct points, then

$$d(0, P) = d(0, Q)$$

only when P and Q are on opposite sides of 0 and the same distance from 0. In this case $\alpha(P) = -\alpha(Q)$. So if $P \neq Q$, we have that $\alpha(P) \neq \alpha(Q)$. If r is any real number, with our assumed measuring device we can find a point P on k so that $\alpha(P) = r$. One simply selects P so that $d(0, P) = r \cdot d(0, E)$. These remarks tell us that α is a 1–1 function from k *onto* R^1. Hence, we have a 1–1 correspondence between the points on any line and the set of real numbers.

It is obvious that, for different choices for 0 and E on the line k, we get different numbers assigned to the same point. When we deal with this process, however, we will usually have in mind a particular choice of 0 and E. This process is called introducing a *coordinate system* on a line.

The fact of the matter is that we usually just pick two points and label them 0 and 1. This is, of course, not different from the process described, but merely the usual practice of labeling a point with its coordinate.

Consider k:

with various points labeled. We assume the coordinates of P_{-2} to be -2, P_{-1} to be -1, P_2 to be 2 and P_3 to be 3. Of course it would be all right, and probably more meaningful, to label k by

where the number is the coordinate of the point. Following this practice, we will refer to the point 3 rather than to the point with coordinate 3.

This process of introducing a coordinate system on a line can be extended to associate with each point in a plane an ordered pair of real numbers. In fact, there will be established by this process a 1–1 correspondence between the points in a plane and $R^1 \times R^1$. Such a correspondence will be called a *coordinate system* for the plane. The way we go about this is as follows. Let X be a plane. Draw two distinct nonparallel lines k_1 and k_2 in X and call their intersection 0 (Fig. 3.1). Choose on k_1 a point E_1 and on k_2 a point E_2, each different from 0. By doing this, we have introduced a coordinate system on k_1 and k_2 as we did before.

Let P be a point in X. Draw a line through P parallel to k_2. This line intersects k_1 in a point P_1. Now draw a line through P parallel to k_1 which intersects k_2 in a point P_2. We assign to the point P, then, the ordered pair

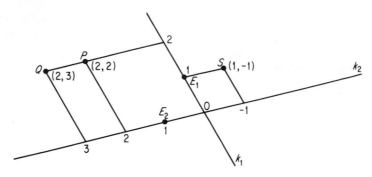

Figure 3.1

$(\alpha(P_1), \alpha(P_2))$ of real numbers, where $\alpha(P_i)$ denotes the coordinate of P_i on k_i; $i = 1, 2$. In Fig. 3.1, as indicated, P has coordinates $(2, 1)$, Q has coordinates $(2, 3)$ and S has coordinates $(1, -1)$.

Now, in the above discussion, the lines k_1 and k_2 (Fig. 3.1) were completely arbitrary so long as they intersected in only one point. It is also the case that $d(0, E_1)$ and $d(0, E_2)$ need not have been the same. Custom, however, has it that we should draw the lines at right angles to one another and that $d(0, E_1) = d(0, E_2)$. Moreover, k_1 is usually drawn horizontally; k_2, then, is vertical. Most of the time we also place E_1 to the right of 0 and E_2 above 0 (Fig. 3.2).

When we set up our coordinate system in this fashion, we call it a *rectangular* or *Cartesian coordinate system*. We will use a Cartesian coordinate system to graph relations and functions. Again, as a matter of custom, we call k_1 the *x* axis, k_2 the *y* axis, the lines k_1 and k_2 are referred to as *coordinate axes*, and the point 0 is called the *origin*.

Another convention that is worth noting is the numbering of the four sections of the plane determined by the introduction of a Cartesian coordinate system. If we insert the unit to the right of the origin on the *x* axis and above

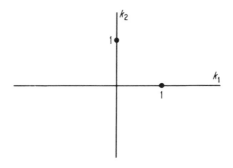

Figure 3.2

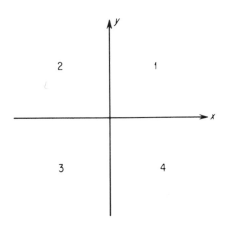

Figure 3.3

the origin on the y axis, we number the four sections of the plane in the manner indicated in Fig. 3.3. These sections are called *quadrants*.

If (a, b) are the coordinates of a point in a plane so coordinatized, we note that $a > 0$ and $b > 0$ if (a, b) is in the first quadrant; $a < 0$ and $b > 0$ if (a, b) is in the second quadrant; $a < 0$ and $b < 0$ if (a, b) is in the third quadrant; and that $a > 0$ and $b < 0$ if (a, b) is in the fourth quadrant.

Exercise 3.1

1. Draw a Cartesian coordinate system and plot the following points. Say in which quadrant each lies. (If a point is on a coordinate axis it is not in a quadrant.)

$$(2, 0), \quad (3, 1), \quad (-2, 2), \quad (-2, -4), \quad (3, -7), \quad (5, -2), \quad (4, 4)$$

2. Sketch on a graph all the points:
   (a)   2 units to the left of the y axis.
   (b)   3 units above the x axis.
   (c)   on the line through the origin making an angle of 45 degrees with the positive half of the x axis; the negative half of the x axis.

3. Sketch the set of points:
   (a)   Whose x and y coordinates are the same.
   (b)   Whose x coordinates are one more than the y coordinates.
   (c)   Whose x and y coordinates are equal in absolute value.
   (d)   Whose coordinates (x, y) satisfy $y < 2$ and $x < 1$.
   (e)   Whose coordinates (x, y) satisfy $-1 \leq x < 1$.
   (f)   Whose coordinates (x, y) take on the values 1, 2, and 3.
   (g)   Whose coordinates (x, y) are such that $2x = y$.
   (h)   Whose coordinates (x, y) satisfy $y = x$ and $x > 0$.

4. Sketch the set of points:

   (a) $\{(x, y) \mid x = -y\}$.
                             (b) $\{(x, y) \mid |x| < 2\}$.

   (c) $\{(x, y) \mid x + y = 0\}$.
                      (d) $\{(x, y) \mid x = 2, y > 0\}$.

   (e) $\{(x, y) \mid |y| < 1 \text{ and } |x| < 2\}$.
      (f) $\{(x, y) \mid -3 < |y|\}$.

   (g) $\{(x, y) \mid |y| > 0\}$.

3.2   Graphing Relations

When we "graph" a relation on R^1 we identify, in a plane on which a Cartesian coordinate system has been introduced, the subset of $R^1 \times R^1$ which is the relation. For example, consider the relation $>$ on R^1. So, formally, the relation is

$$k = \{(x, y) \mid x > y \quad \text{and} \quad x, y \in R^1\} .$$

To graph this relation we introduce a Cartesian coordinate system into a plane and identify this subset. The dotted line (Fig. 3.4) indicates all points (x, y) where $x = y$. All the points below this line (the shaded part of the plane) is the graph of the relation k. For, any point (x, y) in this part of the plane has the property that $x > y$ and, if (x, y) is any point so that $x > y$, it lies in this part of the plane.

To examine this a bit more closely, consider a point P, as indicated (Fig. 3.4) in the first quadrant and in the shaded area. If P has coordinates (a, b), then $a > 0$ and $b > 0$. Now the point P' has coordinates (a, a). Since P is below P', $b < a$. So, certainly, the points in the first quadrant, below the line, belong to our graph. Now consider any point Q in the fourth quadrant. Q will have coordinates (a, b) where $a > 0$ and $0 > b$. Thus, for such a point, $a > b$. As an exercise, the reader should justify that the area shaded in the third quadrant belongs in our graph.

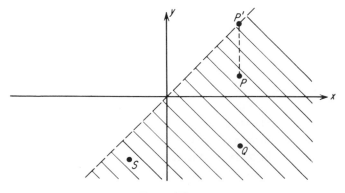

Figure 3.4

It might also be well to note that we can graph real-valued functions whose domains are subsets of R^1. For example, consider the function

$$f : \{1, 2, 3, 4\} \rightarrow R^1$$

defined by

$$f = \{(1, 2), \quad (2, 0), \quad (3, -1), \quad (4, 0)\} \ .$$

The graph of this function is indicated in Fig. 3.5. It consists of exactly 4 points. Note that if (x, y) is a point in f, then (x, y) is one of these 4 points, and if (x, y) is one of these points, it is in f.

We return to problems of this sort in a short time. We should, however, make certain comments concerning our Cartesian coordinate system. If one chooses, he may consider the distance from 0 to 1 on either of the lines drawn as a unit of measurement. So, if the coordinate of a point on the x axis is 2, we would say it is two units away from the origin. We will commonly use this unit of measurement and will refer to the distance between points in terms of this unit without explicitly mentioning this unit. For example, the distance from $(0, 0)$ to $(0, 5)$ is 5 units, and we simply say that the distance from $(0, 0)$ to $(0, 5)$ is 5.

Recall now that for any real number, a, we defined $|a| = a$, if $a \geq 0$; and $|a| = -a$, if $a < 0$. Two properties of absolute value we will need now are

(1) $$|a|^2 = a^2 = (-a)^2$$

and

(2) $$|x - y| = |y - x|$$

for any real numbers a, x, y.

So, on a line, k, on which a coordinate system has been introduced, we define the distance, $d(P, Q)$, between two points P and Q in terms of the distance between 0 and E by

$$d(P, Q) = |\alpha(P) - \alpha(Q)| \ .$$

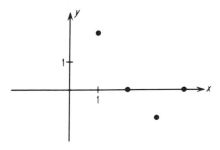

Figure 3.5

If we are now in a plane and if P and Q are both on the x axis or on the y axis, we can obtain their distance in terms of the common unit on the x axis and y axis using this same procedure. For example, if P has coordinates $(x_1, 0)$ and Q has coordinates $(x_2, 0)$, we have that $d(P, Q) = |x_2 - x_1| = |x_1 - x_2|$.

If P and Q are points in a plane on which a Cartesian coordinate system has been introduced, we denote the distance described above by the same notation as before, namely, $d(P, Q)$.

Exercise 3.2

1. Find $d(P, Q)$ when

	P	Q
(a)	$(0, 2)$	$(0, 4)$
(b)	$(2, 0)$	$(-1, 0)$
(c)	$(5, 0)$	$(8, 0)$
(d)	$(0, -10)$	$(0, -6)$
(e)	$(0, -6)$	$(0, -10)$
(f)	$(0, 1)$	$(0, 1)$

2. Graph the relations on R^1 given by

   (a) $\{(x, y) \mid y > x\}$.   (b) $\{(x, y) \mid |y| = x\}$.

   (c) $\{(x, y) \mid y = 2x\}$.   (d) $\{(x, y) \mid x^2 + y^2 = 4\}$.

   (e) $\{(x, y) \mid y > 2x\}$.   (f) $\{(x, y) \mid y > 2x \text{ and } x > 0\}$.

   (g) $\{(x, y) \mid y = x + 5\}$.   (h) $\{(x, y) \mid y > 2x + 5\}$.

   (i) $\{(x, y) \mid |y| = x + 5\}$.   (j) $\{(x, y) \mid |y| \leq x + 5\}$.

3. Graph the relations on R^1 given by:

   (a) $\{(x, y) \mid x \leq 1 \text{ and } y \geq 0\}$.   (b) $\{(x, y) \mid y = -1\}$.

   (c) $\{(x, y) \mid y \geq x + 1\}$.   (d) $\{(x, y) \mid y \leq x + 1\}$.

   (e) $\{(x, y) \mid y \leq x^2\}$.   (f) $\{(x, y) \mid |y| \leq x^2\}$.

   (g) $\{(x, y) \mid y - 1 > 2 + x\}$.   (h) $\{(x, y) \mid y = 1 + |x|\}$.

   (i) $\{(x, y) \mid y = |x| - x\}$.   (j) $\{(x, y) \mid |y| = |x| - x\}$.

3.3   Distance between Points

It is of course true that $d(P, Q) \geq 0$ and that $d(P, Q) = d(Q, P)$, if we are to have our usual notion of distance. One other property of distance is that $d(P, Q) \leq d(P, S) + d(S, Q)$ for any three points P, Q, S in a plane. One of the reasons why we use a rectangular coordinate system is that it makes the computation of distance between points reasonably simple.

Theorem 3.1. Let P, Q be two points in a plane on which a Cartesian coordinate system has been introduced. If P and Q have coordinates (x_1, y_1) and (x_2, y_2) respectively, then

$$d(P, Q) = \sqrt{(x_1 - x_2)^2 + (y_1 - y_2)^2}\,.$$

Proof. Let S (Fig. 3.6) be the point of intersection of lines through P parallel to the x axis and through Q parallel to the y axis. P, Q, and S are, then, vertices of a right triangle. The length of PS is $|x_2 - x_1|$. By the Pythagorean theorem,

$$d(P, Q) = \sqrt{|x_2 - x_1|^2 + |y_2 - y_1|^2}$$
$$= \sqrt{(x_2 - x_1)^2 + (y_2 - y_1)^2}\,.$$

Note that we have here made use of the fact that $|a|^2 = a^2$ for all $a \in R^1$. We also note that the order of subtraction in this formula is not important because, for instance $(x_2 - x_1)^2 = (x_1 - x_2)^2$.

As a simple application of this theorem, we find the distance $d(P, Q)$, where $P : (7, -2)$ and $Q : (-5, 9)$. We apply the formula where $x_1 = 7$, $y_1 = -2$, $x_2 = -5$, $y_2 = 9$. Then

$$d(P, Q) = \sqrt{(7 - (-5))^2 + (-2-(9))^2}$$
$$= \sqrt{12^2 + (-11)^2}$$
$$= \sqrt{144 + 121} = \sqrt{265}\,.$$

So the distance between these points is $\sqrt{265}$ units. Here the unit of measurement is the distance from $(0, 0)$ to $(1, 0)$ (or from $(0, 0)$ to $(0, 1)$).

At times we will be dealing with arbitrary points P and Q whose coordinates are given in terms of symbols. Suppose that $P : (x + h, y + t)$ and $Q : (x, y)$ are such points. Then

$$d(P, Q) = \sqrt{(x + h - x)^2 + (y + t - y)^2}$$
$$= \sqrt{h^2 + t^2}\,.$$

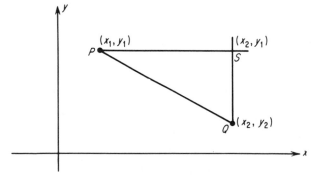

Figure 3.6

We also would point out that the application of Theorem 3.1 to two points $P : (x_1, y_0)$ and $Q : (x_0, y_0)$ with the same y coordinate gives us

$$d(P, Q) = \sqrt{(x_1 - x_0)^2 + (y_0 - y_0)^2}$$

$$= \sqrt{(x_1 - x_0)^2} = |x_1 - x_0|$$

which is the same result we saw earlier.

Exercise 3.3

1. Calculate $d(P, Q)$ when
   - (a) $P : (1, 2), Q : (1, 0)$
   - (b) $P : (1, 2), Q : (1, 2)$
   - (c) $P : (3, 4), Q : (0, 0)$
   - (d) $P : (3, 4), Q : (4, 3)$
   - (e) $P : (-1, -4), Q : (3, -7)$
   - (f) $P : (7, -2), Q : (-2, 7)$
   - (g) $P : (x, y), Q : (0, 0)$
   - (h) $P : (x, y), Q : (1, 1)$
   - (i) $P : (x, y), Q : (h, k)$
   - (j) $P : (x, y), Q : (x + t, y + t)$
   - (k) $P : (a, 0), Q : (a + b, 3b)$
   - (l) $P : (x, k), Q : (0, t)$

2. Find the set (draw a graph of your answer) of all points (x, y):
   - (a) Whose first coordinate is 2; is 0; is -4.
   - (b) Whose x and y coordinates are equal.
   - (c) At a distance 3 from $(0, 0)$; from $(1, 1)$; from $(3, 4)$.
   - (d) Whose second coordinates are twice the first.
   - (e) Whose coordinates satisfy the equation $x + y = 1$.
   - (f) Whose distance from $(0, 0)$ is less than 3; from $(1, 1)$ is greater than 3.

3. What is the perimeter of the triangle with vertices at $(4, 2)$, $(-2, 0)$, and $(-1, -3)$?

4. What is the perimeter of the triangle with vertices at $(0, 0)$, $(4, 5)$, and $(6, 7)$?

5. What is the perimeter of the quadrilateral with vertices at $(1, -1)$, $(5, 3)$, $(3, 4)$, and $(-3, 1)$?

6. What is the perimeter of the quadrilateral with vertices at $(1, 1)$, $(2, 1)$, $(5, 6)$, $(2, 8)$, and $(5, 0)$?

7. Prove that the points $P : (1, -1)$, $Q : (2, 1)$, and $R : (4, 5)$ are collinear (that is, lie on the same straight line) by showing $d(P, Q) + d(Q, R) = d(P, R)$.

8. Show that the triangle with vertices $A : (-1, 1)$, $B : (4, 4)$, $C : (1, -1)$ is isosceles.

9. (a) Show that the triangle with vertices at $A : (8, 6)$, $B : (-3, 3)$, $C : (1, -1)$ is a right triangle
   - (b) Find the area of the triangle in part (a).

10. (a)   Find a point (x, y) which is equidistant from $A : (-1, 2)$, $B : (6, 1)$, and $C : (5, -6)$.

(b) What well-known geometric problem will your work in part (a) enable you to solve?

3.4 Graphs of Equations

We might note that, if we have an equation in two real variables, then the solution set is a relation. In view of this, when we are asked to draw the graph of an equation of this type, we are asked to graph the relation defined by the solution set. As an example, consider the equation $y - x = 1$. The solution set would be

$$\{(x, y) \mid y = x + 1 \quad \text{and} \quad x, y \in R^1\} .$$

Clearly, this is nothing but the relation r defined by

$$r = \{(x, y) \mid y = x + 1, x, y \in R^1\} ,$$

or

$$xry \Leftrightarrow x, y \in R^1 \quad \text{and} \quad y = x + 1 .$$

The graph, then, of this equation is the set of all points in a plane on which a rectangular coordinate system has been introduced for which the second coordinate is one more than the first.

It is easy to find points on the graph (Fig. 3.7) — $(3, 4)$, $(-1, 0)$, $(100, 101)$, and many others are on the graph. We plot some of these points. In fact, if we choose an arbitrary x, mark it on the x axis and mark $x + 1$ on the y axis, we determine a point on the graph. This is noted in Fig. 3.7. It

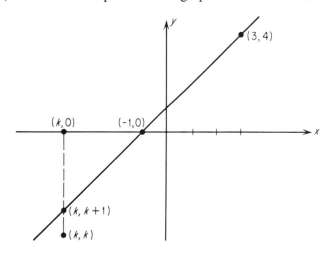

Figure 3.7

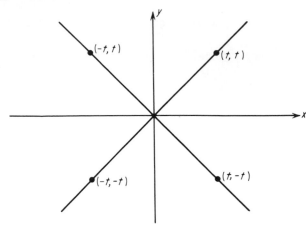

Figure 3.8

would not be hard to guess that the graph of this equation is a straight line determined by any two of these points.

A more complicated problem might be to graph the equation $|y| = |x|$. As a start, we might try to find a few points on the graph of this equation. Remember that (x, y) is on the graph if and only if $|x| = |y|$; that is, if the coordinates have the same absolute value. $(0, 0)$ is certainly such a point. On the other hand $(1, -1), (1, 1), (-1, -1), (-1, 1)$ are all points with this property. Generalizing, if t is any real number, then $(t, t), (t, -t), (-t, -t)$, $(-t, t)$ would be on the graph. Keeping these things in mind, it is not hard to see that the graph would consist of the two lines drawn in Fig. 3.8.

We can also graph inequalities when we consider them as relations. For example, consider the inequality $x + y < 1$. We want to graph, actually, the relation defined by

$$\{(x, y) \mid x, y \in R^1 \text{ and } x + y < 1\}.$$

As before, it is a good idea to find some points which satisfy our inequality. Certainly if $x < 0$ and $y < 0$, $x + y < 0$ and therefore $x + y < 1$. So all points in the third quadrant are in our graph. On the other hand $(5, -4.5)$ is on the graph and $(-10, 10.5)$ are points we want also. We might note that although $(2, -1)$ is not on the graph, $(2, -1.0001)$ is.

As an aid in drawing our graph, let us draw the graph of the points (x, y) where $x + y = 1$. This line is, in a sense, the boundary of the set in which we are interested. At times, boundaries of this sort might be part of the set in question. At other times (as in this example), it is not in our set (see Fig. 3.9).

We have shaded the third quadrant because we know all the points in the third quadrant are in our graph (Fig. 3.9). As an exercise, the reader should complete this graph.

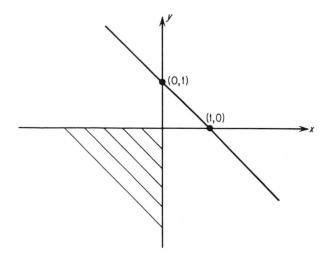

Figure 3.9

Exercise 3.4

1. Graph the following:

(a) $\{(x, y) \mid x = 2\}$.

(b) $\{(x, y) \mid x = y\}$.

(c) $\{(x, y) \mid x + y = 1\}$.

(d) $\{(x, y) \mid y = 0\}$.

(e) The set of all points (x, y), at a distance of 3 from the origin.

(f) The set of all points (x, y), at a distance of 1 from the point $(-1, 0)$.

(g) The set of all points (x, y), equidistant from $(0, 2)$ and $(0, -3)$.

(h) The set of all points (x, y), whose distance from $(2, -3)$ exceeds 1.

(i) $\{(x, y) \mid |x| + |y| = 1\}$.

(j) $\{(x, y) \mid |x| + |y| \leq 1\}$.

(k) $\{(x, y) \mid |xy| > 1\}$.

(l) $\{(x, y) \mid |x| > |y|\}$.

(m) $\{(x, y) \mid |x - y| > 0\}$.

(n) The set of all points (x, y) for which the larger of the numbers $|x|$, $|y|$, is less than 1.

3.5 Midpoints of Line Segments

As an aside, we want to indicate how introducing a coordinate system can be useful in treating certain geometric problems.

As a preliminary step, consider the following theorem:

Theorem 3.2. Let $P : (x_1, y_1)$ and $Q : (x_2, y_2)$ be points in a plane. The midpoint of the line segment connecting the two is:

$$M : \left(\frac{x_1 + x_2}{2}, \frac{y_1 + y_2}{2} \right).$$

Proof. First we show that the point M is equally distant from P and Q by showing that $d(M, P) = d(M, Q)$. We see that

$$d(M, P) = \sqrt{\left(\frac{x_1 + x_2}{2} - x_1 \right)^2 + \left(\frac{y_1 + y_2}{2} - y_1 \right)^2}$$

$$= \sqrt{\left(\frac{x_2 - x_1}{2} \right)^2 + \left(\frac{y_2 - y_1}{2} \right)^2}$$

$$= \frac{1}{2} \sqrt{(x_2 - x_1)^2 + (y_2 - y_1)^2},$$

and

$$d(M, Q) = \sqrt{\left(\frac{x_1 - x_2}{2} \right)^2 + \left(\frac{y_1 - y_2}{2} \right)^2}.$$

This shows that M is equally distant from each of P and Q.

If we show that

$$d(M, P) + d(M, Q) = d(P, Q)$$

we would then have the fact that M is on the line segment connecting the two points, P and Q.

Computing, we get

$$d(M, P) + d(M, Q) = 2d(M, P)$$

$$= 2 \cdot \frac{1}{2} \sqrt{(x_2 - x_1)^2 + (y_2 - y_1)^2}$$

$$= d(P, Q).$$

We might point out that this formula at times will be applied to arbitrary points, points whose coordinates are indicated by letters. For example, if $P : (a, b)$ and $Q : (c, d)$ are given points, then the midpoint, M, of the segment PQ has coordinates $[(a + c)/2, (b + d)/2]$.

A more general problem is that of finding the coordinates of the point M on the segment PQ, where P and Q have coordinates (x_1, y_1) and (x_2, y_2) respectively, when we require that $d(P, m) = r \cdot d(P, Q)$ with $0 < r < 1$. If $y_1 = y_2$ and $x_1 < x_2$, consider the point M with coordinates $(x_1 + r(x_2 - x_1), y_1)$. Then

$$d(P, M) = |x_1 + r(x_2 - x_1) - x_1|$$

$$= r |x_2 - x_1| = r \cdot d(PQ).$$

In the same fashion, if $y_1 = y_2$ but $x_2 < x_1$, consider M with coordinates $(x_1 + r(x_2 - x_1), y_1)$. Then

$$d(P, M) = |x_1 + r(x_2 - x_1) - x_1|$$

$$= r|x_2 - x_1| = r \cdot d(PQ).$$

Of course, if the x-coordinates of the points were the same, the same technique could be used to find M with the desired property.

As examples, consider $P : (2, 1)$ $Q : (6, 1)$. We find M on PQ so that $d(P, M) = \frac{1}{4}d(P, Q)$. By the preceding technique, M has coordinates

$$\left(2 + \frac{1}{4}(6 - 2), 1\right) = (3, 1).$$

If $P : (2, -7)$ $Q : (2, -18)$, let us find M so that $d(P, M) = \frac{1}{9}d(P, Q)$. As indicated above, M has coordinates

$$\left(2, -7 + \frac{1}{9}(-18 + 7)\right) = \left(2, -7 - \frac{11}{9}\right) = \left(2, -8\frac{2}{9}\right).$$

Now consider P and Q, arbitrary, with coordinates (x_1, y_1) and (x_2, y_2) respectively, and let $r \in R^1$, $0 < r < 1$, be given. Suppose that M on PQ is such that $d(P, M) = r \cdot d(P, Q)$. Our problem is to find the coordinates of M. We show that we can do this by reducing the problem to the type of problem just discussed. First consider the triangle PSQ (Fig. 3.10), where S has coordinates (x_2, y_1). Find M_1 on PS by drawing MM_1 parallel to SQ and find M_2 on QS by drawing MM_2 parallel to SP. By a theorem in elementary geometry,

$$d(PM_1) = r \cdot d(P_1S) \quad \text{and} \quad d(SM_2) = r \cdot d(S, Q).$$

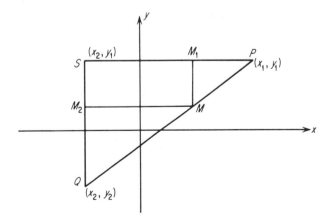

Figure 3.10

But we can find the coordinates of M_1 and M_2. The x coordinate of M_1 is the x coordinate of M and the y coordinate of M_2 is the y coordinate of M. The problem, then, is solved.

As an example, consider the points $P : (1, 2)$ and $Q : (9, 14)$. We find the point M on PQ so that $d(P, M) = \frac{3}{4}d(P, Q)$. As an aid, we draw a rough sketch of what we are after. If M is to have coordinates x_m and y_m, our problem is to determine these numbers (see Fig. 3.11).

By what we have seen,

$$x_m = 1 + \frac{3}{4}(9 - 1)$$

$$= 1 + \frac{3}{4} \cdot 8 = 7$$

and

$$y_m = 2 + \frac{3}{4}(14 - 2) = 2 + \frac{3}{4}(12) = 11 .$$

Our point M, then, has coordinates $(7, 11)$. Using our distance formula, we have

$$d(P, M) = \sqrt{6^2 + 9^2} = \sqrt{117}$$

and

$$d(P, Q) = \sqrt{8^2 + 12^2} = \sqrt{208}$$

But

$$\frac{3}{4}\sqrt{208} = \sqrt{\frac{9 \cdot 208}{16}} = \sqrt{117}$$

which verifies our answer.

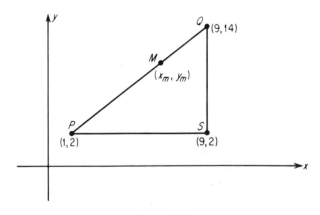

Figure 3.11

Exercise 3.5

1. Find the midpoints of the line segment joining the given points:
   (a) $(1, 1)$, $(5, 5)$.   (b) $(1, 3)$, $(-5, 7)$.
   (c) $(0, 0)$, $(6, 1)$.   (d) $(0, 0)$, $(4, 5)$.
   (e) $(-1, 3)$, $(2, 2)$.   (f) $(-1, -2)$, $(3, 4)$.
   (g) $(h, 0)$, $(0, k)$.   (h) $(0, 0)$, (h, k).
   (i) $(a, 0)$, (b, c).   (j) $(a, 0)$, $(a + 2t, 2s)$.
   (k) $(t, 1 - t)$, $(2 - t, t)$.   (l) $(t, 1 - t)$, $(2 + t, 3 - t)$.

2. In Exercise 1, find the points one-third of the way from the first point to the second point in each of parts (a), (c), (e), (g).

3. Find the point two-fifths of the way from the first to the second of these same points.

4. Find the lengths of the medians of the triangle with vertices at $(5, 1)$, $(-1, 1)$, and $(-3, -3)$.

5. Find the perimeter of the triangle made by joining the midpoints of the triangle with vertices $(1, 2)$, $(5, -4)$, and $(-1, -2)$.

6. Find the perimeter of the triangle made by joining the midpoints of the triangle found in Exercise 5.

3.6   Applications to Geometric Problems

Let us now look at the following problem:
Prove that the diagonals of a rectangle bisect each other.
To solve this problem, draw any rectangle, but be sure to make it general, i.e., do not give it properties that other rectangles do not have. Suppose two of its sides have length h and two have length k (Fig. 3.12). We now introduce a coordinate system into the plane of the rectangle in convenient fashion. It would seem clear that the origin might well go on one of the corners and the x and y axes might well lie on adjacent sides of the rectangle. This will help because the angles of the rectangle are right angles (Fig. 3.13). If we do this,

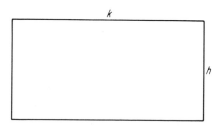

Figure 3.12

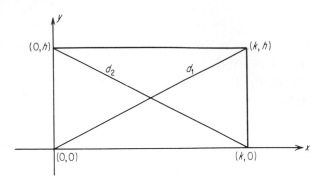

Figure 3.13

as indicated, the coordinates of the corners can be given by assuming the units we introduce in the coordinate system are the same as the unit of length given by the length of the sides of the rectangle.

Now what we wanted to do was to show that the diagonals bisect each other. If we can show that the midpoint of each diagonal is the same point, we have done this.

By Theorem 3.2, the midpoint of d_1 is

$$\left(\frac{k+0}{2}, \frac{h+0}{2}\right) \quad \text{and of } d_2 \text{ is} \quad \left(\frac{0+k}{2}, \frac{h+0}{2}\right).$$

But this shows us that the midpoint of each diagonal is the same.

Another problem of this sort follows: Prove that the medians of an isosceles triangle drawn from the base angles are equal in length. Again draw our triangle with base b and altitude h and introduce a coordinate system. One convenient way of doing this is indicated in Fig. 3.14. (Remember

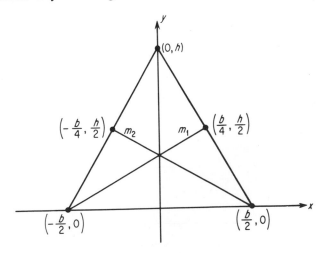

Figure 3.14

that one altitude of an isosceles triangle bisects the opposite side.) The midpoints are labeled and the medians are drawn.

The length of m_1 is

$$\sqrt{\left(\frac{b}{4} + \frac{b}{2}\right)^2 + \left(\frac{h}{2} - 0\right)^2}$$

and the length of m_2 is

$$\sqrt{\left(-\frac{b}{4} - \frac{b}{2}\right)^2 + \left(\frac{h}{2} - 0\right)^2}$$

and these are clearly the same.

Exercise 3.6

1. Find the area of the triangle (Fig. 3.15) with vertices at $(0, 0), (5, 0), (1, 4)$.

2. Find a formula for the area of the triangle shown in Fig. 3.15. (*Hint:* Subtract areas of smaller trapezoids from area of larger trapezoid.)

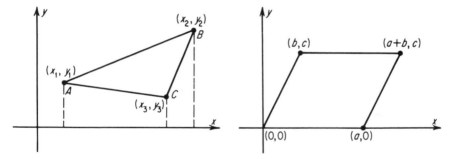

Figure 3.15   Figure 3.16

3. Prove that the diagonals of a parallelogram bisect each other. (*Hint:* Use Fig. 3.16.)

4. Show that, if a triangle has two medians of equal length, then the triangle is isosceles. (*Hint:* Show $a = 0$ in Fig. 3.17.)

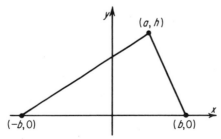

Figure 3.17

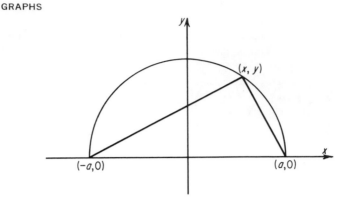

Figure 3.18

5. Show that an angle (Fig. 3.18) inscribed in a semicircle is a right angle. (*Hint:* $x^2 + y^2 = a^2$.)

6. Show that the sum of the squares of the medians of a triangle is equal to three-fourths the sum of the squares of its sides.

7. Prove that the diagonals of any rectangle are equal in length.

8. Prove that the diagonals of an isosceles trapezoid are equal in length.

9. Prove that the medians of any triangle meet in a single point two-thirds of the way from each vertex to the midpoint of the opposite side.

10. Prove that the triangle formed by joining the midpoints of the sides of a right triangle is a right triangle. What is the relation between the areas of the two triangles?

3.7   Graphs of Functions

It is possible to characterize properties of functions in terms of the graphs of the functions. For convenience, we always represent the domain of a function as a horizontal line, or a subset of the x axis, and the image space as a vertical line, or a subset of the y axis. First of all, we should note that, since a function is a subset of a product space which pairs with each element of the domain a unique element in the image space, the graph of a function cannot contain two points one above the other. Thus, if we consider the subset of $R^1 \times R^1$ given by the graph in Fig. 3.19, it cannot be the graph of a function, because P and Q are two points in the set, one above the other.

Now suppose that we have the graph of a function given. If the function is 1–1, for each pair of distinct elements of the domain the functional values are also distinct. So if (x_1, y) is a point on the graph of a function y cannot be paired with x_2, distinct from x_1. So the graph of a 1–1 function, using our

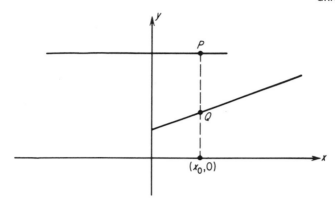

Figure 3.19

agreed convention, cannot have two points on the same line parallel to the x axis.

We also note that, if $f : X \to Y$ is given, then the function is an onto function, if and only if, given $y \in Y$, there is $x \in X$ so that the pair (x, y) is in the function. This means that the graph of an onto function has the property that, given $y \in Y$, the line through y, parallel to the x axis, has on it at least one point of the graph of the function.

In the following examples and exercises we will consider $X = [0, 1] = Y$ and we will consider graphs of subsets of $X \times Y$ that may or may not be functions. As examples, consider the two graphs shown in Fig. 3.20. Part (a) represents a 1–1 onto function, because, for every point y in Y, the line through y parallel to the x axis intersects the graph in one and only one point: (b) represents a function, but not a 1–1 or onto function. The graph in (b) does not represent an onto function because the line through y_0 does not meet the graph. It is not 1–1 because the line through y_1 meets the graph in two points.

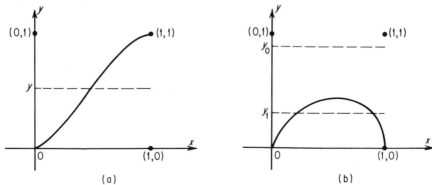

Figure 3.20

Exercise 3.7

Consider the graphs shown in (Fig. 3.21).

(a)   Say which represent functions.

(b)   If a graph represents a function, say whether the function is or is not 1–1 and/or onto.

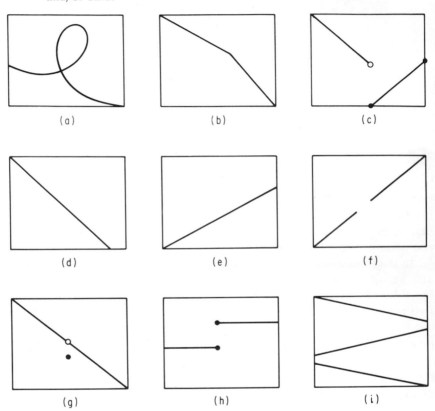

Figure 3.21

Vector
Spaces

4.1 Addition of Pairs of Numbers

We have been dealing with Cartesian coordinate systems for some time and we are now familiar with the identification of points in a plane with ordered pairs of real numbers. We have, in fact, a 1–1 correspondence between the set of all points in a plane and $R^1 \times R^1$.

We now want to consider the possibility of "adding" elements in $R^1 \times R^1$. For convenience, let's denote $R^1 \times R^1$ by R^2. We define a binary operation $+$, called addition, on R^2 as follows:

Definition 4.1. Let (x_1, y_1) and $(x_2, y_2) \in R^2$. We define the *sum* of (x_1, y_1) and (x_2, y_2) by

$$(x_1, y_1) + (x_2, y_2) = (x_1 + x_2, y_1 + y_2).$$

(Observe that here we are defining how to combine two elements of R^2 with an operation called *addition*, represented by the usual symbol for addition. This cannot be thought of as addition of

4

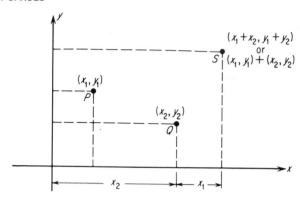

Figure 4.1

real numbers. The $+$ symbol appearing in the pair $(x_1 + x_2, y_1 + y_2)$ denotes, however, the usual addition of real numbers. This is a common bit of confusion and one that most people go along with, because, by the way it is used, we can say whether or not $+$ means addition of real numbers or something else.)

EXAMPLES

$$(1, 5) + (7, -2) = (1 + 7, 5 + (-2)) = (8, 3)$$
$$(-1, 0) + (1, -1) = (0, -1)$$
$$(\pi, 2) + (1, -2) = (\pi + 1, 0) \,.$$

From these examples, it is possible to see that no confusion arises when we use the same symbol to denote two different things.

It is possible to interpret this addition geometrically because of our identification of elements in R^2 and points in a plane. In Fig. 4.1, we see that the point P, with coordinates (x_1, y_1), added to the point Q, with coordinates (x_2, y_2), gives us the point S, whose first coordinate is $x_1 + x_2$ and whose second coordinate is $y_1 + y_2$.

We might well ask what algebraic properties hold for R^2 when considered under this operation of addition. The properties we ask about are listed below as exercises.

Exercise 4.1

1. Compute
   (a) $(2, -1) + (4, 5)$.   (b) $(2, -1) + (2, 3)$.
   (c) $(3, 2) + (0, 0)$.   (d) $(5, 7) + (-5, 1)$.

(e) $(x, y) + (0, 0)$.

(f) $(x, y) + (x, y)$.

(g) $(s, t) + (-s, 1)$

(h) $(s, t) + (s + 1, 1 - t)$.

(i) $(3, -2) + (-3, -2)$.

(j) $(3, 4) + (-3, -4)$.

(k) $(a, b) + (-a, -b)$.

(l) $(x + y, t) + (-x - y, -t)$.

(m) $[(1, -1) + (a, b)]$
       $+ (2 - a, 1 + b)$.

(n) $(1, 1) + (2, 1) + (1, 2)$.

2. Prove that

   (a) $(x_1, y_1) + (x_2, y_2) = (x_2, y_2) + (x_1, y_1)$ for all $(x_1, y_1), (x_2, y_2) \in R^2$.

   (b) $((x_1, y_1) + (x_2, y_2)) + (x_3, y_3) = (x_1, y_1) + ((x_2, y_2) + (x_3, y_3))$
         for all $(x_1, y_1), (x_2, y_2), (x_3, y_3) \in R^2$.

   (c) $(x, y) + (0, 0) = (x, y)$ for all $(x, y) \in R^2$.

   (d) $(x, y) \in R^2 \Rightarrow \exists (u, v) \in R^2$ so that $(x, y) + (u, v) = (0, 0)$.

3. Suppose that $(a, b) - (x, y)$ is taken to mean $(a, b) + (-(x, y))$, where $-(x, y)$
   is the additive inverse of (x, y). (Note that $-(x, y) = (-x, -y)$.) Compute

   (a) $(2, 7) - (3, 4)$.

   (b) $(2, 7) - (2, 7)$.

   (c) $(3, 8) - (-2, -1)$.

   (d) $(-1, 2) - (2, 4)$.

   (e) $(-1, 1) - (-1, 1)$.

   (f) $(1, 1) - (-1, 0)$.

   (g) $(a, b) - (c, d)$.

   (h) $(a + b, x) - (a, y)$.

As a result of these properties we see that R^2 under $+$ satisfies the properties listed as (A1), (A2), (A3), and (A4) for the real numbers relative to
addition.

4.2 Scalar Multiplication

Another question we might ask is whether or not we can multiply elements of R^2 in some sensible fashion. The answer to that is yes, but we might
well defer discussing this for awhile. The answer to "sensible" multiplication
is *not* coordinate-wise multiplication. For, one of the nice properties of real
numbers is that

$$a \cdot b = 0 \Leftrightarrow \text{ either } a = 0 \text{ or } b = 0.$$

If we considered

$$(x_1, y_1) \cdot (x_2, y_2) = (x_1 x_2, y_1 y_2),$$

it would be possible for a product to be $(0, 0)$ but for both the pairs to be
different from $(0, 0)$. For example, $(1, 0) \neq (0, 0)$ and $(0, 3) \neq (0, 0)$, but if
we "multiply" as above, then $(1, 0) \cdot (0, 3) = (0, 0)$.

For the time being, we turn our attention to a way of multiplying a *real
number with an ordered pair of real numbers to get an ordered pair of real*

numbers. Technically, then, we want a function from $R^1 \times R^2$ into R^2. We will call this way of combining a real number k with an ordered pair (x, y) of real numbers, *scalar multiplication*, and denote it as a product $k \cdot (x, y)$. We define *scalar multiplication* by

Definition 4.2. Let $k \in R^1$ and let $(x, y) \in R^2$. We define the *scalar product* $k \cdot (x, y)$ by

$$k \cdot (x, y) = (kx, ky) \,.$$

Again it is possible to represent this geometrically (Fig. 4.2).

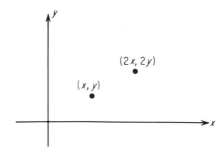

Figure 4.2

Here we use $k = 2$ to show $2 \cdot (x, y)$.

Observe that the distance from $k \cdot (x, y)$ to $(0, 0)$ is $|k|$ times the distance from (x, y) to the origin. For

$$\sqrt{(kx)^2 + (ky)^2} = \sqrt{k^2} \cdot \sqrt{x^2 + y^2}$$
$$= |k| \cdot \sqrt{x^2 + y^2} \,.$$

Remark. In fact, $k \cdot (x, y)$ is on the same straight line through the origin as is (x, y). If $k > 0$, $k \cdot (x, y)$ is on the same side of the origin as is (x, y) and if $k < 0$ it is on the side of the origin away from (x, y).

Exercise

Prove the preceding remark.

We might also list some algebraic properties of this scalar multiplication. We state these properties as a theorem.

Theorem 4.1. Let r, $s \in R^1$ and let (x_1, y_1), $(x_2, y_2) \in R^2$. Then,

(1) $r \cdot ((x_1, y_1) + (x_2, y_2)) = r \cdot (x_1, y_1) + r \cdot (x_2, y_2)$.

(2) $(r + s)(x_1, y_1) = r \cdot (x_1, y_1) + s(x_1, y_1).$

(3) $(r \cdot s) \cdot (x_1, y_1) = r \cdot (s \cdot (x_1, y_1)).$

(4) $1 \cdot (x_1, y_1) = (x_1, y_1); \; 0 \cdot (x_1, y_1) = (0, 0).$

Proof.

(2) $(r + s)(x_1, y_1) = ((r + s)x_1, (r + s)y_1)$

$$= (rx_1 + sx_1, ry_1 + sy_1)$$

$$= (rx_1, ry_1) + (sx_1, sy_1)$$

$$= r(x_1, y_1) + s(x_1, y_1).$$

(3) $(r \cdot s)(x_1, y_1) = ((rs) \cdot (x_1), (rs) \cdot (y_1))$

$$= (r(sx_1), r(sy_1))$$

$$= r(sx_1, sy_1) = r(s \cdot (x_1, y_1))$$

The other parts are left as exercises for the reader.

Exercise 4.2

1. Complete the proof of Theorem 4.1.

2. Plot (x, y) and $k \cdot (x, y)$ for each of the following:

(x, y)	$(1, 2)$	$(3, 4)$	$(4, 6)$	$(5, -1)$	$(1, -1)$	$(3, -6)$	$(4, 0)$
k	2	-1	$\dfrac{1}{2}$	0	-3	$\dfrac{1}{3}$	$-\dfrac{3}{2}$

3. Plot (on a single graph) the point $(-1, 1) + t \cdot (3, 3)$ for the values $t = 0, 1,$ $\dfrac{1}{2}, \dfrac{1}{4}, \dfrac{3}{4}, \dfrac{2}{3}.$ Comment on the results.

4. Compute

   (a) $3 \cdot (-1, 0) + (-2) \cdot (1, -3).$

   (b) $3 \cdot (5, 7) + 2(-1, 6).$

   (c) $(a_1, b_1) + \dfrac{1}{2}(a_2 - a_1, b_2 - b_1).$

   (d) $(a_2, b_2) - \dfrac{1}{2}(a_2 - a_1, b_2 - b_1).$

   (e) $h \cdot (1, 0) + b(0, 1).$

   (f) $\dfrac{1}{2}(a, b) + \dfrac{1}{2}(c, d).$

5. Find values of s and t so that

(a) $s \cdot (-1, 2) + t \cdot (3, 1) = (-4, 1)$.

(b) $s \cdot (5, -1) + t \cdot (-1, 3) = (2, 1)$.

(c) $s \cdot (-2, -2) + t \cdot (1, -5) = (-7, 11)$.

(d) $s \cdot (4, 2) + t \cdot (3, 2) = (2, 1)$.

(e) $s \cdot (1/2, 2) + (4, 6) = t \cdot (-5, 0)$.

4.3 Geometric Interpretation of Addition in R²

For our later work we need a better look at the addition in R^2. Consider the points P and Q (Fig. 4.3), with coordinates (x_1, y_1) and (x_2, y_2) respectively. Let $S = P + Q$. Then S has coordinates $(x_1 + x_2, y_1 + y_2)$. Draw OP, OQ, QS, and PS. If we look at the length of OP and QS we see they are the same. It is clear that the length of PS and OQ are also the same. It follows, then, that the figure is a parallelogram. Thus, graphically, to add

$$P : (x_1, y_1) \quad \text{and} \quad Q : (x_2, y_2),$$

draw OP and OQ, draw the lines through Q parallel to OP and through P parallel to OQ. Where these lines intersect, say at S, we find the point with coordinates $(x_1 + x_2, y_1 + y_2)$. By this method, we have found the sum of P and Q graphically.

Exercise

Carefully plot $(1, 1)$ and $(2, 5)$ and graphically find the sum of the two. Does it turn out all right? Do the same with $(-4, 1)$ and $(4, 2)$.

One might realize that this procedure is the same as moving the segment OP so that O falls on Q, but so that the direction of the segment is not changed. P, then, falls on the point that is the sum of P and Q.

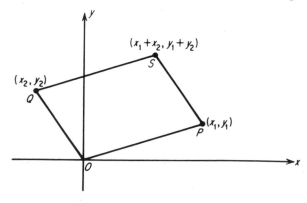

Figure 4.3

4.4   Vectors

Some of the readers by this time might recognize what we have been doing as nothing but the algebra of vectors in a plane. The terminology of vectors is useful, and we will introduce it here.

First consider the concept of directed line segment. We make no attempt here to define line segment but assume that, if P and Q are points in a plane, the reader understands what is meant by the line segment determined by them. We agree to distinguish between the segment from P to Q and that from Q to P. Thus, notationally, we denote the segment from P to Q by **PQ** and that from Q to P by **QP**. We refer to these as *directed line segments*. In the segment **PQ** we call P the *initial point* and Q the *terminal point* of the segment.

In all that follows we assume that we are operating in a plane on which a Cartesian coordinate system has been introduced.

Definition 4.3. Let P and Q be points with coordinates (x_1, y_1) and (x_2, y_2) respectively. Let S and T be points with coordinates (x_3, y_3) and (x_4, y_4) respectively. The segments **PQ** and **ST** are *equivalent* if and only if

$$x_2 - x_1 = x_4 - x_3 \quad \text{and} \quad y_2 - y_1 = y_4 - y_3.$$

To denote the equivalence of **PQ** and **ST** we will write **PQ** $\sim$ **ST**. (Read this as, **PQ** is equivalent to **ST**.)

Remark. If **PQ** $\sim$ **ST**, then $d(P, Q) = d(S, T)$, the lines are parallel and the segments point in the "same direction."

The fact that $d(P, Q) = d(S, T)$ is simply verified. The argument that the lines are parallel is better left until we discuss slopes of lines. The fact that they point in the same direction is determined by the signs of the numbers involved in determining the equivalence of the segments.

Observe that $\sim$ is a relation on the set of all directed line segments in our plane. It can be shown that it is an equivalence relation. Thus (Sec. 1.11) we have the set of all directed line segments grouped into equivalence classes. Recall that every directed line segment will be in one and only one of these classes.

Exercise

Verify that $\sim$ is an equivalence relation on the set of all directed line segments in our plane.

Now we are in a position to define precisely the concept of vector. A *vector* in a plane is an equivalence class of directed line segments. Clearly, such objects as these are awkward to handle and the technique for handling vectors is that of dealing with representatives of the classes. Thus, if **PQ** is a directed line segment, we deal with the vector that is the set of all line segments equivalent to **PQ**. We *will* refer to the vector **PQ**, meaning the class of all line segments equivalent to **PQ** or the vector determined by **PQ**. The statement that vector **PQ** equals the vector **RS** means that the equivalence classes are equal. Of course, this means that the directed segments **PQ** and **RS** are equivalent. Why?

In much of what we do, we will be interested in finding particular directed line segments rather than classes of equivalent segments. On the other hand, we must keep in mind that each directed segment may be considered as a representative of a class of equivalent segments—a vector.

We add a word concerning notation. The notation **PQ** might mean either a directed line segment or the vector determined by the line segment **PQ**. The context will indicate which is being considered. For example, if we have the statement **PQ** = **RS** we are dealing with vectors unless we specifically say otherwise. Because, unless line segments **PQ** and **RS** are identical ($P = R$ and $Q = S$), they would not normally be related by equality.

Definition 4.4. Let P, Q, R, S be points in our plane with coordinates (x_1, y_1), (x_2, y_2), (x_3, y_3), and (x_4, y_4) respectively. The sum of the vectors **PQ** and **RS**, denoted **PQ** + **RS**, is defined to be the vector **OX**, where X has coordinates

$$(x_2 - x_1 + x_4 - x_3, y_2 - y_1 + y_4 - y_3)$$

and where 0 is the origin, $(0, 0)$.

Thus, if $P : (1, 2)$, $Q : (3, 4)$, $R : (-2, -1)$, and $S : (3, -6)$ are points with the indicated coordinates, **PQ** + **RS** would be the vector determined by the line segment **OX** where X has coordinates $(7, -3)$. Now we could have been asked to find the point Y so that **PY** = **PQ** + **RS**. This means that we must find the coordinates of the point Y so that the vectors **PY** and **OX** are equal or so that the line segments **PY** and **OX** are equivalent. Now we know the coordinates of P, O, and X. Let (x, y) be the coordinates of Y. Then **PY** $\sim$ **OX** if and only if

$$x - 1 = 7 - 0 \quad \text{and} \quad y - 2 = -3 - 0.$$

This means that $x = 8$ and $y = -1$. Thus we have found Y so that the vector determined by **PY** is equal to the sum of the vectors **PQ** and **RS**.

Remark. Let P and Q be points with coordinates (x_1, y_1) and (x_2, y_2) respectively. Let X be any point with coordinates (x_0, y_0). Then, if Y has coordinates $(x_0 + x_2 - x_1, y_0 + y_2 - y_1)$, **XY** $\sim$ **PQ** and **XY** = **PQ**. In particular, if $X = 0$ (that is, has coordinates $(0, 0)$), Y has coordinates $(x_2 - x_1, y_2 - y_1)$ and **OY** = **PQ**.

The proof for this remark follows immediately from the definition of $\sim$ and vectors.

The importance of this remark is that it allows us to represent any vector by a line segment with the origin as initial point. It also allows us to interpret addition of vectors as the addition we defined earlier for R^2. For, if **PQ** and **RS** are vectors determined by the points of Definition 4.4, then $\mathbf{OP^1} = \mathbf{PQ}$ and $\mathbf{OQ^1} = \mathbf{RS}$, if P^1 has coordinates $(x_2 - x_1, y_2 - y_1)$ and Q^1 has coordinates $(x_4 - x_3, y_4 - y_3)$ in R^2. Then $P^1 + Q^1 = X$, where X has coordinates $(x_2 - x_1 + x_4 - x_3, y_2 - y_1 + y_4 - y_3)$. But the vector $\mathbf{OX} = \mathbf{PQ} + \mathbf{RS}$.

It should be pointed out that if $\mathbf{PQ} + \mathbf{RS}$ is found and if $\mathbf{AB} = \mathbf{PQ}$ and $\mathbf{CD} = \mathbf{RS}$ then $\mathbf{AB} + \mathbf{CD} = \mathbf{PQ} + \mathbf{RS}$. This is a consequence of the definition of equivalence of directed line segments. That is, if $\mathbf{AB} = \mathbf{PQ}$ and if $A : (u_1, v_1)$, $B : (u_2, v_2)$, $P : (x_1, y_1)$, and $Q : (x_2, y_2)$, have the coordinates indicated, then $u_2 - u_1 = x_2 - x_1$ and $v_2 - v_1 = y_2 - y_1$. So, in determining the sums $\mathbf{AB} + \mathbf{CD}$ and $\mathbf{PQ} + \mathbf{RS}$, it doesn't matter whether $\mathbf{AB}$ or $\mathbf{PQ}$ is used.

Definition 4.5. Let $k \in R^1$ and let **PQ** be a vector, where P and Q have coordinates (x_1, y_1) and (x_2, y_2) respectively. We define the *scalar product* of k and **PQ**, denoted by $k \cdot \mathbf{PQ}$, to be the vector **OX**, where X has coordinates

$$(k(x_2 - x_1), k(y_2 - y_1))$$

and where 0 is the origin.

Again, by choosing $Y : (x_2 - x_1, y_2 - y_1)$ so that $\mathbf{OY} = \mathbf{PQ}$, we can identify this scalar multiplication as that in R^2.

As an example, consider **PQ** where $P : (2, 4)$ and $Q : (7, -4)$ have the indicated coordinates. Then

$$4 \cdot \mathbf{PQ} = \mathbf{OX}, \quad \text{where } X \text{ has coordinates } (20, -32).$$

We might have been asked to find the coordinates of Y so that

$$\mathbf{PY} = 4 \cdot \mathbf{PQ}.$$

This would mean that, if Y has coordinates (x, y) then $x - 2 = 20 - 0$ and $y - 4 = -32 - 0$. So

$$x = 22 \quad \text{and} \quad y = -28.$$

Then

$$\mathbf{PY} = 4 \cdot \mathbf{PQ} = \mathbf{OX}.$$

As examples of how these notions can be useful, we look at several problems. First note that, if **OX** is the vector with end point $X : (2, -5)$, $3 \cdot \mathbf{OX} = \mathbf{OY}$ where Y has coordinates $(6, -15)$.

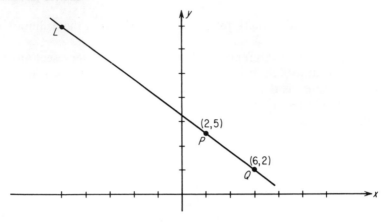

Figure 4.4

Let **PQ** be a directed segment with end points (Fig. 4.4) $P : (2, 5)$ $Q : (6, 2)$. Let us find the point L so that the segment **PL** lies on **PQ** and L is 3 times as far from P as is Q whereas L is on the side of P away from Q.

It is not hard to see that L satisfies the vector equation

$$\mathbf{PL} = -3 \cdot \mathbf{PQ} .$$

Our problem is to find the coordinates (x, y) of L so this equation holds. Now $3 \cdot \mathbf{PQ} = \mathbf{OX}$ where X has coordinates $-3 \cdot (4, -3) = (-12, 9)$. If $\mathbf{PL} = \mathbf{OX}$, then $x - 2 = -12$ and $y - 5 = 9$, or $x = -10$ and $y = 14$. Thus, L has coordinates $(-10, 14)$.

In about the same fashion, we can find the midpoint of the segment **PQ**. The midpoint, K, satisfies the vector equation

$$\mathbf{PK} = \frac{1}{2} \mathbf{PQ} .$$

$\frac{1}{2} \cdot \mathbf{PQ} = \mathbf{OX}$ where X has coordinates $\frac{1}{2}(4, -3) = (2, -\frac{3}{2})$. Then, if $\mathbf{PK} = \mathbf{OX}$ and if K has coordinates (x, y), $x - 2 = 2$ and $y - 5 = -\frac{3}{2}$, or $x = 4$ and $y = 3\frac{1}{2}$. So K has coordinates $(4, 3\frac{1}{2})$.

Exercise 4.3

1. Given the points $O : (0, 0)$, $P : (1, 2)$, $Q : (-1, -3)$, and $R : (-2, 4)$, find coordinates of X so that (sketch your answers):

   (a) $\mathbf{OX} = 3 \cdot \mathbf{OP}$.

   (b) $\mathbf{OX} = \mathbf{OP} + \mathbf{OQ}$.

(c) $\mathbf{OX} = \mathbf{OR} - 2 \cdot \mathbf{OP} + 3 \cdot \mathbf{OQ}$. ($-2 \cdot \mathbf{OP}$ means $+(-2) \cdot \mathbf{OP}$)

(d) $\mathbf{OX} = \mathbf{OP} + \mathbf{PQ} + \mathbf{QR}$.

(e) $\mathbf{PX}$ has the same length and direction as $\mathbf{QR}$.

(f) $\mathbf{OP} + \mathbf{OX} = \mathbf{OR}$.

(g) $\mathbf{PX} + \mathbf{QX} = \mathbf{RP}$.

2. Given the points $O : (0, 0)$, $A : (1, 3)$, $B : (-1, -2)$, $C : (2, -6)$. (The length of a vector is the length of any line segment determining the vector.)

(a)   Compute the length of $\mathbf{OA}$.

(b)   Compute the length of $\mathbf{BC}$.

(c)   Compute the length of $-2 \cdot \mathbf{OB}$.

(d)   Compute the length of $3 \cdot \mathbf{OA} + 4 \cdot \mathbf{OB}$.

(e)   Compute the length of $2 \cdot \mathbf{AB}$.

(f)   Compute the length of $2 \cdot \mathbf{AB} + \mathbf{OA}$.

(g)   Compute the length of $-3 \cdot \mathbf{AB}$.

(h)   Compute the length of $-3 \cdot \mathbf{OC} + 3 \cdot \mathbf{OC}$.

3. Using vectors find the points of trisection of the line segment joining $(-1, 0)$ and $(5, 3)$.

4. Find the coordinates of the point X which is three-fifths of the way from $(2, 1)$ to $(-3, 6)$ lying on the line segment joining the two points.

5. Find the point of quinsection nearest $(4, -1)$ of the line segment joining $(4, -1)$ and $(-6, 9)$.

6. Using vectors find the point three-fourths of the way from $(-5, 4)$ to $(5, -4)$.

7. The vector $\mathbf{OX}$, $O : (0, 0)$, $X : (-4, 3)$ is added to $\mathbf{OY}$ where Y is the midpoint of the segment from $(-3, 2)$ to $(6, -8)$. What is the length of the resulting vector?

4.5   Equations of Sets in R². Straight Line

At this time we want to look at the idea of the equation of a set, K, of points in a plane on which a Cartesian coordinate system has been introduced. In the future, when we speak of a plane on which a rectangular coordinate system has been introduced, we will frequently use the notation R^2 because of the identification we have between the two.

Definition 4.6. Let $K \subset R^2$. By the *equation of K*, we mean an equation, q, so that

$$(x, y) \in K \Leftrightarrow (x, y) \text{ satisfies } q .$$

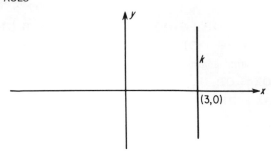

Figure 4.5

This means that, if (x, y) is a point in K, then (x, y) satisfies the equation q and if (x, y) is a pair of numbers satisfying q, then (x, y) is a point in K.

As an example consider the equation $x = 3$ and the set, K, of all points 3 units to the right of the y axis in R^2.

Certainly if $(x, y) \in K$, then $x = 3$ (Fig. 4.5). Moreover, if (x, y) is a pair of numbers so that $x = 3$, $(x, y) \in K$. Thus $x = 3$ is the equation of K.

Now we want to turn our attention to the problem of determining the equation of all points on the straight line determined by the points $P : (x_1, y_1)$ and $Q : (x_2, y_2)$. $(P \neq Q)$. If (x_0, y_0) are the coordinates of a point S (Fig. 4.6) on this straight line, then there is a real number t with the property that $t \cdot \mathbf{PQ} = \mathbf{PS}$. It is true, then, that $\mathbf{OS} = \mathbf{OP} + t \cdot \mathbf{PQ}$. Rewriting this equation in terms of the coordinates involved, we get that

$$(x_0, y_0) = (x_1, y_1) + t \cdot (x_2 - x_1, y_2 - y_1),$$

or that

$$(x_0, y_0) = (x_1 + t(x_2 - x_1), y_1 + t(y_2 - y_1)).$$

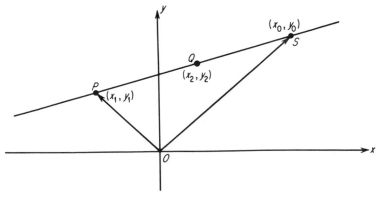

Figure 4.6

So, if (x_0, y_0) is any point on our line, for some real number t, it is true that

$$x_0 = x_1 + t(x_2 - x_1) \quad \text{and} \quad y_0 = y_1 + t(y_2 - y_1).$$

If $x_2 \neq x_1$, we can solve the first of these equations for t and substitute the answer into the second equation to get that

$$y_0 = y_1 + \frac{x_0 - x_1}{x_2 - x_1}(y_2 - y_1),$$

or

$$y_0 - y_1 = \frac{y_2 - y_1}{x_2 - x_1}(x_0 - x_1).$$

This means that the coordinates x_0 and y_0 of any point on the line determined by P and Q satisfy the equation

(α)
$$y - y_1 = \frac{y_2 - y_1}{x_2 - x_1}(x - x_1),$$

provided, of course, that $x_2 \neq x_1$. If $x_2 = x_1$, the coordinates x and y satisfy the equation

(β)
$$x = x_1.$$

If x_a and y_a are any two numbers which satisfy the equation (α), consider the point L with coordinates (x_a, y_a). If we let

$$t = \frac{x_a - x_1}{x_2 - x_1},$$

then $x_a = x_1 + t(x_2 - x_1)$ and we have, since

$$y_a - y_1 = \frac{y_2 - y_1}{x_2 - x_1}(x_a - x_1),$$

that $y_a = y_1 + t(y_2 - y_1)$. Thus $\mathbf{OL} = \mathbf{OP} + t \cdot \mathbf{PQ}$. This means that L lies on our line. So we have shown that, if $x_2 \neq x_1$, (α) is the equation of our straight line. We have also shown that, if $x_2 = x_1$, the coordinates of any point on our line satisfy (β). Suppose that $x_2 = x_1$ and that (x_a, y_a) are any pair of numbers satisfying (β). Then $x_a = x_1$. Now $y_1 \neq y_2$. Let

$$t = \frac{y_a - y_1}{y_2 - y_1}.$$

Then $y_a = y_1 + t(y_2 - y_1)$, and since $x_2 - x_1 = 0$,

$$x_a = x_1 + t(x_2 - x_1).$$

Hence the point L with coordinates (x_a, y_a) satisfies

$$\text{OL} = \text{OP} + t \cdot \text{PQ} .$$

The preceding discussion is, in fact, the proof of Theorem 4.2.

Theorem 4.2. Let P and Q be distinct points in R^2 with coordinates (x_1, y_1) and (x_2, y_2) respectively. The equation of the straight line determined by these two points is

(α) $$y - y_1 = \frac{y_2 - y_1}{x_2 - x_1}(x - x_1), \quad \text{if } x_2 \neq x_1 ,$$

or

(β) $$x = x_1, \quad \text{if } x_2 = x_1 .$$

We now consider an example of this. Let $(3, 1)$ and $(-2, 4)$ be the points P and Q. Then

$$\frac{y_2 - y_1}{x_2 - x_1} = \frac{4 - 1}{-2 - 3} = -\frac{3}{5} .$$

By our theorem, since $x_2 \neq x_1$, the equation of the line through these two points is

$$y - 1 = -\frac{3}{5}(x - 3) .$$

We could, of course, rewrite this as

$$5y + 3x = 14 .$$

Probably the reader wonders what would have happened if we had called $(3, 1)$, Q and $(-2, 4)$, P. If we do this, we would again compute

$$\frac{y_2 - y_1}{x_2 - x_1} \quad \text{to be} \quad \frac{1 - 4}{3 - (-2)} = -\frac{3}{5} .$$

Then the equation would be

$$y - 4 = -\frac{3}{5}(x + 2) .$$

Although this is apparently different from the equations obtained earlier, on simplifying we get the equation $5y + 3x = 14$, which is the same as we obtained earlier.

As another application of Theorem 4.2, consider the points $(3, 5)$ and $(3, -10)$. Since the x coordinates of each are the same, $x_2 - x_1 = 0$ (no matter what we call the points), and the equation is of the form (β) in our theorem. Hence the equation of the line determined by these two points is

$$x = 3 .$$

Exercise 4.4

Write equations of the straight lines determined by the following pairs of points. (Simplify your equation.)

	P	Q			P	Q
(a)	$(0, 0)$	$(1, 1)$	(f)		$(-1, -2)$	$(-3, -4)$
(b)	$(0, 0)$	$(-1, 1)$	(g)		$(0, 3)$	$(4, 5)$
(c)	$(2, 5)$	$(2, 9)$	(h)		$(1, 99)$	$(3, -592)$
(d)	$(3, 4)$	$(6, 7)$	(i)		$(4, 6)$	$(6, 6)$
(e)	$(3, 4)$	$(-4, 10)$	(j)		$(2, -9)$	$(9, -2)$

4.6 Slope of a Line

A few observations concerning equations of straight lines are in order. As we noted, the fraction $(y_2 - y_1)/(x_2 - x_1)$ appears in our equation. It is clear that, when $x_2 - x_1 = 0$, this is not a real number. Let us consider a nonvertical straight line in R^2 and pick a pair of pairs of distinct points on the line. For example let (x_1, y_1), (x_2, y_2), and (x_1', y_1'), (x_2', y_2') be the pairs of points. The fractions

$$\frac{y_2 - y_1}{x_2 - x_1} \quad \text{and} \quad \frac{y_2' - y_1'}{x_2' - x_1'}$$

are, of course, the same, no matter how the points were chosen.

Exercise

Prove the foregoing comment as an exercise using similar triangles.

This number determined by any pair of points on the line in R^2 is called the *slope of the line*. Formally, then, we make the following definition:

Definition 4.7. Let k be a nonvertical straight line in R^2. Let P and Q be distinct points on k with coordinates (x_1, y_1) and (x_2, y_2), respectively. The *slope, m, of k* is defined to be

$$m = \frac{y_2 - y_1}{x_2 - x_1}.$$

Since the slope is the same for any pair of points on the same line, suppose we consider any point (x_0, y_0) and the point $(x_0 + 1, y_1)$. The slope of the line can be determined by evaluating

$$\frac{y_1 - y_0}{x_0 + 1 - x_0} = \frac{y_1 - y_0}{1}.$$

Thus the slope of a line tells us how much the y coordinates of points change when the x coordinates change one unit. That is, the change in the y coordinate per unit change in the x coordinate. So, if the slope of a line is 3, we know the line rises 3 units for every unit change along the x axis. It is possible, of course, that the slope of a line is negative.

We might well note that, if we know one point on a line and the slope of the line, we can write the equation of the line. Because (α) of Theorem 3.4 can be rewritten to be

$$y - y_1 = m(x - x_1) .$$

A very simple example of the type of problem this result allows us to handle is the following:

Give the equation of the straight line with slope $\frac{3}{4}$ passing through the point $(2, -5)$. Since the equation of a line (not parallel to the y axis) can be written as

$$y - y_1 = m(x - x_1) ,$$

we get immediately that the equation of the line in question is

$$y - (-5) = \frac{3}{4}(x - 2) ,$$

or

$$4y - 3x + 26 = 0 .$$

Exercise 4.5

1. (a)   Verify that m is positive when the line rises from left to right; negative when the line falls from left to right.

   (b)   What does a slope of 0 tell us about a line?

   (c)   When does a line have no slope?

   (d)   Write the equations of the x axis; the y axis.

2. Give an equation (in simplified form) for the line passing through the given point and having the given number m as slope:

   (a) $(0, 0)$; $m = 2$.

   (b) $(-1, -1)$; $m = -1$.

   (c) $(2, 1)$; $m = 1$.

   (d) $(3, -2)$; $m = -\dfrac{3}{2}$.

   (e) $(-2, 1)$; $m = \dfrac{1}{2}$.

   (f) $(5, -9)$; $m = \dfrac{1}{10}$.

   (g) $(8, -2)$; $m = -\dfrac{3}{4}$.

   (h) $\left(-3, \dfrac{2}{5}\right)$; $m = 0$.

   (i) $(-8, -2)$, m not defined.

   (j) (x_1, y_1); $m = a$.

3. Show that the points $(2, 0)$, $(0, 3)$, and $(4, -3)$ are collinear. Use the notion of slope.

4. Find the value of y which will make the point $(3, y)$ lie on the line joining $(-6, 1)$ and $(-3, 0)$.

5. A point, X, whose first coordinate is twice its second, lies on the line through $(6, 4)$ and $(-2, 2)$. Find the coordinates of X.

6. Let P and Q be points with coordinates $(1, 1)$ and $(5, 7)$ respectively.

   (a)   Write the equation of the line k through P and Q.

   (b)   Find the y coordinate of the point $(10, y)$ which is on the line through P with slope twice that of k.

7. Let $P : (0, 1)$; $Q : (2, 3)$; $R : (5, -2)$; and $S : (7, 4)$ be given points.

   (a)   Write the equations of the lines through P and Q, through R and S and through Q and S.

   (b)   Write the equations of the lines through the midpoints of PQ and RS.

4.7 More About Straight Lines

Definition 4.8. Let e and f be equations. e and f are called *equivalent* $\Leftrightarrow$ they have the same solution sets.

Exercise 4.6

1. Justify for yourselves that the graph of equivalent equations are the same. Also verify that if e is an equation of a set $K \subset R^2$ and if f is equivalent to e, then f is an equation of set K.

2. Prove that the following equations are equivalent:

   (a) $y - 2 = \dfrac{3}{4}x$ and $4y - 3x = 8$.

   (b) $y = \dfrac{1}{x^2 + 1}$ and $x^2 y + y - 1 = 0$.

   (c) $2x + 4y = 10$ and $\dfrac{x}{5} + \dfrac{2y}{5} = 1$.

   (d) $9x^2 + 16y^2 = 144$ and $\dfrac{x^2}{16} + \dfrac{y^2}{9} = 1$.

   (e) $ax^2 - by^2 = ab$ and $\dfrac{x^2}{b} - \dfrac{y^2}{a} = 1$.

We now consider the following theorems:

Theorem 4.3. Let $e : Ax + By + C = 0$, $A, B, C \in R^1$ be an equation in two real variables so that not both of A and B are 0. Then e is an equation of a straight line.

Proof. Case 1. $B = 0$.

When $B = 0$, e becomes $Ax + C = 0$. Consider the equation $x = -C/A$. This is the equation of a vertical line passing through the point $(-C/A, 0)$. But these equations are equivalent. Hence e is an equation of a straight line.

Case 2. $B \neq 0$.

Consider the equation of a straight line with slope $-A/B$, passing through the point $(0, -C/B)$. This equation is

$$y = -\frac{A}{B} x - \frac{C}{B}.$$

But the equation just arrived at is equivalent to e and, therefore, e is an equation of a straight line.

Theorem 4.4. Let $Ax + By + C = 0$ be an equation of a straight line k where $B \neq 0$. The slope of the line k is $-A/B$.

Proof. Let x_1 and x_2 be any pair of distinct real numbers. The points

$$\left(x_1, -\frac{A}{B} x_1 - \frac{C}{B}\right) \quad \text{and} \quad \left(x_2, \frac{A}{B} x_2 - \frac{C}{B}\right)$$

are an arbitrary pair of distinct points on k. The slope of k is, then,

$$\frac{[-(A/B)x_1 - (C/B)] - [-(A/B)x_2 - (C/B)]}{x_1 - x_2},$$

or

$$\frac{-(A/B)x_1 + (A/B)x_2}{x_1 - x_2},$$

or

$$-\frac{A(x_1 - x_2)}{B(x_1 - x_2)} = -\frac{A}{B}.$$

We are now in a position to make some more remarks about equations for straight lines. If, as in Theorem 3.4, an equation of a straight line is of the form

$$(\alpha) \qquad\qquad y - y_1 = \frac{y_2 - y_1}{x_2 - x_1}(x - x_1),$$

it is seen that the equations

$$(\beta) \qquad (x_2 - x_1)y - (x_2 y_1 - x_1 y_1) = (y_2 - y_1)x - (x_1 y_2 - x_1 y_1),$$

and

$$(\gamma) \qquad (x_2 - x_1)y + (y_1 - y_2)x + (x_1 y_2 - x_2 y_1) = 0$$

are equivalent to (α). (Actually, a given equation has many equations equivalent to it.) For this reason, rather than speaking of an equation of a given line, we will speak of *the* equation of the line, realizing that there are other equations that might be used. In (γ), if we let

$$(x_2 - x_1) = B, \quad (y_1 - y_2) = A \quad \text{and} \quad (x_1y_2 - x_2y_1) = C,$$

we see that (α) is equivalent to an equation of the form $Ax + By + C = 0$. Many books call this the *general form for the equation of a straight line*.

As a result of Theorem 4.4, in order to find the slope of a straight line, one need merely solve the equation for y and read the coefficient of x.

Exercise 4.7

Find the slopes of the straight lines whose equations are as follows:

(a) $3x - 4y + 10 = 0$.   (b) $9x + y - 10 = 0$.

(c) $y + 3 = 0$.   (d) $2x - 4 = 0$.

(e) $8y - 16x + 5 = 0$.   (f) $6y - x + 2 = 0$.

(g) $\dfrac{4y + 2x}{3} = 0$.   (h) $8y - 3x - 8 = 0$.

(i) $\dfrac{2x}{3y} - 6 = 0$.   (j) $5x - 2y + 6 = 0$.

(k) $4x + 6 = y$.   (l) $-2x - y + 2 = 0$.

(m) In the equation in (a), find two points on the line. Using these points, write the equation of the line determined by them and verify that it is the equation in (a).

Remark. In graphing straight lines, it is necessary to plot only two points and then to draw the line through them.

For instance, we might be asked to graph the solution set of the equation $x + y = 4$. We immediately recognize this as the equation of a straight line. If we let $x = 0$, then $y = 4$; if we let $y = 0$, then $x = 4$. This means that we have two points, $(0, 4)$ and $(4, 0)$, on our line. To graph it, then, simply plot these points and draw the line.

Exercise

Graph the lines whose equations are given in Exercise 4.7.

4.8 Slopes of Parallel and Perpendicular Lines

In this section, we discuss the relation of the slopes of parallel lines and lines that are perpendicular to each other. Consider the following theorem:

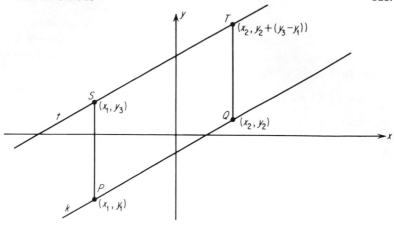

Figure 4.7

Theorem 4.5. Let t be any straight line and suppose that k is any line parallel to t. Then k and t have the same slopes.

Proof. First, observe that if k and t (Fig. 4.7) are both vertical, neither has a slope. Now suppose that k and t are nonvertical parallel straight lines. Suppose that k is the lower line. If not, rename the lines.

Choose points P and Q, with coordinates (x_1, y_1) and (x_2, y_2) respectively, on k. Draw lines through P and Q parallel to the y axis. These lines determine points S and T on t. Now the x coordinates of S and T are x_1 and x_2 respectively. (Why?) Note that the quadrilateral $PQST$ is a parallelogram and that SP is equal in length to TQ. So, if we call the y coordinate of S, y_3, the y coordinate of T will be $y_2 + (y_3 - y_1)$. We now compute the slopes of k and t using the pairs of points we now have on each.

The slope m_1 of k is given by

$$m_1 = \frac{y_2 - y_1}{x_2 - x_1},$$

and the slope m_2 of t is given by

$$m_2 = \frac{y_2 + (y_3 - y_1) - y_3}{x_2 - x_1}$$

$$= \frac{y_2 - y_1}{x_2 - x_1}.$$

These are clearly the same and the theorem is proved.

The theorem establishing the relation between slopes of perpendicular lines is as follows:

Theorem 4.6. Suppose k and t are lines, neither of which is vertical, and suppose $k \perp t$. Then the product of their slopes is -1.

Proof. If one line is vertical, it has no slope, and the theorem is senseless. Assume that k rises from left to right. (If not, rename the lines.) Suppose that (x_0, y_0) is the point of intersection of k and t.

Choose the point $P : (x_0 + 1, y_1)$ on k and the point $M : (x_1, y_0 + 1)$ on t where $x_1 = x_0 - (y_1 - y_0)$.
Construct the triangles as indicated in Fig. 4.8. With the choice of points we made, the triangles MSI and PQI are congruent. The slope, m_1, of k is given by

$$m_1 = \frac{y_1 - y_0}{1},$$

and the slope, m_2, of t is given by

$$m_2 = \frac{1}{x_0 - (y_1 - y_0) - x_0}$$

Clearly $m_1 \cdot m_2 = -1$.

We might note that another way of stating the relation between the slopes of perpendicular lines, neither of which is vertical, is that each slope is the negative reciprocal of the other. In symbols, $m_1 = 1/m_2$, or $m_2 = -1/m_1$. Clearly these are equivalent to $m_1 \cdot m_2 = -1$.

As examples of how this might be used, we note that if a line has slope 2, any line perpendicular to it has slope $-\frac{1}{2}$.

A type of problem of interest is that of determining the equation of a line through a given point and perpendicular to a given line. For example, write

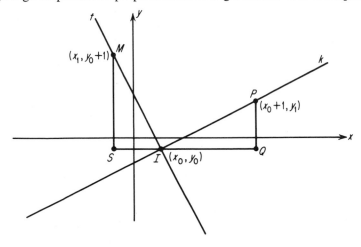

Figure 4.8

the equation of the line, perpendicular to the line with equation $y = 3x + 2$, that passes through $(1, 2)$. The slope of the given line is 3. So the slope of the line we want is $-\frac{1}{3}$. The equation of the line in question is, then,

$$y - 2 = -\tfrac{1}{3}(x - 1), \quad \text{or} \quad 3y + x = 7.$$

Exercise 4.8

1. Write an equation of the line through the origin and (a) parallel, (b) perpendicular to the line whose equation is $x - y + 3 = 0$.

2. Write an equation of the line passing through the point $(1, 4)$ and (a) parallel, (b) perpendicular to the line with equation $3x - y - 2 = 0$.

3. Give an equation of the line through $(-1, 3)$ and (a) parallel, (b) perpendicular to the line whose equation is $x - 1 = 0$.

4. Give an equation of the line through $(1, -1)$ and (a) parallel, (b) perpendicular to the line with equation $y + 3 = 0$.

5. Find an equation for the line which is the perpendicular bisector of the line segment joining the origin and the point $(4, -2)$.

6. Show that the triangle with vertices $(3, -1)$, $(7, 2)$, and $(4, 6)$ is a right triangle.

7. Show that the quadrilateral with vertices $(7, 0)$, $(9, 2)$, $(6, 5)$, and $(4, 3)$ is a rectangle.

8. Given the triangle with vertices $(4, 1)$, $(-4, 3)$, and $(0, 1)$, find the length of the altitude drawn from $(4, 1)$.

9. Let P have coordinates $(3, -2)$. Write the equations of the lines through P that are (a) parallel to (b) perpendicular to the lines whose equations are given below:

   (a) $y = 3$. (b) $y = 4x + 7$.
   (c) $y = -x + 1$. (d) $2y + x = 3$.
   (e) $x - 2y = 1$. (f) $4x + 3y = 0$.
   (g) $x - 10y = 1$. (h) $13x + 17y = 3$.

4.9 Complex Numbers

There are other types of curves whose equations can be derived in ways similar to that for the equation of the straight line. There are also equations that one learns to recognize as being equations of certain curves. This material is treated in courses in analytic geometry. So at this time we turn our attention to other topics. One that we have mentioned before is that of multiplying elements in R^2.

Definition 4.9. Let (x_1, y_1), $(x_2, y_2) \in R^2$. We define a binary operation (denoted by $\cdot$) called *multiplication* on R^2 by

$$(x_1, y_1) \cdot (x_2, y_2) = (x_1 x_2 - y_1 y_2, x_1 y_2 + x_2 y_1) \,.$$

Thus, for example,

$$(3, 2) \cdot (4, -2) = (3 \cdot 4 - (2)(-2), 3(-2) + 2 \cdot 4)$$
$$= (12 + 4, -6 + 8) = (16, 2) \,.$$

Exercise 4.9

Compute the following:

(a) $(-1, 2) \cdot (3, -2)$.

(b) $(2, 1) \cdot (-2, 1)$.

(c) $(1, 0) \cdot (4, -1)$.

(d) $(1, 0) \cdot (0, 1)$.

(e) $(1, 0) \cdot (a, b)$.

(f) $(a, b) \cdot (1, 0)$.

(g) $(3, 1) \cdot (3, -1)$.

(h) $(a, b) \cdot (c, d)$.

(i) $(a, b) \cdot (a, -b)$.

(j) $(1, 1) \cdot \left(\dfrac{1}{2}, -\dfrac{1}{2} \right)$.

(k) $(a, b) \cdot \left(\dfrac{a}{a^2 + b^2}, \dfrac{-b}{a^2 + b^2} \right)$.

(l) $(0, 2) \cdot (0, 1)$.

(m) $(0, 1) \cdot (0, 1)$.

(n) $(a, b) \cdot (3, 1)$.

(o) $(0, 1) \cdot (a, b)$.

(p) $2(0, 1) + (3, 4) \cdot (0, 1)$.

(q) $2 \cdot (-1, -1) + (-2, 1) \cdot (3, 4)$.

(r) $2 \cdot (0, 2) + (0, 1)^2$.

(s) $(0, 2)^2 + (4, 0)$.

(t) $4(4, 0)^2 + (0, 1)^3$.

This multiplication satisfies certain properties. We list some of these as theorems and others as exercises.

Theorem 4.7. Let $(x_j, y_j) \in R^2$; $j = 1, 2, 3$. Then

$$(x_1, y_1) \cdot ((x_2, y_2) \cdot (x_3, y_3)) = ((x_1, y_1) \cdot (x_2, y_2)) \cdot (x_3, y_3) \,.$$

Proof.

$$(x_1, y_1) \cdot ((x_2, y_2) \cdot (x_3, y_3)) = (x_1, y_1) \cdot (x_2 x_3 - y_2 y_3, x_2 y_3 + y_2 x_3)$$
$$= (x_1(x_2 x_3 - y_2 y_3) - y_1(x_2 y_3 + y_2 x_3),$$
$$x_1(x_2 y_3 + y_2 x_3) + y_1(x_2 x_3 - y_2 y_3))$$
$$= (x_1 x_2 x_3 - x_1 y_2 y_3 - y_1 x_2 y_3 - y_1 y_2 x_3,$$
$$x_1 x_2 y_3 + x_1 y_2 x_3 + y_1 x_2 x_3 - y_1 y_2 y_3) \,.$$

$$((x_1, y_1)\cdot(x_2, y_2))\cdot(x_3, y_3) = (x_1x_2 - y_1y_2, x_1y_2 + y_1x_2)\cdot(x_3, y_3)$$
$$= ((x_1x_2 - y_1y_2)x_3 - (x_1y_2 + y_1x_2)y_3,$$
$$(x_1x_2 - y_1y_2)y_3 + (x_1y_2 + y_1x_2)x_3)$$
$$= (x_1x_2x_3 - y_1y_2x_3 - x_1y_2y_3 - y_1x_2y_3,$$
$$x_1x_2y_3 - y_1y_2y_3 + x_1y_2x_3 + y_1x_2x_3).$$

Comparing these expansions, we see that the theorem holds.

Theorem 4.8. Let $(x_1, y_1), (x_2, y_2) \in R^2$. Then

$$(x_1, y_1)\cdot(x_2, y_2) = (x_2, y_2)\cdot(x_1, y_1).$$

Proof. The proof for this theorem is left as an exercise for the reader.

Theorem 4.9. For any

$$(x, y) \in R^2, (x, y)\cdot(1, 0) = (x, y).$$

Proof.

$$(x, y)\cdot(1, 0) = (x\cdot 1 - y\cdot 0, x\cdot 0 + y\cdot 1) = (x, y).$$

Theorem 4.10. Suppose $(x, y) \in R^2$ and not both x and y are 0. Then

$$(x, y)\cdot\left(\frac{x}{x^2 + y^2}, \frac{-y}{x^2 + y^2}\right) = (1, 0).$$

Proof.

$$(x, y)\cdot\left(\frac{x}{x^2 + y^2}, \frac{-y}{x^2 + y^2}\right)$$
$$= \left(\frac{x^2}{x^2 + y^2} - y\cdot\frac{-y}{x^2 + y^2}, x\cdot\frac{-y}{x^2 + y^2} + y\cdot\frac{x}{x^2 + y^2}\right)$$
$$= \left(\frac{x^2 + y^2}{x^2 + y^2}, \frac{-xy}{x^2 + y^2} + \frac{xy}{x^2 + y^2}\right) = (1, 0).$$

Theorem 4.11. $(0, 1)\cdot(0, 1) = (-1, 0).$

Proof.

$$(0, 1)(0, 1) = (0\cdot 0 - 1\cdot 1, 0\cdot 1 + 1\cdot 0) = (-1, 0)$$

Exercise

Prove that $(x, y)\cdot(0, 0) = (0, 0)$ for any $(x, y) \in R^2$.

Theorem 4.12. Let $(x_j, y_j) \in R^2, j = 1, 2, 3.$

Then

$$(x_1, y_1)[(x_2, y_2) + (x_3, y_3)] = (x_1, y_1) \cdot (x_2, y_2) + (x_1, y_1) \cdot (x_3, y_3)$$

Proof. Observe that

$$(x_1, y_1)[(x_2, y_2) + (x_3, y_3)] = (x_1, y_1)(x_2 + x_3, y_2 + y_3)$$
$$= (x_1(x_2 + x_3) - y_1(y_2 + y_3), x_1(y_2 + y_3) + y_1(x_2 + x_3))$$
$$= (x_1 x_2 + x_1 x_3 - y_1 y_2 - y_1 y_3, x_1 y_2 + x_1 y_3 + y_1 x_2 + y_1 x_3)$$

On the other hand,

$$(x_1, y_1)(x_2, y_2) + (x_1, y_1)(x_3, y_3)$$
$$= (x_1 x_2 - y_1 y_2, x_1 y_2 + y_1 x_2) + (x_1 x_3 - y_1 y_3, x_1 y_3 + y_1 x_3)$$
$$= (x_1 x_2 - y_1 y_2 + x_1 x_3 - y_1 y_3, x_1 y_2 + y_1 x_2 + x_1 y_3 + y_1 x_3).$$

Comparing these two expansions, we note the desired equality.

Definition 4.10. The set R^2, with the operations of addition and multiplication as defined earlier, is called the set of *complex numbers*. When we understand that we are dealing with R^2 relative to these operations we denote the set by $\mathcal{C}$.

The matter of notation should be explained somewhat. For, if the reader has encountered complex numbers before, he has seen them in the form $a + bi$, with $a, b \in R^1$ and with i being some kind of number whose square is the real number -1. We would like to reconcile our notation with this usual notation. We first make the observation that, in a sense, $\mathcal{C}$ contains R^1. For example, consider the subset $\mathcal{R}$ of $\mathcal{C}$ defined by

$$\mathcal{R} = \{(x, y) \in \mathcal{C} \mid y = 0\}.$$

If $(x_1, 0), (x_2, 0) \in \mathcal{R}$,

$$(x_1, 0) + (x_2, 0) = (x_1 + x_2, 0),$$
$$(x_1, 0) \cdot (x_2, 0) = (x_1 x_2 - 0 \cdot 0, x_1 \cdot 0 + x_2 \cdot 0) = (x_1 x_2, 0).$$

Thus $\mathcal{R}$ is closed under the addition and multiplication of $\mathcal{C}$. More than this, the operations of addition and multiplication as applied in $\mathcal{R}$ are exactly the binary operations of R^1. This means that if we want to add or multiply $(x_1, 0), (x_2, 0)$, all we really have to know are these operations in R^1 and to insert the results in R^1 into the first positions in the pair that is to be the result of our operation in $\mathcal{C}$.

To be formal about it, there is a 1–1 correspondence between $\mathcal{R}$ and R^1, namely $(x, 0) \leftrightarrow x$, for every $x \in R^1$, with the properties that

$$(x_1, 0) + (x_2, 0) \Leftrightarrow x_1 + x_2$$

$$(x_1, 0) \cdot (x_2, 0) \Leftrightarrow x_1 x_2 \, ,$$

for all $(x_1, 0), (x_2, 0) \in \mathcal{R}$.

In this sense, $\mathcal{R}$ is the same as R^1. Because of this, we say that $\mathcal{C}$ contains R^1 or that R^1 *is imbedded* in $\mathcal{C}$.

With this notion in mind, we will agree to denote the element $(a, 0) \in \mathcal{C}$ by a. Using this agreement $(-1, 0)$ would be written -1. In Theorem 4.11 we proved that $(0, 1) \cdot (0, 1) = (-1, 0)$. If we denote the complex number $(0, 1)$ by the symbol i, we have, in our new notation that $i \cdot i = -1$, or that $i^2 = -1$. With this agreement about notation in $\mathcal{C}$, we can arrive at the usual notation for complex numbers. For let $(a, b) \in \mathcal{C}$. Notice that

$$(a, 0) + (b, 0) \cdot (0, 1) = (a, 0) + (0, b) = (a, b) \, .$$

That is, given any element $(a, b) \in \mathcal{C}$, (a, b) can be written as $(a, 0) + (b, 0) \cdot (0, 1)$. But following our agreement, we then have that $(a, b) = a + bi$. In terms of our new notation, we have that

$$(a + bi) + (c + di) = (a + c) + (b + d)i$$

and

$$(a + bi) \cdot (c + di) = (ac - bd) + (ad + bc)i$$

for any pair of complex numbers $a + bi$, $c + di$.

We also have that, if $a + bi \neq 0$ (that is, $a + bi \neq 0 + 0i$),

$$(a + bi)^{-1} = \frac{a}{a^2 + b^2} - \frac{b}{a^2 + b^2} i \, .$$

Without being overly concerned about this, we might practice a little arithmetic for complex numbers. We will agree that

$$\frac{a + bi}{c + di} = (a + bi)(c + di)^{-1} \, ,$$

just as we did in R^1, and that

$$(a + bi) - (c + di) = (a + bi) + (-(c + di))$$
$$= (a + bi) + (-c - di) \, .$$

Most of the difficulties with the arithmetic of complex numbers concern division and we might observe that there is a trick we can use to make division look simpler. First observe that

$$(c + di) \cdot (c - di) = c^2 + d^2 \, .$$

Then notice that

$$\frac{a + bi}{c + di} = (a + bi)\left(\frac{c}{c^2 + d^2} - \frac{d}{c^2 + d^2} i\right)$$

because

$$\frac{a + bi}{c + di} = (a + bi)(c + di)^{-1} .$$

Then note that

$$\frac{a + bi}{c + di} \cdot \frac{c - di}{c - di} = \frac{(a + bi) \cdot (c - di)}{c^2 + d^2}$$

$$= (a + bi)(c + di)^{-1} .$$

Hence, if a denominator involves $c + di$, we multiply top and bottom of the fractions by $c - di$ to reduce the problem to one of multiplication of complex numbers. For example,

$$\frac{10 + 15i}{3 + 4i} = \frac{10 + 15i}{3 + 4i} \cdot \frac{3 - 4i}{3 - 4i}$$

$$= (10 + 15i)(3 - 4i) \cdot \frac{1}{25}$$

$$= (90 + 5i)\frac{1}{25} = \frac{18}{5} + \frac{1}{5}i .$$

In the preceding discussion, we used the fact that, if k is a real number and if $a + bi \in \mathcal{C}$, then

$$k(a + bi) = (ka) + (kb)i .$$

We can justify this as follows: Consider the real number k as the complex number $k + 0i$ and consider the product $k \cdot (a + bi)$ as $(k + 0i) \cdot (a + bi)$. Then,

$$k(a + bi) = (k + 0i)(a + bi)$$

$$= (ka - 0b) + (kb + 0a)i$$

$$= (ka) + (kb)i .$$

An alternative to this is to define the "scalar multiplication" of a real number with a complex number.

Exercise 4.10

1. Perform the indicated operations and write the result in the form $a + bi$:

    (a) $(5 + i) + (-3 - 2i)$.   (b) i^3.

    (c) i^4.   (d) i^5.

(e) i^{-7}.   (f) i^{19}.

(g) $(-i)^3$.   (h) $(3 + i) \cdot (4 - 2i)$.

(i) $(1 + i)(1 + 2i)(1 + 3i)$.   (j) $\dfrac{5i - 10}{10}$.

(k) $\dfrac{1 + i}{-2}$.   (l) $\dfrac{3 + 2i}{i}$.

(m) $\dfrac{1}{3i - 4}$.   (n) $\dfrac{2 + i}{3 - i}$.

(o) $\dfrac{i + 1}{i - 1}$.   (p) $\dfrac{(1 - i)(2 + i)}{3 + 4i}$.

(q) $\left(-\dfrac{1}{2} + \dfrac{3}{2}i\right)^3$.   (r) $\left(-\dfrac{1}{2} - \dfrac{3}{2}i\right)^3$.

2. Solve the following equations in $\mathcal{C}$.

(a) $x^2 + 1 = 0$.   (b) $2x + 3 - 4i = 0$.

(c) $3 + \dfrac{x}{2} = i$.   (d) $x^2 + x + 1 = 0$.

(e) $x^2 + ix = 0$.   (f) $x^2 + ix - 3 = 0$.

4.10   Vector Spaces

In dealing with R^2, or ordered pairs of real numbers, we defined addition and scalar multiplication. Relative to these operations, certain properties were satisfied. These properties we list here.

For convenience we will use u, v, w to denote arbitrary elements in R^2 and a, b, c to denote real numbers. The properties that hold in this situation are:

(V0) $u + v \in R^2$, $a \cdot u \in R^2$

(V1) $u + v = v + u$

(V2) $(u + v) + w = u + (v + w)$

(V3) $u + \bar{0} = u$ for all $u \in R^2$, where $\bar{0} = (0, 0)$.

(V4)   Given $u = (c, d)$, $-u = (-c, -d)$ has the property that $u + (-u) = \bar{0}$.

(V5) $a \cdot (u + v) = au + av$.

(V6) $(a + b)u = au + bu$.

(V7) $(ab)u = a(bu)$.

(V8) $1 \cdot u = u$ and $0 \cdot u = \bar{0}$.

Definition 4.11. Let W be any set on which an "addition" and "scalar multiplication" is defined. Then, if the properties (V0)–(V8) hold, W is a *vector space over the real numbers* or a *real vector space*.

We have available several examples other than R^2. It should be reasonably clear that the set, $\mathcal{C}$, of complex numbers is also a real vector space when we use the scalar multiplication

$$k(a + bi) = (ka) + (kb)i\,,$$

where $k \in R^1$ and $a + bi \in \mathcal{C}$.

(V1)–(V4) are satisfied as we have seen. Showing that (V5)–(V8) hold is routine. For example, let $k \in R^1$ and let $u = a + bi$ and $v = c + di \in \mathcal{C}$. Then,

$$\begin{aligned}
k(u + v) &= k((a + bi) + (c + di)) \\
&= k((a + c) + (b + d)i) \\
&= k(a + c) + k(b + d)i \\
&= (ka + kc) + (kb + kd)i \\
&= (ka + kbi) + (kc + kdi) \\
&= k(a + bi) + k(c + di) \\
&= ku + kv\,.
\end{aligned}$$

Thus, (V5) holds.

Exercise 4.11

1. Verify that properties (V6)–(V8) hold for $\mathcal{C}$.

2. Let W be the set of all quadratic functions on R^1. Then $f \in W \Leftrightarrow f(x) = ax^2 + bx + c$; $a, b, c \in R^1$. (We consider the cases where some or all of the coefficients are zero to be quadratic functions.) We define $+$ on W by

   $$(ax^2 + bx + c) + (px^2 + mx + n) = (a + p)x^2 + (b + m)x + (c + n).$$

   We define a scalar multiplication by

   $$k(ax^2 + bx + c) = (ka)x^2 + (kb)x + kc \quad \text{for } k \in R^1.$$

   Show that (V0)–(V8) holds for this set.

EXAMPLE. An example we want to examine rather closely is

$$R^3 = \{(x, y, z) \mid x, y, z \in R^1\}\,.$$

The operations (addition and scalar multiplication) that we introduce are obvious extensions of the same operations on R^2.

Let (x_1, y_1, z_1) and $(x_2, y_2, z_2) \in R^3$. We define the sum

$$(x_1, y_1, z_1) + (x_2, y_2, z_2)$$

of these elements by

$$(x_1, y_1, z_1) + (x_2, y_2, z_2) = (x_1 + x_2, y_1 + y_2, z_1 + z_2) .$$

We define scalar multiplication by

$$k(x_1, y_1, z_1) = (kx_1, ky_1, kz_1)$$

for $k \in R^1$ and $(x_1, y_1, z_1) \in R^3$.

With these definitions, it is rather easy to show that the properties (V0)–(V8) hold for R^3. Certainly (V0) holds by definition of addition and scalar multiplication. (V1) and (V2) are immediate consequences of the commutative and associative laws for real numbers. Consider $\bar{0} = (0, 0, 0)$. Then $(x, y, z) + \bar{0} = (x, y, z)$ for all $(x, y, z) \in R^3$. If $u = (x, y, z)$, let $-u = (-x, -y, -z)$ and we can see that $u + (-u) = \bar{0}$. (V6) is proved as follows: Let $k, m \in R^1$ and let $(x, y, z) \in R^3$. Then

$$(k + m)(x, y, z) = ((k + m)x, (k + m)y, (k + m)z)$$

$$= (kx + mx, ky + my, kz + mz)$$

$$= (kx, ky, kz) + (mx, my, mz)$$

$$= k(x, y, z) + m(x, y, z) .$$

Exercise

Prove the remaining properties (V5), (V7), and (V8) for R^3.

Now there is nothing in the foregoing definition that could not extend itself to the situation where we deal with ordered n-tuples $(x_1, x_2, \ldots, x_n)$, of real numbers. In fact, if we define R^n to be the set of all ordered n-tuples of real numbers and if we define addition in R^n by

$$(x_1, x_2, \ldots, x_n) + (y_1, y_2, \ldots, y_n) = (x_1 + y_1, x_2 + y_2, \ldots, x_n + y_n) ,$$

for every $(x_1, x_2, \ldots, x_n), (y_1, y_2, \ldots, y_n) \in R^n$, and scalar multiplication by

$$k \cdot (x_1, x_2, \ldots, x_n) = (kx_1, kx_2, \ldots, kx_n) ,$$

for $k \in R^1$ and $(x_1, x_2, \ldots, x_n) \in R^n$, then R^n is a vector space. We will agree that

$$(x_1, \ldots, x_n) = (y_1, \ldots, y_n) \Leftrightarrow x_i = y_i \quad \text{for } 1 \leq i \leq n .$$

In particular,

$$(x_1, y_1, z_1) = (x_2, y_2, z_2) \Leftrightarrow x_1 = x_2 , \qquad y_1 = y_2 , \qquad z_1 = z_2 .$$

The verification of properties (V0)–(V8) is exactly the same as for R^3 except for the slight variation in notation. We note that R^n is called *euclidean n-space*. In particular, R^3 is euclidean 3-space.

We have seen that in R^2, if P and Q are points, then the vector equation of the straight line determined by P and Q is

$$\mathbf{OX} = \mathbf{OP} + t \cdot \mathbf{PQ}$$

where $t \in R^1$. We should note that, since $\mathbf{OP} + \mathbf{PQ} = \mathbf{OQ}$, we can say that $\mathbf{PQ} = \mathbf{OQ} - \mathbf{OP}$. From this point of view, if W is any vector space and u and v are any two vectors, we can define the "straight line" determined by u and v to be the set of all vectors w where

$$w = u + t(v - u), t \in R^1.$$

This is, of course, an immediate generalization of the notion of straight line to any vector space.

In particular, we can translate this definition to the vector space R^3 or even R^n. In R^3 we identify a vector with the end point of its representative with initial point $(0, 0, 0)$. Thus, if we have a point P with coordinates (x, y, z), we identify the vector $\mathbf{OP}$ with the coordinates (x, y, z). Our general definition of the straight line determined by $P : (x_1, y_1, z_1)$ and $Q : (x_2, y_2, z_2)$ becomes

$$\mathbf{OX} = \mathbf{OP} + t \cdot \mathbf{PQ}, t \in R^1,$$

or

$$\mathbf{OX} = \mathbf{OP} + t \cdot (\mathbf{OQ} - \mathbf{OP}), t \in R^1.$$

This, on further reduction, becomes, if we assume X has coordinates (x, y, z),

$$(x, y, z) = (x_1, y_1, z_1) + t(x_2 - x_1, y_2 - y_1, z_2 - z_1),$$

where $t \in R^1$.

Thus, if $X : (x, y, z)$ is a point on the straight line determined by the points P and Q, its coordinates satisfy the system of equations,

$$\frac{x - x_1}{x_2 - x_1} = \frac{y - y_1}{y_2 - y_1} = \frac{z - z_1}{z_2 - z_1},$$

provided that none of the foregoing denominators is zero. To see this, simply note that, from our definition of equality in R^3, we get

(a)
$$x = x_1 + t(x_2 - x_1)$$
$$y = y_1 + t(y_2 - y_1)$$
$$z = z_1 + t(z_2 - z_1),$$

or that

(b) $$\frac{x - x_1}{x_2 - x_1} = t, \qquad \frac{y - y_1}{y_2 - y_1} = t \qquad \text{and} \qquad \frac{z - z_1}{z_2 - z_1} = t.$$

The system (b) occurs only when none of the denominators, $x_2 - x_1$, $y_2 - y_1$, $z_2 - z_1$, is zero. If we consider those cases where zero occurs among these numbers, it is best to deal with the system (a). Realize that, in order to find points on our line, we replace t in each equation in (a) by the same real number. The resulting values of x, y, and z are the coordinates of a point in R^3 on the line in question.

If, for example, $x_2 - x_1 = 0$, (a) becomes

$$x = x_1 ,$$

$$y = y_1 + t(y_2 - y_1) ,$$

$$z = z_1 + t(z_2 - z_1) .$$

If neither $y_2 - y_1$ nor $z_2 - z_1$ is zero, we rewrite this system as

$$x = x_1, \qquad \frac{y - y_1}{y_2 - y_1} = \frac{z - z_1}{z_2 - z_1} .$$

If two of the numbers, say $x_2 - x_1$ and $y_2 - y_1$, are zero, (a) becomes

$$x = x_1, \qquad y = y_1, \qquad z = z_1 + t(z_2 - z_1) .$$

But as t takes on all real values, z takes on all real values. Remember $(x_1, y_1, z_1) \neq (x_2, y_2, z_2)$, so not all coordinates can be equal. Thus, the condition $z = z_1 + t(z_2 - z_1)$ is no restriction and our system becomes

$$x = x_1, \qquad y = y_1 .$$

An example of determining the equation of a line in R^3 follows: Let P have coordinates $(1, 2, -1)$ and Q have coordinates $(4, 3, 7)$. Then the system of equations is

$$\frac{x - 1}{4 - 1} = \frac{y - 2}{3 - 2} = \frac{z + 1}{7 - (-1)},$$

or

$$\frac{x - 1}{3} = \frac{y - 2}{1} = \frac{z + 1}{8} .$$

An obvious comment is that this equation of a straight line in R^3 should agree with the equation of a straight line obtained any other way. We will now look at the geometric side of what we have been doing and try to justify this equation we have for a straight line in R^3.

Note that, when we introduced a coordinate system on a line, we assigned to every element on the line a real number. When we coordinatized the plane, we assigned to each point of the plane an ordered pair of real numbers. We would expect that introducing coordinates in space would involve ordered triples or 3-tuples or real numbers.

Rather than treat this matter generally, we consider only a Cartesian coordinate system of space. First choose a horizontal plane and introduce a

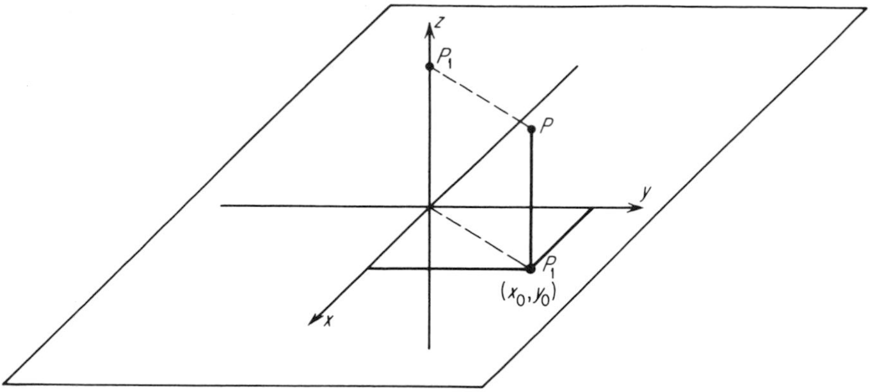

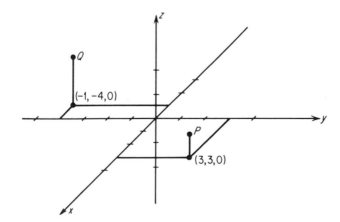

Figure 4.9

rectangular coordinate system on this plane (Fig. 4.9). Then through the origin of this system draw a line perpendicular to the plane. We shall call this the z axis. We introduce the same unit distance on the z axis as on the x and y axes in the given plane. Now, if P is any point in space, draw PP_1 perpendicular to the z axis. P_1 has coordinate z_1 on the z axis. Draw PP_2 perpendicular to the xy plane (the given plane) and find the coordinates (x_1, y_1), of P_2 in the plane. We define the coordinates of P to be (x_1, y_1, z_1).

As a matter of common terminology, we refer to the plane determined by the x and z axes as the xz plane. Similarly, we have the yz plane, the plane determined by the y axis and the z axis.

As a sample of plotting points whose coordinates are given we plot (Fig. 4.10)

$$P : (3, 3, 1) \quad \text{and} \quad Q : (-1, -4, 2) .$$

Observe that we didn't bother to indicate the xy plane except by drawing the x and y axes.

Figure 4.10

Consider, now, two points, $P : (x_1, y_1, z_1)$ and $Q : (x_2, y_2, z_2)$ in R^3. As in R^2, we consider vectors represented by directed line segments from the origin to points in space. It is not hard to see that the addition and scalar multiplication in R^3 defined earlier are geometrically the same as in R^2. That is, the vector sum $\mathbf{OP} + \mathbf{OQ}$ results in $\mathbf{OS}$, where S has coordinates $(x_1 + x_2, y_1 + y_2, z_1 + z_2)$ and $k \cdot \mathbf{OP}$, where $k \in R_1$ results in $\mathbf{OT}$ where T has coordinates (kx_1, ky_1, kz_1). Our analogy is complete when we agree that $\mathbf{PQ} = \mathbf{OK}$, where $\mathbf{OK}$ is parallel to, equal in length to, and points in the same direction as $\mathbf{PQ}$ (that is, $\mathbf{OK}$ is equivalent to $\mathbf{PQ}$). It can be verified that K has coordinates $(x_2 - x_1, y_2 - y_1, z_2 - z_1)$.

With these comments in mind, we look briefly at the idea of the straight line in space determined by P and Q (Fig. 4.11). Just as in R^2, we can consider an arbitrary point X on the line determined by P and Q. Then $\mathbf{PX} = t \cdot \mathbf{PQ}$ for some real number t. Or

$$\mathbf{OX} = \mathbf{OP} + t \cdot \mathbf{PQ} .$$

So, if X is any point on the line through P and Q, it satisfies this equation. On the other hand, we could reverse the argument to conclude that any point satisfying this equation is on this straight line.

For the case of R^n, $n > 3$, pictures are impossible, and we cannot, in the usual geometric sense, justify our equation for a straight line.

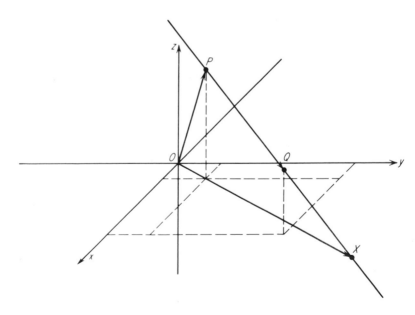

Figure 4.11

Exercise 4.12

1. Plot the following points in R^3:

   (a) $(1, 1, 1)$.   (b) $(0, 1, 0)$.

   (c) $(1, 0, 1)$.   (d) $(-2, 3, 4)$.

   (e) $(1, 1, -2)$.   (f) $(0, 2, 4)$.

   (g) $(-1, -1, 2)$.   (h) $(0, 0, 3)$.

   (i) $(-2, 3, -3)$.   (j) $(4, 6, -2)$.

2. Write the equations of the lines using the pairs of points (a) − (b), (c) − (d), etc.

3. Sketch the following sets of points in R^3:

   (a) $\{(x, y, z) \mid z = 2\}$.   (b) $\{(x, y, z) \mid x = y = z\}$.

   (c) $\{(x, y, z) \mid x = 0, y = 0\}$.   (d) $\{(x, y, z) \mid x = y\}$.

   (e) $\{(x, y, z) \mid x \geq 1\}$.   (f) $\{(x, y, z) \mid |x| = 2\}$.

   (g) $\{(x, y, z) \mid |x| < 2\}$.   (h) $\{(x, y, z) \mid x > 0, y > 0, z > 0\}$.

   (i) $\{(x, y, z) \mid x = 4, y = 3, z > 0\}$.   (j) $\{(x, y, z) \mid x > y\}$.

4.11   Distance in R³

Now we want to consider the problem of finding the distance between points in R^3. As might be expected, we develop a formula that is a direct extension of the formula for distance in R^2.

Consider, then, two points, $P : (x_1, y_1, z_1)$ and $Q : (x_2, y_2, z_2)$ in R^3. In the xy plane, at the points $(x_1, y_1, 0)$, $(x_1, y_2, 0)$, $(x_2, y_1, 0)$, and $(x_2, y_2, 0)$ construct lines parallel to the z axis. Two of these pass through P and Q. Through P and Q construct planes parallel to the xy plane. The intersections of the constructed lines with the constructed planes determine the vertices of a rectangular parallelopiped (a box). We will allow the possibility that certain of the coordinates of P are equal to the corresponding coordinates in Q. This simply gives our box a width or/and a height or/and a length of zero. Nothing is disturbed in our development if this occurs. We have labeled certain of these vertices (Fig. 4.12). We note that the angles QSR and QRP are right angles. We also note that

$$d(S, R) = |y_2 - y_1| \quad \text{and} \quad d(S, Q) = |x_2 - x_1| .$$

Thus,

$$d(Q, R)^2 = |x_2 - x_1|^2 + |y_2 - y_1|^2 .$$

Moreover,

$$d(P, Q)^2 = d(Q, R)^2 + d(R, P)^2 .$$

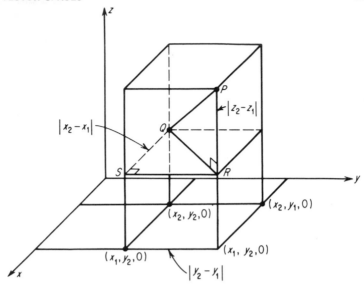

Figure 4.12

With the observation that $d(R, P) = |z_2 - z_1|$, we have

$$d(P, Q)^2 = |x_2 - x_1|^2 + |y_2 - y_1|^2 + |z_2 - z_1|^2$$
$$= (x_2 - x_1)^2 + (y_2 - y_1)^2 + (z_2 - z_1)^2 .$$

Rewriting, we have that

$$d(P, Q) = \sqrt{(x_2 - x_1)^2 + (y_2 - y_1)^2 + (z_2 - z_1)^2} .$$

This is clearly a generalization of the distance formula in R^2. If we desired to extend this to R^n, we would have difficulty in proving a similar formula, but we could (and do) define distance in R^n by an extension of the preceding formula.

In ordinary geometry, we define distance from a point to a line or from a point to a plane in terms of "perpendicular distances." For future use, we shall allow this convention to stand.

We can, of course, use the distance formula to develop equations of curves and surfaces in R^3. For example, a sphere with radius r centered at the origin 0 is a surface, K, with the property that if X is on K, $d(X, 0) = r$. Then, if X has coordinates (x, y, z), these coordinates satisfy the equation $d(X, 0) = r$. Expanding this, we have that X satisfies

$$(x - 0)^2 + (y - 0)^2 + (z - 0)^2 = r^2$$

or

$$x^2 + y^2 + z^2 = r^2.$$

It can be shown that, if X is any point whose coordinates (x, y, z) satisfy this equation, then $d(X, 0) = r$ and X is on the sphere.

Another general consideration is that of a plane in R^3. There are a number of ways of developing the equation for a plane. One way might be through the use of vectors. We will look at a plane as the set of all points equally distant from two fixed points, $P : (x_1, y_1, z_1)$ and $Q : (x_2, y_2, z_2)$, and we use the distance formula to find its equation.

If X is any point on the plane, then

$$d(X, P) = d(X, Q) \quad \text{and} \quad d(X, P)^2 = d(X, Q)^2 \,.$$

But

$$(x - x_1)^2 + (y - y_1)^2 + (z - z_1)^2$$
$$= (x - x_2)^2 + (y - y_2)^2 + (z - z_2)^2 \,,$$

or

$$2(x_2 - x_1)x + 2(y_2 - y_1)y + 2(z_2 - z_1)z$$
$$= (x_2^2 + y_2^2 + z_2^2) - (x_1^2 + y_1^2 + z_1^2) \,.$$

Realizing that x_1, y_1, z_1, x_2, y_2, and z_2 are all constants, this equation can be written in the form

$$Ax + By + Cz = D \,,$$

where $A, B, C, D \in R^1$.

We have shown that, if X is on a plane, it satisfies this equation. Reversing this to show that if X is a point whose coordinates satisfy this equation, then X is on the plane is a bit difficult and we omit this part of the proof.

In particular, suppose we consider the points $(1, 1, 1)$ and $(-1, -1, -1)$ and ask the equation of the plane bisecting the segment determined by these points. Then by the foregoing procedure we get the equation of the plane as

$$2(1 - (-1))x + 2(1-(-1))y + 2(1-(-1))z$$
$$= (1^2 + 1^2 + 1^2) - ((-1)^2 + (-1)^2 + (-1)^2)$$

or

$$4x + 4y + 4z = 0 \,,$$

or

$$x + y + z = 0 \,.$$

Exercise 4.13

1. Find the distance between the following points in R^3:

   (a) $(1, 1, 1)$ and $(0, 0, 0)$.   (b) $(1, 1, 1)$ and $(0, 1, 0)$.

   (c) $(-1, -1, 0)$ and $(2, 3, 4)$.   (d) $(-1, -1, 0)$ and $(3, -1, 2)$.

   (e) $(0, 1, 0)$ and $(-2, -4, 1)$.   (f) $(1, 2, 0)$ and $(4, 0, 6)$.

   (g) $(1, 2, 1)$ and $(0, 3, -3)$.   (h) $(9, 0, 8)$ and $(1, -1, -1)$.

(i) (a, b, c) and $(1, 1, 0)$.   (j) $(1, 0, 1)$ and $(a, b, 0)$.

(k) $(1 + t, 1 + t, 0)$ and   (l) $(1 + t, 1 - t, 0)$ and
      $(1 - t, t - 1, 1)$. $(t, 2 + t, 1)$.

2. Sketch the following sets of points in R^3:

   (a) $\{X : (x, y, z) \mid X$ is two units away from the xy plane$\}$.

   (b) $\{X : (x, y, z) \mid d(X, P) \leq 3$, where P is $(1, 0, 1)\}$.

   (c) $\{X : (x, y, z) \mid d(X, 0) < 3\}$.

   (d) $\{X : (x, y, z) \mid d(X, u) = 1$, where u is the y axis$\}$.

3. Write the equation of the plane each point of which is equally distant from

   (a) $(4, 4, 4)$ and $(0, 0, 0)$.   (b) $(4, 4, 4)$ and $(2, 2, 2)$.

   (c) $(4, 6, 8)$ and $(2, 4, 6)$.   (d) $(4, 6, 8)$ and $(-4, -6, 8)$.

   (e) $(2, 0, 0)$ and $(0, 0, 0)$.   (f) $(2, 0, 0)$ and $(4, 0, 0)$.

4. Write the equation of the sphere,

   (a)   Centered at $(1, 1, 1)$ with radius 3.

   (b)   Centered at $(0, 1, 1)$ with radius 2.

5. Write the equations of the straight lines in R^3 determined by the pairs of points in 1.

Linear
Programming

As a sample of the usefulness of studying the straight line, consider the following problem. A person, X, wants to buy x units of an item from an outlet F and y units of this same item from an outlet G. He needs at least 600 units. He has trucks at F and G capable of hauling 500 and 300 units, respectively. The trucker at F agrees to haul at the rate of $1.50 per unit plus $300. The trucker at G agrees to haul at $1.00 per unit plus $400. F will sell at $6.00 per unit if at least 100 units are ordered; G will sell at $4.00 per item if 150 units are ordered. X refuses to pay more than $1,500 for transportation, but agrees to make at least the minimum purchase at each outlet. The problem is ordering the proper amount from each source in order to minimize his total cost subject to the stated restrictions.

Let us set up this problem in algebraic terms. Let x be the number of units X will order from F and y be the number of units he will order from G. His total cost, K (in dollars) will be:

5

$$K = x(6 + 1.5) + 300 + y(4 + 1) + 400$$

$$= (7.5x + 5y + 700) \text{ dollars.}$$

Now the variables, x and y, are not free to vary at will. For example, A needs 600 units. So $x + y \geq 600$. Also F won't sell fewer than 100 units at the price of \$6.00/unit and G won't sell fewer than 150 units at the price of \$4.00/unit. So we have the further restrictions that $x \geq 100$, $y \geq 150$. More than this, $x \leq 500$ and $y \leq 300$ because of the capacities of the trucks. Then we have X's refusal to pay more than \$1,500 for transportation of the item. So

$$x(1.5) + 300 + y \cdot 1 + 400 \leq 1,500$$

or

$$1.5x + y \leq 800 .$$

So our problem is to make the value of K,

$$K = K(x, y) = 7.5x + 5y + 700 ,$$

as small as possible by choosing x and y restricted by the conditions

$$100 \leq x \leq 500$$

$$150 \leq y \leq 300$$

$$x + y \geq 600$$

$$1.5x + y \leq 800$$

Now it's entirely possible that no pairs of numbers, x and y, satisfy all these restrictions. We now are in a position to check this out graphically. For example, we can graph the set of all points (x, y) so that $x + y \geq 600$, and the set of all points (x, y) so that $1.5x + y \leq 800$.

In fact, the set of points in which we are interested is

$$\{(x, y) \mid 100 \leq x \leq 500\} \cap \{(x, y) \mid 150 \leq y \leq 300\}$$

$$\cap \{(x, y) \mid 1.5x + y \leq 800\}$$

$$\cap \{(x, y) \mid x + y \geq 600\}$$

In our example this set is not empty (see Fig. 5.1). Our problem, then, is determining which point (or points) in this set make K as small as possible.

Later, we will prove a theorem that this minimum value is attained at one of the vertices of our area. If we evaluate K at these points we get

$$K(300, 300) = 7.5(300) + 5(300) + 500$$

$$= 2,250 + 1,500 + 500 = 4,250$$

$$K(400, 200) = 3,000 + 1,000 + 500 = 4,500$$

$$K(333\tfrac{1}{3}, 300) > K(300, 300) .$$

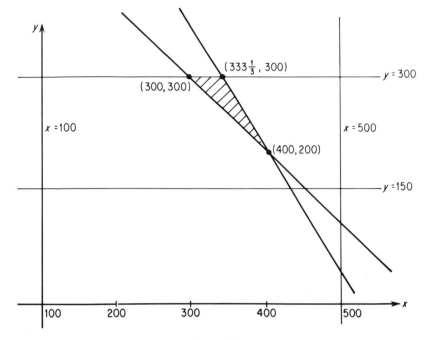

Figure 5.1

So the minimum total cost to X would be $4,250, under the restrictions we imposed, and this is obtained by ordering 300 units from each of F and G.

5.2 Solution to Simultaneous Equations

First we note in this probelm that we need to determine the coordinates of points common to pairs of lines. So we look at this procedure in a general setting. Suppose that $a_1x + b_1y + c_1 = 0$ and $a_2x + b_2y + c_2 = 0$ are the equations of the lines l_1 and l_2 respectively. If (x_0, y_0) is any point on both l_1 and l_2, then

$$a_1x_0 + b_1y_0 + c_1 = 0 \quad \text{and} \quad a_2x_0 + b_2y_0 + c_2 = 0.$$

If $a_1 \neq 0$,

$$x_0 = -\frac{b_1y_0 + c_1}{a_1},$$

and we can rewrite the second statement as,

$$a_2\left(-\frac{b_1y_0 + c_1}{a_1}\right) + b_2y_0 + c_2 = 0.$$

But this can be rewritten as

$$-a_2 b_1 y_0 - a_2 c_1 + a_1 b_2 y_0 + a_1 c_2 = 0 ,$$

or, if $a_1 b_2 - a_2 b_1 \neq 0$, as

$$y_0 = \frac{a_2 c_1 - a_1 c_2}{a_1 b_2 - a_2 b_1} .$$

Then

$$x_0 = -\frac{b_1[(a_2 c_1 - a_1 c_2)/(a_1 b_2 - a_2 b_1)] + c_1}{a_1} ,$$

or

$$x_0 = \frac{1}{a_1}\left(\frac{-b_1 a_2 c_1 + b_1 a_1 c_2 - c_1 a_1 b_2 + a_2 b_1 c_1}{a_1 b_2 - a_2 b_1}\right)$$

$$= \frac{b_1 c_2 - c_1 b_2}{a_1 b_2 - a_2 b_1} .$$

This, of course, guarantees a unique pair of numbers (x_0, y_0) under the proper conditions on the coefficients of the equations for the lines l_1 and l_2.

At this time, we merely want to point out that, knowing the equations of the lines involved, one can algebraically determine coordinates of points on both lines. This can be done by solving two linear equations in two variables simultaneously. Any technique the reader might have learned for doing this will give the result. As an example, consider the lines (their equations) in the preceding example:

$$x + y = 600 \quad \text{and} \quad 1.5x + y = 800 .$$

Suppose (x_0, y_0) is a point on each.

Then

$$x_0 + y_0 = 600 \quad \text{or} \quad x_0 = 600 - y_0 ,$$

and

$$1.5(600 - y_0) + y_0 = 800 ,$$

or

$$900 - 1.5 y_0 + y_0 = 800$$

or

$$100 = 0.5 y_0 \quad \text{or} \quad y_0 = 200 .$$

We also have $x_0 = 600 - 200 = 400$.

So, if (x_0, y_0) is a point on both lines, then $x_0 = 400$ and $y_0 = 200$.

These numbers could have been determined in other ways. For example, assuming (x_0, y_0) to satisfy both equations gives us

$$x_0 + y_0 = 600 \quad \text{and} \quad 1.5x_0 + y_0 = 800 .$$

Subtracting the first of these from the second, we get

$$0.5x_0 = 200 \quad \text{or} \quad x_0 = 400 .$$

Exercise 5.1

1. Find the points common to both lines in the following pairs of lines.

(a) $x - y = 6.$
     $x + y = 4.$

(b) $x - y = 5.$
     $x + y = 7.$

(c) $x - 9y = 10.$
     $2x - y = 1.$

(d) $y - 2x = 4.$
     $x + y = 6.$

(e) $x + 3y = 1.$
     $4x + 12y = 4.$

(f) $x + 3y = 2.$
     $y = 10.$

(g) $2x + 3y = 7.$
     $3x - 2y = 11.$

(h) $2x + 3y = 5.$
     $6x - 4y = 2.$

(i) $x + y = 7.$
     $2x + 2y = 9.$

(j) $x - 3y = 7.$
     $-3x + 9y = -21.$

2. Graph the set of all points (x, y) whose coordinates satisfy the inequalities:

(a) $0 \le x \le 5, 0 \le y \le 10, x + y \ge 2.$

(b) $y \le 15, y + x \ge 15, y - x \le 5, 5x - y \le 45.$

(c) $x \le 10, y \le 10, y - x \le 4, y + 2x \ge 7, 4y - 2x \ge -7.$

(d) $x - 5y + 18 > 0, x - 3y + 2 \le 0, x - y - 2 \le 0, 3x - y - 2 \ge 0.$

(e) $0 \le y \le 3, y \ge x, y + x \le 4, y - 3x + 6 \le 0.$

5.3 Another Example

Let us now look at a problem of the same sort as that treated in Sec. 5.1. This time we do not consider a real-world problem but one given simply as a problem in algebra.

Consider the set, K, of all points (x, y) satisfying the conditions

$$x \ge 0, \qquad 0 \le y \le 3, \qquad y \le x + 2 \quad \text{and} \quad y \le 6 - x.$$

Let $F(x, y) = 3x - 4y + 2.$ Find the values of (x, y) in K that
   (1) make $F(x, y)$ as large as possible,
   (2) make $F(x, y)$ as small as possible.

Algebraically, this problem is of the same type as that treated earlier. Here, the conditions defining the set K are given to us and the function to maximize and minimize is explicitly stated. In the earlier problem, this information had to be extracted and set up from the problem.

The procedure is essentially the same as before. First we graphically verify that K is not empty and then we apply the theorem alluded to before.

If we sketch the set, K, we get the shaded area shown in Fig. 5.2.

The vertices, as labeled, were obtained by solving the proper equations in pairs. Now the problem is simply that of evaluating

$$F(x, y) = 3x - 4y + 2$$

at these vertices.

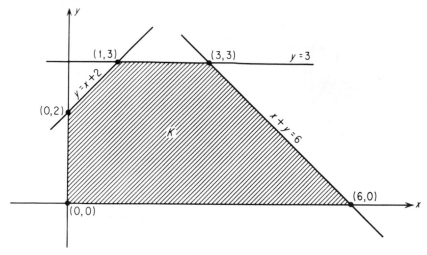

Figure 5.2

$$F(0, 0) = 2, \quad F(0, 2) = -6, \quad F(1, 3) = -7,$$

$$F(6, 0) = 20 \quad \text{and} \quad F(3, 3) = -1 \,.$$

So the maximum value for F, obtained by using only those points in K, is 20 and this happens when $(x, y) = (6, 0)$. The minimum value, -7, is obtained when $(x, y) = (1, 3)$.

Exercise 5.2

   Let

$$F(x, y) = 3x - 4y + 2, \quad G(x, y) = 3x + 4y - 3,$$

$$H(x, y) = x + y \quad \text{and} \quad J(x, y) = 9x - 2y + 1.$$

1. Find the points in K of the preceding section that maximize and minimize G, H, and J.

2. Find the points in the sets in parts (a) and (b) of Exercise 5.1(2) which maximize and minimize each of F, G, H, and J.

3. Repeat Exercise 5.1(1) and (2) for the functions:
   $F(x, y) = 2x + 3y.$
   $G(x, y) = x - 2y + 10.$
   $H(x, y) = 2x + 3.$
   $J(x, y) = x + 10y - 89.$

5.4   The Basic Theorem

To prove the necessary theorem for the solution of our original problem we need yet another fact.

Remark. Suppose that P and Q are points determining a line k. Suppose X is any point on k between P and Q. Then ∃ a real number t so that

$$OX = t \cdot OQ + (1 - t)OP, \quad \text{where} \quad 0 \le t \le 1.$$

Clearly, if X is P, then $t = 0$ would work, and if X is Q, then $t = 1$ would work. Suppose, now, that P has coordinates (x_1, y_1), Q has coordinates (x_2, y_2), and that X has coordinates (x_0, y_0). All we need to note is that for X on k between P and Q, ∃ $t \in R^1$ with $0 \le t \le 1$, so that

$$OX = OP + t \cdot PQ.$$

But $PQ = OQ - OP$. Thus

$$OX = OP + t(OQ - OP) = (1 - t)OP + t(OQ).$$

Definition 5.1. A subset K of R^2 is *convex* ⇔ if P and Q are points in K, then the line segment PQ is in K.

EXAMPLES. In Fig. 5.3, (a) and (b) are convex, but (c) is not.

Definition 5.2. A function $L = L(x, y)$ defined on a subset of R^2 is called *linear* if it is of the form:

$$L(x, y) = ax + by + c; \quad a, b, c \in R^1.$$

Theorem 5.1. Let $L(x, y) = ax + by$ be a function on a convex polygon K in R^2. Then L achieves its minimum (maximum) value at a vertex of the polygon.

Proof. Suppose that we consider $L(x, y)$ at all the vertices. (There are of course only a finite number to consider.) Let P, with coordinates (x_0, y_0), be the one where $L(x, y)$ has the smallest value.

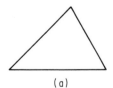   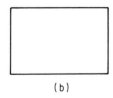

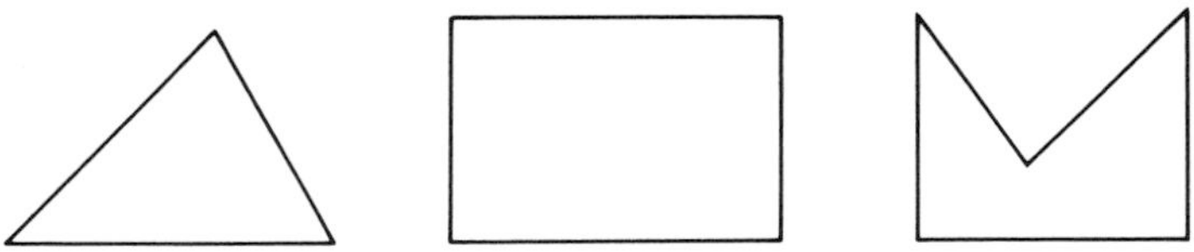

(a)   (b)   (c)

Figure 5.3

Suppose Q_1 and Q_2 are points in K with coordinates (x_1, y_1) and (x_2, y_2), respectively. Suppose X, with coordinates (u, v), is any point on the line segment between Q_1 and Q_2.

Suppose that $L(x_1, y_1) \leq L(x_2, y_2)$.

By the remark preceding this theorem, $\exists\, t \in R^1$, $0 \leq t \leq 1$, so that

$$u = tx_1 + (1 - t)x_2 \quad \text{and} \quad v = ty_1 + (1 - t)y_2 .$$

Then

$$L(u, v) = au + by$$

$$= atx_1 + a(1 - t)x_2 + bty_1 + b(1 - t)y_2$$

$$= t(ax_1 + by_1) + (1 - t)(ax_2 + by_2)$$

$$= tL(x_1, y_1) + (1 - t)L(x_2, y_2)$$

$$= L(x_2, y_2) - t(L(x_2, y_2) - L(x_1, y_1)) .$$

But $t \geq 0$ and $L(x_2, y_2) - L(x_1, y_1) \geq 0$ implies

$$t \cdot (L(x_2, y_2) - L(x_1, y_1)) \geq 0 .$$

So $L(u, v) \leq L(x_2, y_2)$. On the other hand,

$$0 \leq t \leq 1 \quad \text{and} \quad L(x_2, y_2) - L(x_1, y_1) \geq 0$$

$$\Rightarrow -t(L(x_2, y_2) - L(x_1, y_1)) \geq -(L(x_2, y_2) - L(x_1, y_1))$$

$$\Rightarrow L(x_2, y_2) - t(L(x_2, y_2) - L(x_1, y_1))$$

$$\geq L(x_2, y_2) - (L(x_2, y_2) - L(x_1, y_1))$$

$$\Rightarrow L(u, v) \geq L(x_1, y_1) .$$

We have the result that, for any two points, Q_1 and Q_2, the value of L at any point on the segment connecting the two points lies between the values of L at Q_1 and Q_2.

Now we have that, for all the values $L(x, y)$ at the vertices of K, $L(x_0, y_0)$ is the least. But, by what we have just done, we can see that $L(x_0, y_0) \leq L(u, v)$ for any (u, v) on a side of K. For if (u, v) is on a side it lies "between" two vertices Q_1 and Q_2. But $L(u, v)$ is then greater than, or equal to, L at one of the vertices. But then $L(u, v) \geq L(x_0, y_0)$.

Now let $X : (s, t)$ be any point in K. Then PX is in K and we can extend the segment PX to a point Q on a side of K. But if Q has coordinates (u, v), we have $L(u, v) \geq L(x_0, y_0)$. Again by what we have proved, $L(s, t) \geq L(x_0, y_0)$.

We have proved our theorem for the minimum value of L. A completely dual proof holds for the maximum value.

Realizing that the maximum or minimum of $ax + by + c$ occurs at the point where $ax + by$ is a maximum or minimum, we have a slightly more general theorem.

Theorem 5.2. Let $L(x, y) = ax + by + c$ be a function defined on a convex polygon K in R^2. Then L achieves its minimum (maximum) value at a vertex of K.

5.5   An Application

Before trying some exercises that require application of Theorem 5.2, let us look at an example similar to the one introducing this chapter.

Suppose that a lawyer handles exactly 300 clients per year. For divorce cases he receives \$200, for civil cases, \$250; for criminal cases, \$400. Divorce cases are easy, so he wants at least 100 such cases per year. Criminal cases are time-consuming, and he wants no more than 100 of these each year. His business expenses are \$20,000 each year. How many of each type of case should he handle each year in order to maximize his profit, subject, of course, to the foregoing restrictions?

Let x denote the number of divorce cases he handles each year. Now $x \geq 100$. Let y denote the number of civil cases he takes. Then the number of criminal cases he will deal with is $300 - x - y$. But this number must not exceed 100. Thus $300 - x - y \leq 100$, or $200 \leq x + y$. One further observation is needed. He will handle at most 300 cases. Thus $x + y \leq 300$. The restrictions on the possible choices for x and y, then are

$$100 \leq x$$

$$200 \leq x + y \leq 300 \,.$$

Other conditions, such as $0 \leq x \leq 300$, $0 \leq y \leq 300$, could be mentioned but these are implied by the stated restrictions. If we plot the set of all points (x, v) subject to the foregoing restrictions, we obtain the set, K, shaded in Fig. 5.4.

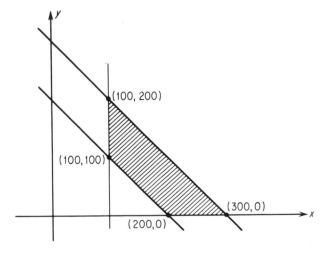

Figure 5.4

Now the lawyer's profit is given by $P(x, y) = P$ (in dollars) where

$$P(x, y) = 200x + 250y + 400(300 - x - y) - 20,000 .$$

Simplifying, we get

$$P(x, y) = 100,000 - 200x - 150y .$$

But, by Theorem 5.2, to maximize this function we need only consider the vertices of K and choose the vertex yielding the largest number $P(x, y)$. Now,

$$P(100,100) = 65,000 \text{ dollars}$$

$$P(100,200) = 50,000 \text{ dollars}$$

$$P(200,0) = 60,000 \text{ dollars}$$

$$P(300,0) = 40,000 \text{ dollars} .$$

So, in order to make as much money as possible, he should handle 100 divorce cases, 100 civil cases, and 100 criminal cases.

The following set of exercises includes several problems of the sort discussed in the introduction to this chapter. Although lengthy, we hope the reader finds them interesting.

Exercise 5.3

1. Find a point in each of the (nondegenerate)* convex polygons described in Exercise 5.1(2) where the function,

$$L(x, y) = 412 + 2x + 6y$$

achieves its maximum. Its minimum.

2. Do the same for the function,

$$L(x, y) = 2 + 0.3x - 0.7y .$$

3. (a)   A television producer is trying to arrange a half-hour show. He plans to use a comedian, an orchestra, and commercials to fill the time. The comic requires a guarantee of $2,000 and works at the rate of $200 per minute. (This means that he will have to be used at least 10 minutes.) The orchestra gets paid at the rate of $500 per minute and requires a $2,500 guarantee. The commercials cost $100 per minute to produce and the sponsor demands that there be at least 3 minutes of commercials. The producer refuses to produce a show having more than 10 minutes of commercials.

Let x denote the number of minutes the comic is used and y the number of minutes the orchestra is used. (Then $30 - x - y$ is the number of minutes of commercials.) Find values of these which will allow the producer to produce a show at minimum cost.

* That is, polygons that are not a straight line, not a point, or not empty.

(b)   When the orchestra leader learns that the producer plans to use his band for only 5 minutes he tells the producer that, if he will use the band for at least 10 minutes, then the band will work for $300 per minute.
Does this affect the producer's earlier decision?

(c)   Suppose that 100,000 people will watch the television show no matter what is on, but that 1,000 of these turn off their sets for each minute of commercials. Suppose, also, that for every minute the band is on, 30,000 more viewers will watch the show and that for every minute the comedian is on, 25,000 more viewers will watch the show. Choose x and y so that the number of viewers of the show is a maximum.

4. (a)   A student is taking courses in history, English, mathematics, and chemistry. His numerical grade in each course can be predicted from the following formula:

Course	*Grade*
History	$40 + 7t$
English	$40 + 6t$
Math	$30 + 4t$
Chemistry	$50 + 3t$

Here t represents the number of hours per week spent in studying the course.
The student plans to spend exactly 30 hr per week studying. His math course requires twice as much time as his history course, and required reading in English and history consumes at least 3 hr per week for each course. Since he is a science major he feels that not less than 18 hr per week should be spent on math and chemistry (combined) and at least 6 hr per week should be spent on chemistry alone.
Let x denote the number of hours per week devoted to history and y the number of hours per week devoted to English. (Math and chemistry receive $2x$ and $30 - (x + y + 2x)$ hr per week respectively.) Find a study timetable which will allow the student to achieve the highest possible numerical average for the four courses.

(b)   Although the preceding program yields the highest possible over-all average for the student, he discovers that it will leave him with an average of 68 in chemistry. He feels that he should not have an average below 77 in chemistry. Modify the program by imposing this additional restriction. What is the best study program for the student now?

(c)   By using the modified program the student will bring his chemistry grade up to 77, but his math grade will be 66. Impose the additional restriction that his math grade be not lower than 70. Find a program that will yield the highest over-all average and at the same time keep both science grades up.

(d)   The student finds that this last program is satisfactory. His only regret is that if he follows it, each of his course averages will be in the 70's. He thinks that he should be able to lift his grade in English to 80 or above with none of his other grades falling below 70. Show that he is mistaken

5. (a)   A farmer has 1,200 watermelons to sell. He may sell up to 300 melons locally at $.25 per melon without paying a trucking fee, or he may ship melons either to point A, where he can sell at $.39 per melon, or to point B, where he can sell at $.50 per melon. The fee for shipping melons to B is $.07 per melon. He can, however, expect a 10% loss of melons en route and he must pay for the shipment on the basis of the number of melons sent. Moreover the trucker cannot handle over 800 melons. The fee for shipping melons to A is $80 plus $.05 per melon. This trucker can handle no more than 700 melons but guarantees that there will be no loss en route. A regulation prohibits the farmer's shipping more than twice as many melons to one point as to another.

Let x denote the number of melons shipped to A, y the number shipped to B and $1,200 - x - y$ the number sold locally. Find values of x and y so that the farmer's income will be a maximum.

(b)   Suppose that the farmer can expect to lose 20% of the melons shipped to point B. How does this affect the first solution to the problem above? Why might "politics" enter into the disposition of the melons in this case? Suggest a "fair" way for the farmer to ship his melons and still make a maximum amount of money.

Matrix Theory

Comment. At different stages of our course of studies, we have considered sets on which binary operations were defined. Now we want to look at a system of this sort that has widespread applications in many areas, ranging from sociology to electrical engineering. The types of application range from merely notational advantage to techniques for solving systems of equations.

Although we introduce this topic as a matter of interest to the person who wants to discover what mathematicians do, we also introduce it to show the power of certain symbolism. A word of warning to the reader is probably in order. Do not be panic-stricken by the notation involved in this chapter. It is introduced to shorten arguments and can be mastered easily with some practice. You will, of course, be given plenty of chance to practice.

6

6.1 Notation

Frequently we wish to deal with finite sets of numbers. For example,

$$\{1, 2, 3, 4, 5, 6, 7, 8, 9, 10, 11, 12, 13, 14, 15\}$$

is such a set. In the past, we have indicated this set by

$$\{n \mid n \in I, 1 \le n \le 15\} \ .$$

Recall that the symbol n has nothing to do with the set and that we could have just as well have denoted the set by

$$\{t \mid t \in I, 1 \le t \le 15\}$$

or

$$\{i \mid i \in I, 1 \le i \le 15\} \ .$$

A frequently used notation for this same set is

$$\{i\}_{i=1}^{15}$$

where this means that i takes on the integral values from 1 to 15. Other samples of this would be

$$\{2i\}_{i=1}^{5} = \{2 \cdot 1, 2 \cdot 2, 2 \cdot 3, 2 \cdot 4, 2 \cdot 5\}$$
$$= \{2, 4, 6, 8, 10\}$$

or

$$\left\{\frac{1}{3n}\right\}_{n=2}^{5} = \left\{\frac{1}{6}, \frac{1}{9}, \frac{1}{12}, \frac{1}{15}\right\}.$$

Clearly, in the preceding examples, not much is saved by the notation. However, consider $\{2^n\}_{n=1}^{10,000}$. Here one saves considerable effort by this notation. Again, in theoretical discussion, one might want to speak of an arbitrary set of n real numbers. A notation frequently used is

$$\{a_1, a_2, a_3, \ldots, a_n\} \quad \text{or} \quad \{a_i\}_{i=1}^{n} \ .$$

For one reason or another, men are forever adding the numbers in such sets. As an example, we can form the sum of the numbers in $\{1, 2, 3, \ldots, 11\}$ or $\{i\}_{i=1}^{11}$. We would indicate this sum by

$$1 + 2 + 3 + 4 + 5 + 6 + 7 + 8 + 9 + 10 + 11 \ .$$

It is rather tedious to write this out and we can, and do, indicate this sum by

$$1 + 2 + \cdots + 11 \ .$$

If we want to indicate the sum of the members in the set $\{a_i\}_{i=1}^{n}$ we would do this by writing $a_1 + a_2 + \cdots + a_n$. Another notation frequently used to denote the sum of the elements of such sets is as follows:

$$a_1 + a_2 + \cdots + a_n \quad \text{is denoted} \quad \sum_{i=1}^{n} a_i \ .$$

This means, simply, replace i by 1, 2, ..., n and add the numbers. (The symbol $\sum\limits_{i=1}^{n} a_i$ is read, "summation a_i, i from 1 to n.") Thus, $\sum\limits_{i=1}^{5} 2i$ means, replace i by 1, 2, 3, 4, 5, getting 2, 4, 6, 8, 10, and add these numbers, getting $2 + 4 + 6 + 8 + 10$, or 30. As another example

$$\sum_{n=2}^{6} \frac{1}{3n} = \frac{1}{3\cdot 2} + \frac{1}{3\cdot 3} + \frac{1}{3\cdot 4} + \frac{1}{3\cdot 5} + \frac{1}{3\cdot 6}$$

$$= \frac{1}{6} + \frac{1}{9} + \frac{1}{12} + \frac{1}{15} + \frac{1}{18}$$

$$= \frac{29}{60}$$

Exercise 6.1

1. Write out the sets indicated:

(a) $\left\{\dfrac{1}{k}\right\}_{k=1}^{5}$.

(b) $\left\{\dfrac{2^{n-1}}{3^n}\right\}_{n=1}^{3}$.

(c) $\{2k - 1\}_{k=1}^{4}$.

(d) $\left\{\dfrac{(-1)^n}{2n + 1}\right\}_{n=1}^{4}$.

(e) $\{2i\}_{i=1}^{4}$.

(f) $\left\{\dfrac{1}{j(j+1)}\right\}_{j=1}^{3}$.

(g) $\{2^i\}_{i=1}^{4}$.

(h) $\left\{\dfrac{(-1)^{m+1}}{m^2 + 1}\right\}_{m=0}^{4}$.

(i) $\left\{\dfrac{1}{2^{m-1}}\right\}_{m=3}^{7}$.

(j) $\{x^i\}_{i=0}^{4}$.

(k) $\{n!\}_{n=1}^{3}$.

(l) $\left\{\dfrac{(-1)^{p+1}}{p!}\right\}_{p=1}^{5}$.

(m) $\left\{\dfrac{k}{2}\right\}_{k=0}^{6}$.

(n) $\{(-1)^n \cdot 3^n\}_{n=2}^{5}$.

2. Compute:

(a) $\sum\limits_{k=1}^{5} k$.

(b) $\sum\limits_{k=0}^{3} \left(\dfrac{1}{2}\right)^k$.

(c) $\sum\limits_{j=1}^{6} (2j - 1)$.

(d) $\sum\limits_{k=0}^{5} (2k + 1)$.

(e) $\sum\limits_{i=1}^{4} (-1)^i$.

(f) $\sum\limits_{k=1}^{4} \dfrac{(k+1)!}{2^k}$.

(g) $\displaystyle\sum_{n=1}^{50} 1$.

(h) $\displaystyle\sum_{k=0}^{3} \frac{k^2}{(k+1)!}$. *

(i) $\displaystyle\sum_{n=0}^{7} 2^n$.

(j) $\displaystyle\sum_{n=1}^{5} \frac{3^n}{(n+1)^2}$.

3. Abbreviate the following in the notation we have introduced:

(a) $\dfrac{1}{2}, \dfrac{1}{4}, \dfrac{1}{8}, \dfrac{1}{16}$.

(b) $0, 1, 2, 3$.

(c) $2, -5, 10, -17$.

(d) $\dfrac{2}{3}, \dfrac{3}{8}, \dfrac{4}{15}, \dfrac{5}{24}$.

(e) $1, \dfrac{2}{3}, \dfrac{3}{7}, \dfrac{4}{13}, \dfrac{5}{21}$.

(f) $1 + \dfrac{1}{2} + \dfrac{1}{3} + \dfrac{1}{4} + \dfrac{1}{5}$.

(g) $1 + 2 + 3 + \ldots + 100$.

(h) $1 \cdot 2 + 2 \cdot 3 + 3 \cdot 4 + 4 \cdot 5 + 5 \cdot 6$.

Now this notation can be generalized a bit. First let us say that the symbol n in $\{a_n\}_{n=1}^{100}$ is called an *index*. n is also an index in $\displaystyle\sum_{n=1}^{100} a_n$. Of course, other letters might have been used and would have been called indices; for example, k is an index in $\displaystyle\sum_{k=1}^{23} 2^k$; j is an index in $\displaystyle\sum_{j=2}^{10} \frac{j!}{3j}$.

Now certain situations arise where two indices might appear. For example, consider the set

$$\left\{ \frac{1}{2}, \frac{1}{2^2}, \ldots, \frac{1}{2^{10}}, \frac{2}{2}, \frac{2}{2^2}, \ldots, \frac{2}{2^{10}}, \ldots, \frac{8}{2}, \ldots, \frac{8}{2^{10}} \right\} .$$

Using two letters as indices, we have this set indicated simply by

$$\left\{ \frac{k}{2^i} \right\}_{k=1,\ \ i=1}^{8 \qquad 10}$$

or

$$\left\{ \frac{k}{2^i} \right\}_{\substack{1 \le k \le 8 \\ 1 \le i \le 10}}$$

With this notation, $\displaystyle\sum_{i=1}^{10} \frac{k}{2^i}$ would indicate, for k fixed,

$$\frac{k}{2} + \frac{k}{2^2} + \cdots + \frac{k}{2^{10}} .$$

---

* For any positive integer n, $n!$ (read n factorial) is defined to be $n \cdot (n-1) \cdot \ \cdots \ \cdot 3 \cdot 2 \cdot 1$. Thus $4! = 4 \cdot 3 \cdot 2 \cdot 1 = 24$. By definition $0! = 1$.

Then $\sum\limits_{k=1}^{8}\left(\sum\limits_{i=1}^{10}\dfrac{k}{2^i}\right)$ would indicate the sum of all the terms in the preceding set.

From our commutative and associative laws for addition in R^1, we see, without too much trouble,

$$\sum_{k=1}^{8}\left(\sum_{i=1}^{10}\frac{k}{2^i}\right) = \sum_{i=1}^{10}\left(\sum_{k=1}^{8}\frac{k}{2^i}\right).$$

So we would write

$$\sum_{k=1}^{8}\;\sum_{i=1}^{10}\frac{k}{2^i}$$

without fear of being misunderstood.

To see that this is so, consider the set

$$\{a_{ij}\}_{\substack{1\le k\le 3 \\ 1\le j\le 4}}$$

and form the sums

$$\sum_{i=1}^{3}\left(\sum_{j=1}^{4}a_{ij}\right),\qquad \sum_{j=1}^{4}\left(\sum_{i=1}^{3}a_{ij}\right)$$

and see that they are the same.

$$\sum_{j=1}^{4}\left(\sum_{i=1}^{3}a_{ij}\right) = \sum_{j=1}^{4}\left(a_{1j}+a_{2j}+a_{3j}\right)$$

$$= (a_{11}+a_{21}+a_{31}) + (a_{12}+a_{22}+a_{32})$$

$$+ (a_{13}+a_{23}+a_{33}) + (a_{14}+a_{24}+a_{34}).$$

$$\sum_{i=1}^{3}\left(\sum_{j=1}^{4}a_{ij}\right) = \sum_{i=1}^{3}\left(a_{i1}+a_{i2}+a_{i3}+a_{i4}\right)$$

$$= (a_{11}+a_{12}+a_{13}+a_{14}) + (a_{21}+a_{22}+a_{23}+a_{24})$$

$$+ (a_{31}+a_{32}+a_{33}+a_{34})$$

But, except for order, these are the same sums.

Some techniques of manipulating expressions of the preceding sort probably should be mastered. For our purposes, we simply indicate these where they are needed and demonstrate them (by example) or leave the validation of the technique as an exercise for the reader.

Exercise 6.2

1. Write out the sets indicated:

(a) $\{j^i\}_{j=1,\ i=1}^{3\ \ \ 2}$.

(b) $\left\{\dfrac{k}{2^i}\right\}_{i=0,\ k=1}^{2\quad 3}$

(c) $\{m+n\}_{n=1,\ m=1}^{3\qquad 3}$

(d) $\{k^n\}_{k=1,\ n=0}^{2\quad 3}$

(e) $\{x - z\}_{x=2,\ z=1}^{4\quad 2}$

(f) $\left\{\dfrac{2^n}{t}\right\}_{t=2,\ n=0}^{4\quad 3}$

(g) $\{(-1)^n \cdot k\}_{n=1,\ k=2}^{2\quad 4}$

(h) $\{2^{ij}\}_{i=1,\ j=0}^{5\quad 2}$

2. Compute

(a) $\displaystyle\sum_{i=0}^{2}\sum_{j=1}^{3}\frac{i}{j}$.

(b) $\displaystyle\sum_{x=2}^{4}\sum_{y=0}^{2} x - y$.

(c) $\displaystyle\sum_{m=4}^{5}\sum_{n=1}^{2}\frac{m+n}{m-n}$.

(d) $\displaystyle\sum_{k=1}^{2}\sum_{n=0}^{3} k^n$.

(e) $\displaystyle\sum_{k=0}^{3}\sum_{x=2}^{4}\frac{k}{2x}$.

3. Write in the notation above,

(a) $\{1+1,\ 1+2,\ 1+3,\ 2+1,\ 2+2,\ 2+3\}$.

(b) $\{1^1,\ 1^2,\ 2^1,\ 2^2,\ 3^1,\ 3^2,\ 4^1,\ 4^2\}$.

(c) $\{2,\ 3,\ 4,\ 4,\ 9,\ 16,\ 8,\ 27,\ 64\}$.

(d) $\left\{a,\ a^2,\ a^3,\ \dfrac{a}{2},\ \dfrac{a^2}{2},\ \dfrac{a^3}{2}\right\}$.

(e) $\left\{\dfrac{1}{2},\ \dfrac{1}{3},\ \dfrac{1}{4},\ \dfrac{2}{2},\ \dfrac{2}{3},\ \dfrac{2}{4},\ \dfrac{3}{2},\ \dfrac{3}{3},\ \dfrac{3}{4}\right\}$.

6.2 Matrices

A (real) *matrix* is a finite rectangular array of real numbers. More sophisticated definitions could be used, but for our purposes this will suffice. Thus, for example,

$$\begin{pmatrix} 1 & 2 & 3 \\ -1 & 0 & -\pi \end{pmatrix}, \quad \begin{pmatrix} 1 & 0 & 1 & 0 & 1 \\ 1 & 1 & 1 & 1 & 1 \\ 0 & 0 & 0 & 0 & 0 \end{pmatrix}, \quad \begin{pmatrix} 1 \\ 5 \\ -7 \end{pmatrix} \quad \text{and} \quad (-1, \ -2, \ 10, \ 12)$$

are matrices. In our work, we will use only matrices with real numbers and will not use the term *real matrix* but simply *matrix*. Observe that when we deal with such an array we put parentheses around it. If there are m rows of numbers and n columns in a matrix, we call it an $m \times n$ (m by n) matrix. Thus our examples are 2×3, 3×5, 3×1, and 1×4 matrices respectively. We call the numbers in the matrix *entries* in the matrix.

One might ask where matrices arise. An obvious place is in systems of linear equations. Consider the system of equations:

$$2x - 3y + 4z = 1$$
$$x + y - z = 1$$
$$x + z = 2 .$$

The matrix

$$\begin{pmatrix} 2 & -3 & 4 \\ 1 & 1 & -1 \\ 1 & 0 & 1 \end{pmatrix}$$

is called the *coefficient* matrix for this system.

Another way in which they arise might be shown by example. Let a, b, c, and d represent persons. Suppose that in chess, a can beat b and c, b can beat c and d, c can beat only d, and that d can beat only a. We can describe this situation by a matrix as follows:

$$\begin{array}{c} \\ a \\ b \\ c \\ d \end{array} \begin{array}{cccc} a & b & c & d \\ \begin{pmatrix} 0 & 1 & 1 & 0 \\ 0 & 0 & 1 & 1 \\ 0 & 0 & 0 & 1 \\ 1 & 0 & 0 & 0 \end{pmatrix} \end{array}$$

An entry of 1 indicates that the person on the left can beat the person whose letter is above the entry. An entry of 0 means that the person on the left cannot beat the person above.

As another example, suppose that 5 cities, A, B, C, D, E, are connected directly by roads as indicated in Fig. 6.1.

We can indicate this network of roads by a matrix as follows:

$$\begin{array}{c} \\ A \\ B \\ C \\ D \\ E \end{array} \begin{array}{ccccc} A & B & C & D & E \\ \begin{pmatrix} 0 & 1 & 1 & 1 & 0 \\ 1 & 0 & 1 & 0 & 1 \\ 1 & 1 & 0 & 1 & 1 \\ 1 & 0 & 1 & 0 & 1 \\ 0 & 1 & 1 & 1 & 0 \end{pmatrix} \end{array}$$

In this matrix, 1 to the right of D and under C, for example, indicates that there is a direct road between D and C.

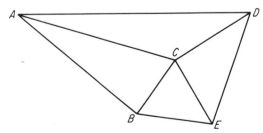

Figure 6.1

As an exercise, verify that the matrix below tells the number of routes between cities that pass through exactly one other city.

$$
\begin{array}{c}
\begin{array}{ccccc} A & B & C & D & E \end{array} \\
\begin{array}{c} A \\ B \\ C \\ D \\ E \end{array}
\begin{pmatrix}
③ & 1 & 2 & 1 & 3 \\
1 & ③ & 2 & 3 & 1 \\
2 & 2 & ④ & 2 & 2 \\
1 & 3 & 2 & ③ & 1 \\
3 & 1 & 2 & 1 & ③
\end{pmatrix}
\end{array}
$$

The significance of the numbers circled is that they give the number of roads from (or to) a given city. To reach A from A by going through another city, one would take one of these roads then turn around and return.

To compute the number of one- or two-stage routes between cities we should add position by position to get a new matrix. This type of consideration gives reason for a natural definition of addition of matrices of the same shape. To define this addition adequately and to prove certain properties of addition, we must introduce a notation adequate for our purposes.

First we will use capital letters to denote matrices. So we will speak of matrices A, B, C, ... Let A be an $m \times n$ matrix. Recall, then, that A has m rows and n columns. The entry that appears in the ith row and jth column of A we call the i,jth or simply the i,j entry. So in the matrix

$$
\begin{pmatrix}
1 & 0 & -1 & 1 \\
3 & 2 & -5 & \dfrac{1}{2} \\
0 & 0 & 1 & \pi
\end{pmatrix}
$$

the 2, 2 entry is 2, the 3, 4 entry is π. This gives rise to the convention of representing an arbitrary $m \times n$ matrix A by:

$$
A = \begin{pmatrix}
a_{11} & a_{12} & \cdots & a_{1n} \\
a_{21} & a_{22} & \cdots & a_{2n} \\
\multicolumn{4}{c}{\dotfill} \\
a_{m1} & a_{m2} & \cdots & a_{mn}
\end{pmatrix}
$$

Here the symbol a_{ij} represents the number in the ith row and jth column (for example, a_{25} is the entry in the second row, fifth column). This is commonly abbreviated:

$$
A = (a_{ij}) = (a_{ij})_{m \times n}
$$

Notice here that i and j are indices with $-1 \leq i \leq m$ and $1 \leq j \leq n$. Also realize that we could speak of $a_{\mu\nu}$ where $a_{\mu\nu}$ is the entry in the μth row and νth column. In fact, any symbols could be used as subscripts, but recall that the first subscript refers to the number of the row and the second refers to the number of the column in which the entry stands.

Exercise 6.3

1. Consider the 3×4 matrix A given by

$$A = \begin{pmatrix} 2 & -1 & 3 & 6 \\ -2 & 0 & 0 & -1 \\ \pi & 7 & 10 & 99 \end{pmatrix}.$$

Give the following entries:

(a) 1, 1 (b) 3, 4 (c) 2, 2 (d) 3, 3.

2. Write out the 2×4 matrix (a_{ij}) where

(a) $a_{ij} = i + j$.

(b) $a_{ij} = i \cdot j$.

(Here $i = 1, 2$ and $j = 1, 2, 3, 4$)

3. Write out the 10×1 matrix (a_{ij}), where $a_{ij} = (-1)^i$.

4. Write out the 5×5 matrix (a_{ij}), where

(a) $a_{ij} = i - j$. (b) $a_{ij} = i^2 + j^2$.

(c) $a_{ij} = |i - j| + i^2$. (d) $a_{ij} = \dfrac{i}{j}$.

(e) $a_{ij} = i + j$. (f) $a_{ij} = i \cdot j - i$.

(g) $a_{ij} = (i \cdot j)^2$. (h) $a_{ij} = (i + j) + 3$.

6.3 Algebra of Matrices

With our notation, we define, rather simply, the notion of equality of matrices.

Definition 6.1. Let $A = (a_{ij})$ and $B = (b_{ij})$ be two $m \times n$ matrices.

$$A = B \Leftrightarrow a_{ij} = b_{ij} \quad \text{for every } i, j; \qquad 1 \le i \le m, \qquad 1 \le j \le n.$$

Exercise

Write the meaning of this definition in words.

Definition 6.2. Let $A = (a_{ij})$ and $B = (b_{ij})$ be two $m \times n$ matrices. We define the *sum of A and B*, denoted $A + B$, as follows:

$$A + B = C, \quad \text{where} \quad C = (a_{ij} + b_{ij}), 1 \le i \le m, 1 \le j \le n.$$

This means that C is an $m \times n$ matrix whose ijth entry is the sum of the ijth entries of A and B. Notice that it is possible only to add matrices of the same shape. Thus, we can add two 2×3 matrices but we cannot add a 2×3 to a 2×4 matrix.

As examples, consider the following sums:

$$\begin{pmatrix} 2 & 4 & 3 \\ 0 & -1 & -2 \end{pmatrix} + \begin{pmatrix} -1 & -4 & 2 \\ 1 & 1 & 1 \end{pmatrix} = \begin{pmatrix} 1 & 0 & 5 \\ 1 & 0 & -1 \end{pmatrix}.$$

$$(1 \quad 3 \quad -\pi) + (2 \quad 6 \quad 1) = (3 \quad 9 \quad 1 - \pi).$$

Exercise 6.4

Find the indicated sums where possible.

(a) $\begin{pmatrix} 1 & 0 & 1 & 0 \\ 0 & 1 & 0 & 1 \\ 1 & 0 & 1 & 0 \end{pmatrix} + \begin{pmatrix} 0 & 0 & 1 & 1 \\ 0 & 1 & 1 & 0 \\ 1 & 1 & 0 & 0 \end{pmatrix}.$

(b) $\begin{pmatrix} 2 & 4 \\ 5 & 7 \\ 3 & 1 \end{pmatrix} + \begin{pmatrix} 2 & 1 \\ 1 & -1 \\ 1 & -1 \end{pmatrix}.$

(c) $(1 \quad 2 \quad 3) + (-1 \quad -2 \quad -3).$

(d) $\begin{pmatrix} 1 & 0 & 1 & 0 \\ 0 & 1 & 0 & 1 \\ 1 & 0 & 1 & 0 \end{pmatrix} + \begin{pmatrix} 0 & 0 & -1 & -1 \\ 0 & 1 & -1 & 0 \\ -1 & -1 & 0 & 0 \end{pmatrix}.$

(e) $\begin{pmatrix} 1 & 3 \\ 2 & -1 \end{pmatrix} + \begin{pmatrix} -1 & -3 \\ -2 & 1 \end{pmatrix}.$

(f) $(1, \quad 2, \quad 3) + (3, \quad 2, \quad 1).$

(g) $\begin{pmatrix} 1 & 0 \\ 0 & 1 \end{pmatrix} + \begin{pmatrix} 2 & 3 & 3 \\ 3 & 2 & 0 \end{pmatrix}.$

(h) $\begin{pmatrix} 1 \\ 2 \\ 1 \end{pmatrix} + \begin{pmatrix} 0 \\ 0 \\ 0 \end{pmatrix}.$

Let $M_{m \times n}$ be the set of all $m \times n$ matrices. Then $+$ is a binary operation on $M_{m \times n}$. From our definition of "$+$", it is clear that $M_{m \times n}$ is closed under $+$.

Certain other properties hold. For example, let (a_{ij}), (b_{ij}), and (c_{ij}) be any three $m \times n$ matrices. Then

$$[(a_{ij}) + (b_{ij})] + (c_{ij}) = (a_{ij} + b_{ij}) + (c_{ij})$$

$$= ((a_{ij} + b_{ij}) + c_{ij}) = (a_{ij} + (b_{ij} + c_{ij}))$$

$$= (a_{ij}) + (b_{ij} + c_{ij}) = (a_{ij}) + [(b_{ij}) + (c_{ij})].$$

Thus our addition is an associative binary operation.

Moreover, if (a_{ij}) and (b_{ij}) are arbitrary elements of $M_{m \times n}$, then $(a_{ij}) + (b_{ij}) = (b_{ij}) + (a_{ij})$.

Exercise

Prove this commutative law for addition of $m \times n$ matrices.

Let $\bar{0} = (k_{ij}) \in M_{m \times n}$ be the matrix with $k_{ij} = 0$ for all i, j. Then, if $A = (a_{ij}) \in M_{m \times n}$,

$$A + \bar{0} = (a_{ij}) + (k_{ij}) = (a_{ij}) = A .$$

It is also true that, if $A = (a_{ij})$ and $-A = (-a_{ij})$, then $A + (-A) = \bar{0}$.

These results give us, then,

Theorem 6.1. $M_{m \times n}$ is closed under addition and the commutative and associative laws hold. There exists a zero matrix; and every $A \in M_{m \times n}$ has an additive inverse.

Exercise 6.5

1. Let

$$A = \begin{pmatrix} 1 & 2 & 3 \\ -1 & 0 & -1 \end{pmatrix} \qquad B = \begin{pmatrix} 1 & 0 & 1 \\ 1 & 1 & 0 \end{pmatrix}$$

$$C = \begin{pmatrix} 1 & 0 & -1 \\ 0 & 1 & 0 \end{pmatrix} \qquad \bar{0} = \begin{pmatrix} 0 & 0 & 0 \\ 0 & 0 & 0 \end{pmatrix}.$$

Prove that

(a) $(A + B) + C = A + (B + C)$.   (b) $A + B = B + A$.

(c) $A + (-A) = \bar{0}$.   (d) $C + \bar{0} = C$.

2. Suppose $A = (a_{ij})$ is a real $m \times n$ matrix and let $k \in R^1$. Define a scalar multiplication by

$$k \cdot A = (k \cdot a_{ij}),$$

that is, multiply every entry in A by k. The product $kA \in M_{m \times n}$.

(a) For A, B, C in Problem 1, compute

(1) $2 \cdot A$.   (2) $2(A + B)$.

(3) $2A + 2B$.   (4) $A + 2B - 3C$.

(b) Prove, for arbitrary $m \times n$ matrices, A, B, and real numbers, r and s, that

(1) $r(A + B) = rA + rB$.   (2) $(r + s)A = rA + sA$.

(3) $(r \cdot s)A = r \cdot (sA)$.   (4) $1 \cdot A = A, OA = \bar{0}$.

Remark. Exercise 2(b) and Theorem 6.1, together, show that $M_{m \times n}$ is a vector space.

6.4 Matrix Multiplication

We next want to define a multiplication for matrices. Justifying the definition we make is a bit more difficult. In certain contexts, we can show it is the natural definition. To make it seem more natural consider the following problem.

A manufacturer of an item L uses three raw materials for L, let us say steel, aluminum, and plastic. In one model of L, he uses 15 units of aluminum, 70 units of steel, and 15 units of plastic. In another model, he uses 5 units of aluminum, 75 units of steel, and 30 units of plastic. If aluminum costs \$500 per unit, steel, \$50 per unit, and plastic, \$5 per unit, we can compute the cost of raw materials for each model. One model would cost

$$15 \cdot 500 + 70 \cdot 50 + 15 \cdot 5 = 11{,}075 \text{ dollars},$$

whereas the other would cost

$$5 \cdot 500 + 75 \cdot 50 + 30 \cdot 5 = 6{,}400 \text{ dollars}.$$

If we would represent the proportions used in each model as a matrix Q, we might get

$$\begin{array}{cc} & \begin{array}{ccc} A & S & P \end{array} \\ \begin{array}{c} M_1 \\ M_2 \end{array} & \begin{pmatrix} 15 & 70 & 15 \\ 5 & 75 & 30 \end{pmatrix} \end{array} = Q.$$

If we represent the cost per various items as a matrix C, we might get

$$\begin{pmatrix} 500 \\ 50 \\ 5 \end{pmatrix} \begin{array}{c} A \\ S \\ P \end{array} = C.$$

The answer, a total-cost-per-model matrix, might be

$$T = \begin{pmatrix} 11{,}075 \\ 6{,}400 \end{pmatrix} \begin{array}{c} M_1 \\ M_2. \end{array}$$

We would like to define our matrix multiplication so that $Q \cdot C = T$. If we set these matrices down in this order we get

$$\begin{pmatrix} 15 & 70 & 15 \\ 5 & 75 & 30 \end{pmatrix} \cdot \begin{pmatrix} 500 \\ 50 \\ 5 \end{pmatrix} = \begin{pmatrix} 11{,}075 \\ 6{,}400 \end{pmatrix}$$

It seems as if we would have to superimpose the matrix C on the rows in Q in the natural order, multiply the numbers that coincide, and then add the products.

This is, in fact, the way we want to define matrix multiplication. Of course, the general case will be a bit more complex. Note that in order to multiply two matrices, A and B, in the order $A \cdot B$, the number of columns in A and the number of rows in B must be the same.

Before we formally define this operation on matrices, notice that, so far, little has been said about how to position the numbers we get into the product matrix. We will do this in a systematic way, but at this time we cannot make it seem like *the* thing to do. Also note that the example preceding has a column matrix (a matrix with only one column) as the right factor in our product. We do not want restrictions of this type.

Consider, then, two matrices $A = (a_{ij})_{m \times k}$ and $B = (b_{ij})_{k \times n}$ of size $m \times k$ and $k \times n$, respectively. We are going to define our multiplication by saying what the ij entry of $A \cdot B$ is. We indicate the matrices A and B, writing explicitly only the ith row of A and the jth column of B.

$$A \cdot B = \begin{pmatrix} \cdots\cdots\cdots\cdots \\ a_{i1} \quad a_{i2} \quad \dots \quad a_{ik} \\ \cdots\cdots\cdots\cdots \end{pmatrix} \cdot \begin{pmatrix} \cdot & b_{1j} & \cdot \\ \cdot & b_{2j} & \cdot \\ \cdot & \cdot & \cdot \\ \cdot & \cdot & \cdot \\ \cdot & \cdot & \cdot \\ \cdot & b_{kj} & \cdot \end{pmatrix}$$

The ij entry of $A \cdot B$ will be

$$a_{i1}b_{1j} + a_{i2}b_{2j} + \dots a_{ik}b_{kj} = \sum_{v=1}^{k} a_{iv}b_{vj} .$$

Note that all possible choices of i and j will give us a matrix with m rows and n columns.

Formally, then, we make the definition:

Definition 6.3. Let $A = (a_{ij})$ be an $m \times k$ matrix and let $B = (b_{ij})$ be a $k \times n$ matrix. The *product*, $A \cdot B$, (read A times B) of A and B is defined to be the $m \times n$ matrix $C = (c_{ij})$, where, for $1 \leq i \leq m$, $1 \leq j \leq n$,

$$c_{ij} = \sum_{v=1}^{k} a_{iv}b_{vj} .$$

Without doubt, we should now look at some examples. First, without using explicit numbers, consider

$$\begin{pmatrix} a_{11} & a_{12} & a_{13} \\ a_{21} & a_{22} & a_{23} \\ a_{31} & a_{32} & a_{33} \end{pmatrix} \cdot \begin{pmatrix} b_{11} & b_{12} \\ b_{21} & b_{22} \\ b_{31} & b_{32} \end{pmatrix} = A \cdot B = \begin{pmatrix} c_{11} & c_{12} \\ c_{21} & c_{22} \\ c_{31} & c_{32} \end{pmatrix} .$$

Remember, to find c_{11}, we use the first row in A and the first column in B. Our definition then gives us $c_{11} = a_{11}b_{11} + a_{12}b_{21} + a_{13}b_{31}$. Similarly c_{12} would be obtained with the first row of A and the second column of B. Then $c_{12} = a_{11}b_{12} + a_{12}b_{22} + a_{13}b_{32}$.

Continuing, we get that

$$A \cdot B = \begin{pmatrix} a_{11}b_{11} + a_{12}b_{21} + a_{13}b_{31} & a_{11}b_{12} + a_{12}b_{22} + a_{13}b_{23} \\ a_{21}b_{11} + a_{22}b_{21} + a_{23}b_{31} & a_{21}b_{12} + a_{22}b_{22} + a_{23}b_{32} \\ a_{31}b_{11} + a_{32}b_{21} + a_{33}b_{31} & a_{31}b_{12} + a_{32}b_{22} + a_{33}b_{32} \end{pmatrix}$$

Now consider another example with numbers:

$$\begin{pmatrix} 2 & 3 & 2 \\ 0 & 1 & 0 \\ 1 & 1 & 1 \end{pmatrix} \cdot \begin{pmatrix} -1 & -2 \\ 1 & 2 \\ -1 & -4 \end{pmatrix}$$

$$= \begin{pmatrix} 2 \cdot (-1) + 3 \cdot 1 + 2(-1) & 2 \cdot (-2) + 3 \cdot 2 + 2 \cdot (-4) \\ 0 \cdot (-1) + 1 \cdot 1 + 0(-1) & 0 \cdot (-2) + 1 \cdot 2 + 0 \cdot (-4) \\ 1 \cdot (-1) + 1 \cdot 1 + 1(-1) & 1 \cdot (-2) + 1 \cdot 2 + 1 \cdot (-4) \end{pmatrix}$$

$$= \begin{pmatrix} -1 & -6 \\ 1 & 2 \\ -1 & -4 \end{pmatrix}.$$

Notice that this is exactly the process previously described with letters. For example, the third row in the first matrix is (1 1 1) and the second column in the second matrix is

$$\begin{pmatrix} -2 \\ 2 \\ -4 \end{pmatrix}.$$

If we let $a_{31} = 1$, $a_{32} = 1$, $a_{33} = 1$, and $b_{12} = -2$, $b_{22} = 2$, $b_{32} = -4$, we compute c_{32} to be

$$a_{31}b_{12} + a_{32}b_{22} + a_{33}b_{32} = (1)(-2) + (1)(2) + (1)(-4) = -4.$$

Exercise 6.6

1. Perform the indicated operations (where possible):

(a) $\begin{pmatrix} 2 & 4 \\ 3 & 1 \\ 7 & -6 \end{pmatrix} \cdot \begin{pmatrix} 1 & -1 \\ -1 & 1 \end{pmatrix}.$

(b) $\begin{pmatrix} 1 & 3 \\ 2 & 6 \end{pmatrix} \cdot \begin{pmatrix} -3 & -3 \\ 1 & 1 \end{pmatrix}.$

(c) $\begin{pmatrix} 2 & 1 & -2 \\ -7 & -3 & 8 \\ 3 & 1 & -3 \end{pmatrix} \cdot \begin{pmatrix} 1 & 1 & 2 \\ 3 & 0 & -2 \\ 2 & 1 & 1 \end{pmatrix}.$

(d) $\begin{pmatrix} 1 & 1 & 1 \\ 1 & 1 & 1 \\ 1 & 1 & 1 \end{pmatrix} \cdot \begin{pmatrix} 1 & 1 & 1 \\ -1 & -1 & -1 \\ 1 & 1 & 1 \end{pmatrix}.$

(e) $(1 \ 2 \ 3) \cdot \begin{pmatrix} 1 \\ 2 \\ 3 \end{pmatrix}.$

(f) $\begin{pmatrix} 1 \\ 2 \\ 3 \end{pmatrix} \cdot (1 \ 2 \ 3).$

(g) $\begin{pmatrix} 0 & 1 \\ 0 & 0 \end{pmatrix} \cdot \begin{pmatrix} a & b \\ c & d \end{pmatrix}.$

(h) $\begin{pmatrix} 1 & 0 & 0 & 0 \\ 1 & 1 & 0 & 0 \\ 1 & 1 & 1 & 0 \\ 1 & 1 & 1 & 1 \end{pmatrix} \cdot \begin{pmatrix} 1 & 0 & 0 & 0 \\ 1 & 1 & 0 & 0 \\ 1 & 1 & 1 & 0 \\ 1 & 1 & 1 & 1 \end{pmatrix}.$

(i) $\begin{pmatrix} 1 & 0 & 1 \\ 0 & 1 & 0 \end{pmatrix} \cdot \begin{pmatrix} 2 & -1 \\ 1 & 0 \end{pmatrix}.$

(j) $\begin{pmatrix} 2 & -6 \\ 1 & -3 \end{pmatrix} \cdot \begin{pmatrix} 2 & -6 \\ 1 & -3 \end{pmatrix} + \begin{pmatrix} 2 & -6 \\ 1 & -3 \end{pmatrix}.$

(k) $\begin{pmatrix} a & b & c \\ d & e & f \end{pmatrix} \cdot \begin{pmatrix} 1 & 2 \\ 4 & 6 \\ 1 & 1 \end{pmatrix}.$

(l) $\begin{pmatrix} a & b \\ c & d \end{pmatrix} \cdot \begin{pmatrix} e & f \\ g & h \end{pmatrix}.$

(m) $\begin{pmatrix} a_{11} & a_{12} \\ a_{21} & a_{22} \end{pmatrix} \cdot \begin{pmatrix} b_{11} & b_{12} \\ b_{21} & b_{22} \end{pmatrix}.$

2. Let $A = (a_{ij})_{3 \times 3}$ and $B = (b_{ij})_{3 \times 3}$ be matrices of the sizes indicated. Express the 2, 3 entry of the product $A \cdot B$ in a summation formula. Do the same for the 1, 2 entry in $A \cdot B$ and for the 2, 3 entry in the product $B \cdot A$.

6.5 More Algebra

Observe that this multiplication is not in general a binary operation on $M_{m \times n}$. In fact, only when $m = n$ can we multiply the elements of $M_{m \times n}$. We could restrict ourselves to the special case where $m = n$ but we will maintain a general point of view a while longer.

Let

$$A = (a_{ij})_{m \times n}, \qquad B = (b_{ij})_{n \times k}, \quad \text{and} \quad C = (c_{ij})_{k \times s}$$

be matrices of the sizes indicated. We might well ask whether $(A \cdot B) \cdot C = A \cdot (B \cdot C)$. It was for considerations of this sort that we introduced the notation we now have for matrices. As an exercise the reader should carry out the computation for the foregoing using 2×2 matrices in general form i.e., let

$$A = \begin{pmatrix} a_{11} & a_{12} \\ a_{21} & a_{22} \end{pmatrix}, \quad \text{etc.}$$

For the general situation, we will compute $(A \cdot B) \cdot C$ and $A \cdot (B \cdot C)$.

$$(A \cdot B) \cdot C = ((a_{ij}) \cdot (b_{ij})) \cdot C$$

$$= \left(\sum_{v=1}^{n} a_{iv} b_{vj} \right) \cdot C .$$

Let

$$d_{ij} = \sum_{v=1}^{n} a_{iv} b_{vj} \quad \text{for } 1 \leq i \leq m \quad \text{and} \quad 1 \leq j \leq k .$$

Then

$$(A \cdot B) \cdot C = (d_{ij}) \cdot (c_{ij}) = \sum_{\mu=1}^{k} d_{i\mu} c_{\mu j} .$$

Thus the ij entry in $(A \cdot B) \cdot C$ is $\sum_{\mu=1}^{k} d_{i\mu} c_{\mu j}$

Replacing $d_{i\mu}$ by $\sum_{v=1}^{n} a_{iv} b_{v\mu}$, we have that the ij entry in our present product is

$$Z_1 = \sum_{\mu=1}^{k} \left(\sum_{v=1}^{n} a_{iv} b_{v\mu} \right) c_{\mu j} = \sum_{\mu=1}^{k} \left(\sum_{v=1}^{n} \left(a_{iv} b_{v\mu} \right) c_{\mu j} \right)$$

In the same fashion (without some of the intermediate steps),

$$A \cdot (B \cdot C) = (a_{ij}) \cdot ((b_{ij}) \cdot (c_{ij}))$$

$$= (a_{ij}) \left(\sum_{\mu=1}^{k} b_{i\mu} c_{\mu j} \right) = \left(\sum_{v=1}^{n} \left(a_{iv} \sum_{\mu=1}^{k} b_{v\mu} c_{\mu j} \right) \right)$$

$$= \left(\sum_{v=1}^{n} \left(\sum_{\mu=1}^{k} (a_{iv} b_{v\mu}) c_{\mu j} \right) \right).$$

Let Z_2 be the ij entry in $A \cdot (B \cdot C)$. Then

$$Z_2 = \sum_{v=1}^{n} \sum_{\mu=1}^{k} (a_{iv} b_{v\mu}) c_{\mu j} .$$

But $Z_1 = Z_2$ as we pointed out earlier.

We state this result as

Theorem 6.2. Let $A_{m \times n}$, $B_{n \times k}$, $C_{k \times s}$ be matrices of the indicated sizes. Then

$$(A \cdot B) \cdot C = A \cdot (B \cdot C) .$$

Immediately, we think of the possibility of whether or not $A \cdot B = B \cdot A$. In general, both multiplications may not be possible. For if A is $m \times n$ and B is $n \times k$, $A \cdot B$ exists but $B \cdot A$ need not be possible. But even in less general circumstances, the multiplication need not be commutative.

For example,

$$\begin{pmatrix} 1 & 1 \\ 1 & 0 \end{pmatrix} \cdot \begin{pmatrix} 1 & 1 \\ 0 & 0 \end{pmatrix} = \begin{pmatrix} 1 & 1 \\ 1 & 1 \end{pmatrix}.$$

But

$$\begin{pmatrix} 1 & 1 \\ 0 & 0 \end{pmatrix} \cdot \begin{pmatrix} 1 & 1 \\ 1 & 0 \end{pmatrix} = \begin{pmatrix} 2 & 1 \\ 0 & 0 \end{pmatrix}.$$

Another property that does hold is the (left, right) distributive law.

Theorem 6.3. Let $A = (a_{ij})_{m \times n}$, $B = (b_{ij})_{n \times k}$ and $C = (c_{ij})_{n \times k}$ be matrices of the sizes indicated.
Then

$$A \cdot (B + C) = A \cdot B + A \cdot C.$$

Proof.

$$A \cdot (B + C) = (a_{ij})((b_{ij}) + (c_{ij}))$$

$$= (a_{ij}) \cdot (b_{ij} + c_{ij}) = \left(\sum_{v=1}^{n} a_{iv}(b_{vj} + c_{vj}) \right)$$

$$= \left(\sum_{v=1}^{n} (a_{iv}b_{vj} + a_{iv}c_{vj}) \right)$$

$$= \left(\sum_{v=1}^{n} a_{iv}b_{vj} \right) + \left(\sum_{v=1}^{n} a_{iv}c_{vj} \right)$$

$$= (a_{ij}) \cdot (b_{ij}) + (a_{ij}) \cdot (c_{ij})$$

$$= A \cdot B + A \cdot C.$$

If we restrict ourselves to the situation where $m = n$, that is, deal only with square matrices with n rows and columns, then we have that $M_{n \times n}$ is closed under multiplication; that $\cdot$ is an associative binary operation on $M_{n \times n}$ and that a (left, right) distributive law holds.

We also notice that the matrix $I_n \in M_{n \times n}$,

$$I_n = \begin{pmatrix} 1 & 0 & 0 & \ldots & 0 \\ 0 & 1 & 0 & \ldots & 0 \\ \cdots\cdots\cdots\cdots\cdots \\ 0 & 0 & 0 & \ldots & 1 \end{pmatrix},$$

(I_n has 1 in the ii positions and 0 everywhere else) has the property that for $A \in M_{n \times n}$, $A \cdot I_n = I_n \cdot A = A$. To see this, let $A = (a_{ij})$ and consider the product $A \cdot I_n$. The ij entry in this is obtained by considering the ith row, $a_{i1}, a_{i2} \ldots a_{in}$ in A and the jth column $0 \, 0 \ldots 1 \ldots 0$. In pairing these up, only the jth entry in the column is non-zero. Thus the ij entry in the product is a_{ij}. This is for any i and j. So our statement is true and $A \cdot I_n = A$. The proof that $I_n \cdot A = A$ is of the same sort. This means that there is an element in $M_{n \times n}$ that has the role that the real number 1 has in R^1.

Exercise 6.7

1. Given the matrices

$$A = \begin{pmatrix} 1 & 2 \\ 2 & 4 \end{pmatrix}, \qquad B = \begin{pmatrix} 1 & 3 \\ -2 & -1 \end{pmatrix}, \qquad C = \begin{pmatrix} -7 & 5 \\ 2 & -2 \end{pmatrix},$$

show that $AB = AC$. What is unexpected about this?

2. Given

$$A = \begin{pmatrix} 1 & 1 & 1 \\ 1 & 1 & 1 \\ 1 & 1 & 1 \end{pmatrix}, \qquad J = \begin{pmatrix} 1 & 1 & 1 \\ -1 & -1 & -1 \\ 1 & 1 & 1 \end{pmatrix}$$

show that $AJ = A$. Are there other 3×3 matrices such that $BJ = B$? Is $XJ = X$ for every matrix X of order 3? Is $JA = A$? Are there matrices C of order 3* such that $JC = C$?

3. Prove that there is only one matrix of order n* which has the properties of the identity matrix. (*Hint:* Suppose I and J are two identity matrices.) Then show that $I = J$.

4. Verify that $(A \cdot B) \cdot C = A \cdot (B \cdot C)$ and that $A \cdot (B + C) = A \cdot B + A \cdot C$ for the following choices of A, B, and C.

(a) $A = \begin{pmatrix} 2 & 1 & 0 \\ -1 & 0 & 1 \\ 1 & 3 & 2 \end{pmatrix}, \qquad B = \begin{pmatrix} 0 & 0 & 1 \\ 0 & 1 & 0 \\ 1 & 0 & 0 \end{pmatrix},$

$C = \begin{pmatrix} 1 & 0 & 0 \\ 0 & 2 & 0 \\ 0 & 0 & 3 \end{pmatrix}.$

(b) $A = \begin{pmatrix} 1 & 1 \\ 1 & 1 \end{pmatrix}, \qquad B = \begin{pmatrix} 1 & -1 \\ -1 & 1 \end{pmatrix}, \qquad C = \begin{pmatrix} -1 & 1 \\ 1 & -1 \end{pmatrix}.$

6.6   Inverses

In $M_{2\times2}$ we observe that, for certain matrices A, $\exists\, B \in M_{2\times2}$ so that $A \cdot B = B \cdot A = I_2$ but that no such matrix, B, exists for others. For example,

$$\begin{pmatrix} 1 & -1 \\ 0 & 1 \end{pmatrix} \cdot \begin{pmatrix} 1 & 1 \\ 0 & 1 \end{pmatrix} = \begin{pmatrix} 1 & 0 \\ 0 & 1 \end{pmatrix} = \begin{pmatrix} 1 & 1 \\ 0 & 1 \end{pmatrix} \cdot \begin{pmatrix} 1 & -1 \\ 0 & 1 \end{pmatrix}$$

Then consider $\begin{pmatrix} 1 & 1 \\ -1 & -1 \end{pmatrix}$ and suppose $\begin{pmatrix} a & b \\ c & d \end{pmatrix}$ is such that

$$\begin{pmatrix} 1 & 1 \\ -1 & -1 \end{pmatrix} \cdot \begin{pmatrix} a & b \\ c & d \end{pmatrix} = \begin{pmatrix} 1 & 0 \\ 0 & 1 \end{pmatrix}.$$

* A matrix of order n is of size $n \times n$.

Then,

$$\begin{pmatrix} a + c & b + d \\ -a - c & -b - d \end{pmatrix} = \begin{pmatrix} 1 & 0 \\ 0 & 1 \end{pmatrix}.$$

But this means that $a + c = 1$ and $-a - c = 0$, or on adding, that $0 = 1$. Thus the assumption that a matrix with the foregoing property exists gives us a contradiction.

If A is an $n \times n$ matrix, we could ask whether or not there exists a matrix B ($n \times n$) with the property that $A \cdot B = BA = I_n$.

We can show that, if B and C are two matrices such that $AB = BA = I_n$ and $AC = CA = I_n$, then $B = C$. For consider BAC. Remembering that multiplication in $M_{n \times n}$ is associative, we have, on the one hand,

$$BAC = (BA)C = I_nC = C,$$

and on the other hand,

$$BAC = B(AC) = BI_n = B.$$

Thus $B = C$. This means that, if a matrix B exists so that $AB = BA = I$, then B is the only matrix for which this is true.

We can now make the following definition:

Definition 6.4. Let $A \in M_{n \times n}$. If there exists $B \in M_{n \times n}$ such that

$$A \cdot B = B \cdot A = I_n$$

we call B the *inverse of A*. As we have shown, B is unique if it exists and we denote it by A^{-1}.

Theorem 6.4. Suppose that A and B are in $M_{n \times n}$ and that A^{-1} and B^{-1} exists. Then $(AB)^{-1}$ exists and is, in fact, $B^{-1}A^{-1}$.

Proof. All we need note is that

$$(AB)(B^{-1}A^{-1}) = A(BB^{-1})A^{-1}$$
$$= (AI_n)A^{-1}$$
$$= AA^{-1} = I_n$$

and that

$$(B^{-1}A^{-1})(AB) = B^{-1}(A^{-1}A)B$$
$$= B^{-1}(I_nB)$$
$$= B^{-1}B = I_n.$$

Exercise 6.8

1. Suppose that A, B, and C in $M_{n \times n}$ all have inverses. Show that $A \cdot B \cdot C$ has an inverse.

2. Suppose that A, B, and C are in $M_{n \times n}$ and that $AC = BA = I_n$. Show that $C = B$.

The problem of saying whether or not a matrix has an inverse and of finding it, if it exists, is a bit complicated and we will not here deal with this problem except in the simplest fashion. For example, we might, in a naive fashion, find the inverses of 2×2 matrices.

Consider the matrix $\begin{pmatrix} a & b \\ c & d \end{pmatrix}$. The problem of finding the inverse of this matrix is that of finding a matrix $\begin{pmatrix} x & y \\ u & v \end{pmatrix}$ so that

$$\begin{pmatrix} x & y \\ u & v \end{pmatrix} \cdot \begin{pmatrix} a & b \\ c & d \end{pmatrix} = \begin{pmatrix} 1 & 0 \\ 0 & 1 \end{pmatrix}.$$

Multiplying the left side of this equation, we see that this means that we must find real numbers x, y, u, and v so that $ax + cy = 1$ and $bx + dy = 0$ and $au + cv = 0$ and $bu + dv = 1$. Thus, we must find solutions to two sets of two equations in two variables.

Carrying out this process in an example is not difficult. Consider

$$A = \begin{pmatrix} 1 & 2 \\ 4 & -2 \end{pmatrix}.$$

Suppose that $A^{-1} = \begin{pmatrix} x & y \\ u & v \end{pmatrix}$. Then, as indicated,

$$A^{-1} \cdot A = \begin{pmatrix} x + 4y & 2x - 2y \\ u + 4v & 2u - 2v \end{pmatrix} = \begin{pmatrix} 1 & 0 \\ 0 & 1 \end{pmatrix}.$$

Or

$$x + 4y = 1, \qquad 2x - 2y = 0 \quad \text{and} \quad u + 4v = 0, \qquad 2u - 2v = 1 .$$

Solving the first pair for x and y, we see that $y = \frac{1}{5}$, $x = \frac{1}{5}$. Solving the second pair for u and v, we have that $u = \frac{2}{5}$, $v = \frac{1}{10}$. Multiplying, we get

$$\begin{pmatrix} \frac{1}{5} & \frac{1}{5} \\ \frac{2}{5} & -\frac{1}{10} \end{pmatrix} \cdot \begin{pmatrix} 1 & 2 \\ 4 & -2 \end{pmatrix} = \begin{pmatrix} \frac{1}{5} + \frac{4}{5} & \frac{2}{5} - \frac{2}{5} \\ \frac{2}{5} - \frac{4}{10} & \frac{4}{5} + \frac{1}{5} \end{pmatrix}$$

$$= \begin{pmatrix} 1 & 0 \\ 0 & 1 \end{pmatrix}.$$

Thus, we see that $\begin{pmatrix} \frac{1}{5} & \frac{1}{5} \\ \frac{2}{5} & -\frac{1}{10} \end{pmatrix}$ is, indeed, the inverse of A.

The problem of finding the inverse of a 3×3 matrix is considerably more complex using the foregoing technique because it would involve solving 3 sets of 3 equations in 3 variables. It might be well to point out that a technique exists that allows one to find the inverse of a given matrix, if it exists, in reasonably short order, provided that the given matrix is not very large.

If we now have the system of equations $x + 2y = 20$, $4x - 2y = 15$, we can write these equations in matrix form. For consider

$$\begin{pmatrix} 1 & 2 \\ 4 & -2 \end{pmatrix} \cdot \begin{pmatrix} x \\ y \end{pmatrix} = \begin{pmatrix} 20 \\ 15 \end{pmatrix}.$$

This is a matrix equation and, if x_0, y_0 is a solution to our system of equations, then $\begin{pmatrix} x_0 \\ y_0 \end{pmatrix}$ is a solution to our matrix equation and vice versa. We know the inverse of $\begin{pmatrix} 1 & 2 \\ 4 & -2 \end{pmatrix}$. Multiplying both sides of our matrix equation on the left by this inverse, we get

$$\begin{pmatrix} \frac{1}{5} & \frac{1}{5} \\ \frac{2}{5} & -\frac{1}{10} \end{pmatrix} \cdot \begin{pmatrix} 1 & 2 \\ 4 & -2 \end{pmatrix} \cdot \begin{pmatrix} x_0 \\ y_0 \end{pmatrix} = \begin{pmatrix} \frac{1}{5} & \frac{1}{5} \\ \frac{2}{5} & -\frac{1}{10} \end{pmatrix} \cdot \begin{pmatrix} 20 \\ 15 \end{pmatrix}$$

Multiplying out the left and right sides, we get that

$$\begin{pmatrix} x_0 \\ y_0 \end{pmatrix} = \begin{pmatrix} 7 \\ 6\frac{1}{2} \end{pmatrix}.$$

So that, if $\begin{pmatrix} x_0 \\ y_0 \end{pmatrix}$ is a solution to our matrix equation, then $x_0 = 7$ and $y_0 = 6\frac{1}{2}$. But $7 + 2 \cdot \frac{13}{2} = 20$ and $4 \cdot 7 - 2 \cdot \frac{13}{2} = 15$. Thus x_0, y_0 is a solution to our system of equations.

If the problem of finding an inverse to a matrix were easy, this would be a simple way to solve certain systems of equations. In fact, computers frequently use this technique. Programs for finding inverses of matrices are commonplace and a large computer easily performs the matrix operations.

Exercise 6.9

1. Find the inverse (if it exists) of the following matrices:

(a) $\begin{pmatrix} 2 & 5 \\ -1 & -3 \end{pmatrix}$.

(b) $\begin{pmatrix} 3 & 1 \\ 13 & 5 \end{pmatrix}$.

(c) $\begin{pmatrix} 2 & -6 \\ 1 & -3 \end{pmatrix}$.

(d) $\begin{pmatrix} 0 & -1 \\ -1 & 0 \end{pmatrix}$.

2. (a)   Which of the matrices

$$B = \begin{pmatrix} 1 & 1 & 2 \\ 3 & 0 & -1 \\ 2 & 1 & 1 \end{pmatrix} \qquad C = \begin{pmatrix} 2 & 1 & -2 \\ -7 & -3 & 8 \\ 3 & 1 & -3 \end{pmatrix}$$

$$D = \begin{pmatrix} 1 & 1 & \frac{1}{2} \\ \frac{1}{3} & 0 & -1 \\ \frac{1}{2} & 1 & 1 \end{pmatrix} \qquad E = \begin{pmatrix} 2 & 1 & -2 \\ 7 & -3 & -8 \\ -3 & 1 & 3 \end{pmatrix}$$

is the inverse of

$$A = \begin{pmatrix} 1 & 1 & 2 \\ 3 & 0 & -2 \\ 2 & 1 & 1 \end{pmatrix} ?$$

(b)   Use the result of (a) to solve the system of equations

$$\begin{array}{rcl} x + y + 2z & = & 3 \\ 3x \qquad - 2z & = & 4 \\ 2x + y + z & = & 1 . \end{array}$$

3. (a)   Which of the matrices

$$B = \begin{pmatrix} 2 & 1 & 1 \\ -2 & 3 & 0 \\ 1 & 2 & 1 \end{pmatrix} \qquad C = \begin{pmatrix} \frac{1}{2} & 1 & 1 \\ -\frac{1}{2} & \frac{1}{3} & 0 \\ 1 & \frac{1}{2} & 1 \end{pmatrix}$$

$$D = \begin{pmatrix} 3 & 1 & -3 \\ 2 & 1 & -2 \\ -7 & -3 & 8 \end{pmatrix} \qquad E = \begin{pmatrix} -3 & -1 & 3 \\ -2 & 2 & 0 \\ 1 & \frac{1}{2} & 1 \end{pmatrix}$$

is the inverse of

$$A = \begin{pmatrix} 2 & 1 & 1 \\ -2 & 3 & 0 \\ 1 & 2 & 1 \end{pmatrix} ?$$

(b)   Use the result of (a) to solve the system of equations

$$\begin{array}{rcl} 2x + y + z & = & 2 \\ -2x + 3y & = & 1 \\ x + 2y + z & = & 3 . \end{array}$$

4. Give a matrix equation equivalent to the system

$$\begin{array}{rcl} 2x - y + z - u & = & 3 \\ x \qquad + z + u & = & 2 \\ 3x + 3y & = & 4 \\ y \qquad + u & = & -2 . \end{array}$$

5. By examining the system of equations

$$\begin{array}{rcl} x + y + z & = & 2 \\ x + y + z & = & -4 \\ x - y + 3z & = & 0 \end{array}$$

conclude that the matrix

$$S = \begin{pmatrix} 1 & 1 & 1 \\ 1 & -1 & 3 \\ 1 & 1 & 1 \end{pmatrix}$$

does not have an inverse. Explain your reasoning completely.

6. Using a matrix equation, solve

$$\begin{aligned} x + y + z &= 3 \\ 2x - y + z &= -1 \\ 3x + 2y + 6z &= 0. \end{aligned}$$

6.7 An Application

An example we considered earlier involved the counting of one and two stage routes between cities. The "map" we considered was Fig. 6.2. The matrix from which we could reconstruct this map is

$$M = \begin{pmatrix} & A & B & C & D & E & \\ 0 & 1 & 1 & 1 & 0 & A \\ 1 & 0 & 1 & 0 & 1 & B \\ 1 & 1 & 0 & 1 & 1 & C \\ 1 & 0 & 1 & 0 & 1 & D \\ 0 & 1 & 1 & 1 & 0 & E \end{pmatrix}$$

If we find $M^2 = M \cdot M$ we get

$$M^2 = \begin{pmatrix} & A & B & C & D & E & \\ 3 & 1 & 2 & 1 & 3 & A \\ 1 & 3 & 2 & 3 & 1 & B \\ 2 & 2 & 4 & 2 & 2 & C \\ 1 & 3 & 2 & 3 & 1 & D \\ 3 & 1 & 2 & 1 & 3 & E \end{pmatrix}$$

We note that this matrix counts the number of two-stage routes between cities. This is not surprising. For consider how we arrived at a particular entry. As an example, consider the entry giving us the number of two-stage routes between D and B. We used the row in M giving the number of one-stage routes from D to various cities and the column giving the number of one-stage routes from various cities into B. In determining our entry 3, we evaluated

$$1 \cdot 1 + 0 \cdot 0 + 1 \cdot 1 + 0 \cdot 0 + 1 \cdot 1.$$

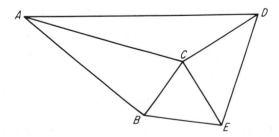

Figure 6.2

1 "paired" with a 1 indicated that there is a route from D to a city and that a route from that city to B exists. The over-all computation gives the total number of such routes.

Suppose that we wanted a matrix that would give us the number of three-stage routes between cities. One might suspect that M^3 might be such a matrix. Indeed, such is the case. Before writing down this matrix, let us consider the way we would find the number of three-stage routes from A to E. Considering the fact that the first row of M^2 gives us the number of two-stage routes from A to various cities, we have that there are 3 two-stage routes from A to A, 1 from A to B, 2 from A to C, 1 from A to D, and 3 from A to E. We also have, considering the fifth column in M, that there are 0 one-stage routes from A to E, 1 from B to E, 1 from C to E, 1 from D to E, and 0 from E to E. So to get from A to E in three stages, we go to various cities from A in two stages and then go one more step to E. Thus, if we get to A, it is not possible to get to E in one more step. Thus $0 = 3 \cdot 0$ is the number of ways we get to E in three steps, being in A after two stages. $1 \cdot 1 = 1$ is the number of ways to get from A to E, being in B after two stages. Continuing, $1 \cdot 2 = 2$, $1 \cdot 1 = 1$ and $1 \cdot 0 = 0$ are the number of ways of getting from A to E being in C, D, E, respectively at the end of two stages. To find the total number of three-stage routes from A to E, then, we merely need add these numbers to get 4; that is,

$$1 \cdot 0 + 1 \cdot 1 + 1 \cdot 2 + 1 \cdot 1 + 1 \cdot 0 = 4 .$$

But this is precisely the way we get the 1,5 entry in M^3.

Thus, the number of three-stage routes between cities can be read from the matrix

$$M^3 = \begin{pmatrix} 4 & 8 & 8 & 8 & 4 \\ 8 & 4 & 8 & 4 & 8 \\ 8 & 8 & 8 & 8 & 8 \\ 8 & 4 & 8 & 4 & 8 \\ 4 & 8 & 8 & 8 & 4 \end{pmatrix}.$$

As an example, let us enumerate the three-stage routes from D to E. According to our matrix, there are 8 of these. We list these routes by giving the sequence of towns passed through. Enumerating we get

D–A–D–E,	D–C–D–E,	D–E–D–E,
D–A–C–E,	D–A–B–E,	D–C–B–E,
D–E–C–E,	D–E–B–E.	

Although this example gives us a procedure not much simpler than counting, suppose a network of 25 cities is involved. The counting procedure might not be so simple, but the matrix technique is not too complicated.

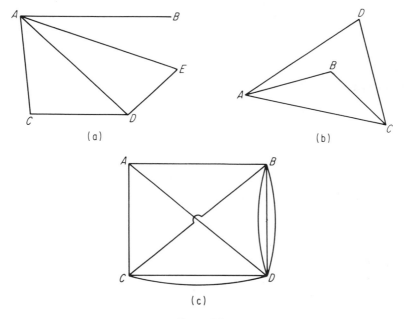

Figure 6.3

Exercise 6.10

For each map in Fig. 6.3 find matrices which give the number of one-, two-, and three-stage routes between cities. Also find a matrix which gives the number of paths which are *one-* or *two*-stage routes.

6.8 Matrices as Functions

As an example of what we want to do in this section, consider the 2×2 matrix

$$A = \begin{pmatrix} \frac{1}{2} & \frac{1}{2} \\ \frac{1}{2} & \frac{1}{2} \end{pmatrix}$$

We define a function $a : R^2 \rightarrow R^2$ by

$$a(x, y) = (x\ y)A$$

for every $(x, y) \in R^2$. Now on the right we consider the product of the 1×2 matrix, (xy), with the 2×2 matrix, A, to get a 1×2 matrix, (uv), which we identify with the point (u, v). As specific examples

$$a(2, 6) = (2\ 6) \cdot \begin{pmatrix} \frac{1}{2} & \frac{1}{2} \\ \frac{1}{2} & \frac{1}{2} \end{pmatrix} = (4, 4)\,,$$

$$a(-8, 2) = (-8\ 2) \cdot \begin{pmatrix} \frac{1}{2} & \frac{1}{2} \\ \frac{1}{2} & \frac{1}{2} \end{pmatrix} = (-3, -3)\,.$$

In general,

$$a(x, y) = \left(\frac{x + y}{2}, \quad \frac{x + y}{2}\right).$$

One property we notice is that, if (x, y) is a point such that $x = y$,

$$a(x, x) = \left(\frac{x + x}{2}, \frac{x + x}{2}\right) = (x, x).$$

In particular, $a(0, 0) = (0, 0)$. (See Fig. 6.4.)

Considering the geometry of the problem, every point in R^2, or the plane, is mapped into the line $y = x$. Indeed consider the points

$$P : (x, y), \qquad Q : a(x, y) = \left(\frac{x + y}{2}, \frac{x + y}{2}\right)$$

and the origin 0: $(0, 0)$.

Note, now, that

$$d_1^2 = d(P, Q)^2 = \left(x - \frac{x + y}{2}\right)^2 + \left(y - \frac{x + y}{2}\right)^2$$

$$= 2\left(\frac{x}{2} - \frac{y}{2}\right)^2,$$

and that

$$d_2^2 = d(0, Q)^2 = \left(\frac{x + y}{2} - 0\right)^2 + \left(\frac{x + y}{2} - 0\right)^2$$

$$= 2\left(\frac{x}{2} + \frac{y}{2}\right)^2,$$

whereas

$$d_3^2 = d(0, P)^2 = x^2 + y^2.$$

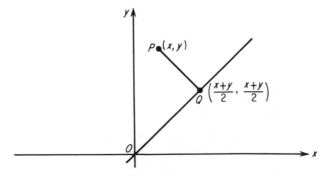

Figure 6.4

A simple computation gives us that

$$d_1^2 + d_2^2 = 2\left(\frac{x-y}{2}\right)^2 + 2\left(\frac{x+y}{2}\right)^2$$

$$= \frac{2}{4}(x^2 - 2xy + y^2) + \frac{2}{4}(x^2 + 2xy + y^2)$$

$$= \frac{1}{2}(2x^2 + 2y^2) = x^2 + y^2$$

$$= d_3^2.$$

Thus we have that the angle PQO is a right angle and that to find $a(x, y)$ geometrically, we simply draw a perpendicular from (x, y) to the line $y = x$. The point, Q, where our line meets $y = x$ is $a(x, y)$.

Now if we consider an arbitrary 2×2 matrix,

$$A = \begin{pmatrix} a_{11} & a_{12} \\ a_{21} & a_{22} \end{pmatrix},$$

we cannot expect to characterize the function $a : R^2 \to R^2$ defined by

$$a(x, y) = (x \; y) \cdot A$$

for $(x, y) \in R^2$ so completely. We can, however, discover certain things about such functions. One obvious remark is that, for any matrix A,

$$a(0, 0) = (0, 0).$$

Another remark is this. Suppose that (x_1, y_1) and (x_2, y_2) are two points (or vectors in R^2). Then

(1) $$a((x_1, y_1) + (x_2, y_2)) = a(x_1, y_1) + a(x_2, y_2).$$

To see this, consider

$$a((x_1, y_1) + (x_2, y_2)) = ((x_1 y_1) + (x_2 y_2))A$$
$$(*)$$
$$= (x_1 y_1)A + (x_2 y_2)A = a(x_1, y_1) + a(x_2, y_2).$$

(The equality (*) is simply the distributive law for multiplication of matrices over addition of matrices.) Finally we notice that, for any $k \in R^1$,

(2) $$a(k(x, y)) = ka(x, y).$$

This is seen from the following:

$$a(k(x, y)) = a(kx, ky) = (kx \; ky)A$$
$$= (k(x \; y))A = k((x \; y)A)$$
$$= ka(x, y).$$

The two results listed previously can be stated as a single property, namely,

(3) $a(k(x_1, y_1) + m(x_2, y_2)) = ka(x_1, y_1) + ma(x_2, y_2)$

for (x_1, y_1), $(x_2, y_2) \in R^2$ and $k, m \in R^1$.

Now there is nothing in the above development that cannot be extended to 3×3 matrices, which induce functions from R^3 into R^3, or to $n \times n$ matrices, which induce functions from R^n into R^n.

Even more generally, consider the $m \times n$ matrix

$$A = \begin{pmatrix} a_{11} & a_{12} & \cdots & a_{1n} \\ a_{21} & a_{22} & \cdots & a_{2n} \\ \cdots\cdots\cdots\cdots\cdots\cdots \\ a_{m1} & a_{m2} & \cdots & a_{mn} \end{pmatrix}.$$

Let $a : R^m \to R^n$ be defined by

$$a(x_1, x_2, \ldots, x_m) = (x_1 x_2 \ldots x_m) \cdot A.$$

for $(x_1, x_2, \ldots, x_m) \in R^m$. To be a bit more specific,

$$a(x_1, x_2, \ldots, x_m) = (u_1, u_2, \ldots, u_n),$$

where

$$u_i = \sum_{j=1}^{m} x_j a_{ji}, 1 \leq i \leq n.$$

This function has all of the properties listed above for the 2×2 case.

Exercise 6.11

1. Let $A = \begin{pmatrix} 0 & 1 \\ 1 & 0 \end{pmatrix}$ and consider the function induced as above by A on R^2.

   (a) Show that this function has property (3).

   (b) Show the geometric interpretation of this function.

2. Let

$$A = \begin{pmatrix} 1 & 0 & 0 \\ 0 & 0 & 0 \\ 0 & 0 & 0 \end{pmatrix}$$

   and consider the function induced on R^3 by A.

   (a) Show that this function has property (3).

   (b) Show the geometric interpretation of this function.

3. Give the geometric interpretation for the functions induced by the following matrices:

(a) $\begin{pmatrix} 0 & 0 \\ 0 & 1 \end{pmatrix}$.

(b) $\begin{pmatrix} -1 & 0 \\ 0 & -1 \end{pmatrix}$.

(c) $\begin{pmatrix} 2 & 0 \\ 0 & 2 \end{pmatrix}$.

(d) $\begin{pmatrix} \cos 30° & \sin 30° \\ -\sin 30° & \cos 30° \end{pmatrix}$.

(e) $\begin{pmatrix} \cos \alpha & \sin \alpha \\ -\sin \alpha & \cos \alpha \end{pmatrix}$.

6.9   Linear Transformations on R²

Definition 6.5. Suppose W is any vector space. A function $a : W \to W$ satisfying the condition,

$$(4) \qquad\qquad a(ru + sv) = ra(u) + sa(v)$$

for $u, v \in W$ and $r, s \in R^1$, is called a *linear transformation* on W.

As we have seen, the functions induced on R^2 by 2×2 matrices are linear transformations (and the functions induced on R^n by $n \times n$ matrices are linear transformations) on vector spaces. In what follows, we restrict ourselves to dealing with the vector space R^2.

We would like to ask whether, given a linear transformation a on R^2, there is a matrix $B(2 \times 2)$ so that a is the function induced by B. To help us solve this problem, we make the following observations. If $(x, y) \in R^2$, $(x, y) = x(1, 0) + y(0, 1)$. Moreover, this is a unique representation of x and y in terms of $(1, 0)$ and $(0, 1)$. Because

$$a(x, y) = x \cdot a(1, 0) + y \cdot a(0, 1)$$

(property 3) we see that, to know a linear transformation a, it is enough to know $a(1, 0)$ and $a(0, 1)$. For then we simply compute $x \cdot a(1, 0) + y \cdot a(0, 1)$. For example, if $a(1, 0) = (\frac{1}{2}, \frac{1}{2})$ and $a(0, 1) = (-1, 0)$, $a(2, 3) = 2(\frac{1}{2}, \frac{1}{2}) + 3(-1, 0) = (-2, 1)$ and $a(4, 7) = 4(\frac{1}{2}, \frac{1}{2}) + 7(-1, 0) = (-5, 2)$.

Now let us consider a general case. Suppose that a is a linear transformation on R^2 and suppose that

$$a(1, 0) = (a_{11}, a_{12}) \quad \text{and that} \quad a(0, 1) = (a_{21}, a_{22}).$$

Now

$$a(x, y) = xa(1, 0) + ya(0, 1)$$

$$= x(a_{11}, a_{12}) + y(a_{21}, a_{22})$$

$$= (xa_{11} + ya_{21}, xa_{12} + ya_{22}).$$

On the other hand, consider the matrix

$$B = \begin{pmatrix} a_{11} & a_{12} \\ a_{21} & a_{22} \end{pmatrix}$$

and consider the linear transformation, b, induced by B. Then $b(x, y) = (x\ y)B = (xa_{11} + ya_{21},\ xa_{12} + ya_{22})$. But clearly the functions a and b are the same.

So the answer to our question of this section is that every linear transformation on R^2 can be induced by a matrix. For convenience, when a is a linear transformation, let us denote the matrix inducing a by $[a]$.

Let us take another look at the example of Sec. 6.8. We characterized our function a as the one that "projected" a point (x, y) onto the line $y = x$. Clearly $a(1, 0) = (\frac{1}{2}, \frac{1}{2})$ and $a(0, 1) = (\frac{1}{2}, \frac{1}{2})$.
But then

$$[a] = \begin{pmatrix} \frac{1}{2} & \frac{1}{2} \\ \frac{1}{2} & \frac{1}{2} \end{pmatrix}.$$

This of course agrees with the matrix A of our example.

As another example, consider the linear transformation p on R^3 that projects a point (x, y, z) onto the line $y = x$ in the xy plane (Fig. 6.5). We will assume that this is a linear transformation. Here the image, $p(x, y, z)$, of a point (x, y, z) is obtained by drawing the line through the point (x, y, z) perpendicular to the line $y = x$ in the xy plane and by determining the point, $p(x, y, z)$, of intersection of the two lines. We propose to find $p(-4, 2, -7)$ and $p(1, 1, 9)$. Realizing that (x, y, z) is expressible in unique fashion as

$$x(1, 0, 0) + y(0, 1, 0) + z(0, 0, 1),$$

we extend our technique in R^2 to finding $[p]$, the matrix inducing p.

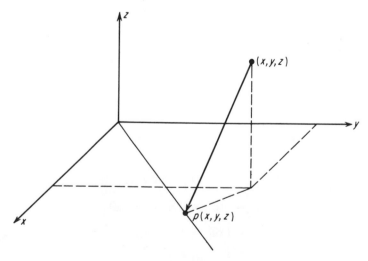

Figure 6.5

As earlier

$$[p] = \begin{pmatrix} \frac{1}{2} & \frac{1}{2} & 0 \\ \frac{1}{2} & \frac{1}{2} & 0 \\ 0 & 0 & 0 \end{pmatrix}$$

because

$$p(1, 0, 0) = (\tfrac{1}{2}, \tfrac{1}{2}, 0), \qquad p(0, 1, 0) = (\tfrac{1}{2}, \tfrac{1}{2}, 0)$$

and

$$p(0, 0, 1) = (0, 0, 0).$$

Then, in general,

$$p(x, y, z) = (xyz) \cdot [p]$$

and in particular,

$$p(-4, 2, 7) = (-4\ 2\ 7) \cdot \begin{pmatrix} \frac{1}{2} & \frac{1}{2} & 0 \\ \frac{1}{2} & \frac{1}{2} & 0 \\ 0 & 0 & 0 \end{pmatrix} = (-1, -1, 0)$$

and

$$p(1, 1, 9) = (1\ 1\ 9) \cdot \begin{pmatrix} \frac{1}{2} & \frac{1}{2} & 0 \\ \frac{1}{2} & \frac{1}{2} & 0 \\ 0 & 0 & 0 \end{pmatrix} = (1, 1, 0).$$

Exercise 6.12

Consider the following linear transformations, a, on R^2. Find $[a]$. Then find $a(2, 4)$, $a(-2, 3)$, and $a(7, -5)$.

(a) $a = $ the projection of (x, y) onto the line $y = 0$.

(b) $a = $ the projection of (x, y) onto the line $y = -x$.

(c) $a = $ the projection of (x, y) onto the line $y = 2x$.

(d) $a = $ the clockwise rotation about the origin of $45°$.

(e) $a = $ the stretching of a vector by a factor of $\frac{3}{2}$.

6.10 Products of Linear Transformations

Suppose that a and b are linear transformations on a vector space W. We define a new function c from W into W by

$$c(u) = a(b(u)) \quad \text{for all } u \in W.$$

Now notice that, when $u \in W$, then $b(u) = t \in W$ and $a(t) = a(b(u))$ makes sense and is, indeed, an element of W. We point out that c is also a linear transformation on W. To verify this, it is enough to show that c has property (3). This is,

$$c(ru + sv) = rc(u) + sc(v) \quad \text{for} \quad u, v \in W \quad \text{and} \quad r, s \in R^1.$$

Now

$$c(ru + sv) = a(b(ru + sv)).$$

Since b is a linear transformation,

$$b(ru + sv) = r \cdot b(u) + s \cdot b(v)$$

$$= ru_1 + sv_1 \, .$$

Then since a is a linear transformation

$$a(ru_1 + sv_1) = r \cdot a(u_1) + s \cdot a(v_1) \, .$$

But

$$ra(u_1) + s \cdot a(v_1) = r \cdot a(b(u)) + s \cdot a(b(v)) \, .$$

However,

$$a(b(u)) = c(u) \quad \text{and} \quad a(b(v)) = c(v) \, .$$

Hence,

$$c(ru + sv) = r \cdot c(u) = s \cdot c(v) \, .$$

In the case of $W = R^2$, we want to point out the relationship between $[c]$ and $[a]$ and $[b]$.

As a matter of common terminology, c is called the *product* of a and b and is frequently denoted $a \circ b$. Thus $[c]$ could be written $[a \circ b]$.

First we will agree that

$$a(1, 0) = (a_{11}, a_{12}), \quad a(0, 1) = (a_{21}, a_{22})$$

$$b(1, 0) = (b_{11}, b_{12}), \quad b(0, 1) = (b_{21}, b_{22})$$

and thus that

$$[a] = \begin{pmatrix} a_{11} & a_{12} \\ a_{21} & a_{22} \end{pmatrix} \quad \text{and} \quad [b] = \begin{pmatrix} b_{11} & b_{12} \\ b_{21} & b_{22} \end{pmatrix}.$$

Now we find $[c] = [a \circ b]$.

$$c(1, 0) = a(b(1, 0)) = a((b_{11}, b_{12})) \, ,$$

$$= a(b_{11}(1, 0) + b_{12}(0, 1)) \, ,$$

$$= b_{11} \cdot a(1, 0) + b_{12} \cdot a(0, 1) \, ,$$

$$= b_{11}(a_{11}, a_{12}) + b_{12}(a_{21}, a_{22}) \, ,$$

$$= (b_{11}a_{11} + b_{12}a_{21}, \; b_{11}a_{12} + b_{12}a_{22}) \, .$$

In the same fashion,

$$c(0, 1) = (b_{21}a_{11} + b_{22}a_{21}, \; b_{21}a_{12} + b_{22}a_{22}) \, .$$

So

$$[c] = \begin{pmatrix} b_{11}a_{11} + b_{12}a_{21} & b_{11}a_{12} + b_{12}a_{22} \\ b_{21}a_{11} + b_{22}a_{21} & b_{21}a_{12} + b_{22}a_{22} \end{pmatrix},$$

$$= [b] \cdot [a] \, .$$

This relationship is an important one and could be used as the reason why multiplication of matrices is defined as it is.

To illustrate this notion, consider the following two linear transformations in R^3. Let b be the projection of points onto the xy plane. Then

$$[b] = \begin{pmatrix} 1 & 0 & 0 \\ 0 & 1 & 0 \\ 0 & 0 & 0 \end{pmatrix}.$$

Let a be the projection of points onto the plane $x = y$. Then

$$[a] = \begin{pmatrix} \frac{1}{2} & \frac{1}{2} & 0 \\ \frac{1}{2} & \frac{1}{2} & 0 \\ 0 & 0 & 1 \end{pmatrix}.$$

Now if we consider the linear transformation $a \circ b$, we see that, for a point (x, y, z), $b(x, y, z)$ takes the point into a point $(x, y, 0)$ of the xy plane. Then $a(x, y, 0)$ is a point on the line $x = y$ in the xy plane. Thus $a \circ b$ is the linear transformation of the example in Sec. 6.9. Its matrix should be given by the product $[b] \cdot [a]$. Computing this product, we see that

$$[a \circ b] = \begin{pmatrix} \frac{1}{2} & \frac{1}{2} & 0 \\ \frac{1}{2} & \frac{1}{2} & 0 \\ 0 & 0 & 0 \end{pmatrix},$$

which is indeed the matrix of the example of Sec. 6.9.

Exercise 6.13

1. In R^3 consider the linear transformations:

$a = $ the projection of points into the yz plane,

$b = $ the projection of points into the xy plane .

 (a)   What is the transformation $a \circ b$?

 (b)   Find $[a]$, $[b]$, and $[a \circ b]$.

2. In R^2 consider the linear transformations:

$a = $ the reflection of points through $y = x$,

$b = $ stretching by a factor of 2.

 (a)   Find $[a]$ and $[b]$.

 (b)   Find $[a \circ b]$.

3. In R^2 consider the linear transformations:

$a = $ the reflection through $y = x$,

$b = $ the reflection through $(0, 0)$.

 (a)   Find $[a]$, $[b]$, and $[a \circ b]$.

 (b)   What is $[a \circ b]$?

6.11 Determinants

As we have indicated, given a system, S, of n linear equations in the n real variables, $x_1, x_2, \ldots, x_n$,

$$
\begin{aligned}
a_{11}x_1 + a_{12}x_2 + \ldots + a_{1n}x_n &= y_1 \\
a_{21}x_1 + a_{22}x_2 + \ldots + a_{2n}x_n &= y_2 \\
&\cdots\cdots\cdots\cdots\cdots\cdots\cdots \\
a_{n1}x_1 + a_{n2}x_2 + \ldots + a_{nn}x_n &= y_n ,
\end{aligned}
$$

(S)

we may consider (S) as a single matrix equation

(SM) $$AX = Y ,$$

where

$$
A = (a_{ij})_{n \times n}, \; X = \begin{pmatrix} x_1 \\ \vdots \\ x_n \end{pmatrix} \quad \text{and} \quad Y = \begin{pmatrix} y_1 \\ \vdots \\ y_n \end{pmatrix}.
$$

If the matrix A has an inverse A^{-1}, then there is a unique solution X_0 of (SM) (and therefore of (S)) given by

$$
x_0 = A^{-1}Y .
$$

It would profit us, then, to look at a technique for determining the inverse of a matrix. In what we shall do, we will not be extremely rigorous but will attempt to develop a tool for handling problems of this sort. This tool will not be, necessarily, the easiest computational tool available, but will work.

We first need the concept of the *determinant of a square matrix A*. We will denote this by det A. This is a rather complicated definition and we will treat it rather informally.

First det is a function from $M_{n \times n}$ into R^1. That is, it is a function that assigns to every square (real) matrix a real number. We proceed inductively. If A is a matrix with single entry, a, we define det A to be a. That is, $\det(a) = a$. Assume that, if A is an $(n-1) \times (n-1)$ matrix, we know how to find det A. Now let $A = (a_{ij})_{n \times n}$ be an $n \times n$ matrix. Let A_{i1} denote the matrix obtained from A by deleting the ith row and 1st column of A. Thus A_{11} would be the matrix* obtained by eliminating the first row and first column of $A \cdot A_{21}$ would be the matrix left after eliminating the second row and first column, A_{31} the third row and first column. Now all of these A_{i1} are $(n-1) \times (n-1)$ matrices and we have assumed that we can obtain the determinants of these.

---

* The matrix A_{i1} is called the $i1$ minor. In general, A_{ij}, the matrix obtained by deleting the ith row and jth column of a matrix is called the ij *minor*.

We define det $(a_{ij})_{n \times n}$ as follows:

$$\det A = a_{11} \det A_{11} - a_{21} \det A_{21} + \ldots + (-1)^{n+1} a_{n1} \det A_{n1}$$

$$= \sum_{k=1}^{n} (-1)^{k+1} a_{k1} \det A_{k1} .$$

Now this is not as formidable as it sounds. For example, if

$$\begin{pmatrix} a_{11} & a_{12} \\ a_{21} & a_{22} \end{pmatrix} \text{ is a } 2 \times 2 \text{ matrix },$$

$$\det \begin{pmatrix} a_{11} & a_{12} \\ a_{21} & a_{22} \end{pmatrix} = a_{11} \det A_{11} - a_{21} \det A_{21} .$$

But

$$\det A_{11} = a_{22} \quad \text{and} \quad \det A_{21} = a_{12} .$$

Thus

$$\det \begin{pmatrix} a_{11} & a_{12} \\ a_{21} & a_{22} \end{pmatrix} = a_{11} a_{22} - a_{21} a_{12} .$$

For future convenience we will simply deal with 2×2 determinants with this formula. So

$$\det \begin{pmatrix} a & b \\ c & d \end{pmatrix} = ad - bc .$$

EXAMPLES

$$\det \begin{pmatrix} 1 & 1 \\ 2 & 1 \end{pmatrix} = 1 \cdot 1 - 1 \cdot 2 = -1$$

$$\det \begin{pmatrix} 1 & 0 \\ 1 & 1 \end{pmatrix} = 1 \cdot 1 - 1 \cdot 0 = 1$$

$$\det \begin{pmatrix} 3 & x \\ 4 & \pi \end{pmatrix} = 3\pi - 4x .$$

Another notation commonly used for det A is $|A|$. Except for 1×1 matrices, this leads to no confusion and we will use it freely.

Consider now

$$\begin{vmatrix} a_{11} & a_{12} & a_{13} \\ a_{21} & a_{22} & a_{23} \\ a_{31} & a_{32} & a_{33} \end{vmatrix} = \det A .$$

From our definition,

$$\det A = a_{11} \cdot \begin{vmatrix} a_{22} & a_{23} \\ a_{32} & a_{33} \end{vmatrix} - a_{21} \cdot \begin{vmatrix} a_{12} & a_{13} \\ a_{32} & a_{33} \end{vmatrix} + a_{31} \cdot \begin{vmatrix} a_{12} & a_{13} \\ a_{22} & a_{23} \end{vmatrix} .$$

As an example, consider $\det\begin{pmatrix} 1 & 1 & 1 \\ 1 & 0 & 1 \\ 1 & 1 & 0 \end{pmatrix}$.

$$\det\begin{pmatrix} 1 & 1 & 1 \\ 1 & 0 & 1 \\ 1 & 1 & 0 \end{pmatrix} = 1\cdot\begin{vmatrix} 0 & 1 \\ 1 & 0 \end{vmatrix} - 1\cdot\begin{vmatrix} 1 & 1 \\ 1 & 0 \end{vmatrix} + 1\cdot\begin{vmatrix} 1 & 1 \\ 0 & 1 \end{vmatrix}$$

$$= 1\cdot(-1) - 1(-1) + 1\cdot(1) = 1 \ .$$

Also by way of example,

$$\begin{vmatrix} 3 & 1 & 0 \\ 7 & 0 & 1 \\ 0 & 1 & 0 \end{vmatrix} = 3\cdot\begin{vmatrix} 0 & 1 \\ 1 & 0 \end{vmatrix} - 7\cdot\begin{vmatrix} 1 & 0 \\ 1 & 0 \end{vmatrix} + 0\cdot\begin{vmatrix} 1 & 0 \\ 0 & 1 \end{vmatrix}$$

$$= 3\cdot(-1) - 7\cdot(0) + 0\cdot(1) = -3 \ .$$

One more example of a larger determinant is this:

$$\begin{vmatrix} 1 & 1 & 1 & 1 & 0 \\ 1 & 0 & 2 & 2 & 0 \\ 0 & 0 & 0 & 1 & 0 \\ 1 & 0 & 0 & 1 & 1 \\ 0 & 0 & 0 & 1 & 1 \end{vmatrix} = 1\cdot\begin{vmatrix} 0 & 2 & 2 & 0 \\ 0 & 0 & 1 & 0 \\ 0 & 0 & 1 & 1 \\ 0 & 0 & 1 & 1 \end{vmatrix} - 1\cdot\begin{vmatrix} 1 & 1 & 1 & 0 \\ 0 & 0 & 1 & 0 \\ 0 & 0 & 1 & 1 \\ 0 & 0 & 1 & 1 \end{vmatrix} + 0\cdot\begin{vmatrix} 1 & 1 & 1 & 0 \\ 0 & 2 & 2 & 0 \\ 0 & 0 & 1 & 1 \\ 0 & 0 & 1 & 1 \end{vmatrix}$$

$$- 1\cdot\begin{vmatrix} 1 & 1 & 1 & 0 \\ 0 & 2 & 2 & 0 \\ 0 & 0 & 1 & 0 \\ 0 & 0 & 1 & 1 \end{vmatrix} + 0\cdot\begin{vmatrix} 1 & 1 & 1 & 0 \\ 0 & 2 & 2 & 0 \\ 0 & 0 & 1 & 0 \\ 0 & 0 & 1 & 1 \end{vmatrix} \ .$$

Now each of the terms of this sum involves 4×4 determinants which can be expressed in terms of 3×3 determinants which we can evaluate.

Exercise

Evaluate the above 4×4 determinants completely.

There are a number of remarks that we can make but will not prove here. These remarks are helpful in evaluating determinants.

Remarks.
(1) The definition we gave of det A involved the first column. We could have used any other column or any row in the same fashion to obtain det A. (Thus, we could expand our determinant, using the column or row with the most zeroes.)

(2) If any row or column contains only zeroes, the determinant is zero. (Simply expand using this row or column.)

(3) Exchanging two adjacent rows or two adjacent columns of a determinant merely changes the sign of the determinant.

(4) Replacing a row (or column) by that row (column), added position by position to a constant multiple of any other row (column), does not change the value of the determinant.

(5) Multiplying a column (row) by a constant is the same as multiplying the value of the determinant by that constant.

(6) If two columns (rows) are the same, the value of the determinant is zero. (Replace one of them by the column added to -1 times the other.)

Exercise 6.14

1. Evaluate:

(a) $\begin{vmatrix} 1 & 1 \\ 1 & 1 \end{vmatrix}$
(b) $\begin{vmatrix} 4 & 6 \\ 1 & 2 \end{vmatrix}$
(c) $\begin{vmatrix} 5 & 6 \\ 0 & 0 \end{vmatrix}$

(d) $\begin{vmatrix} 1 & 1 & 1 \\ 1 & 1 & 1 \\ 0 & 1 & 1 \end{vmatrix}$
(e) $\begin{vmatrix} 2 & 6 & 7 \\ 0 & 1 & 3 \\ 0 & 0 & 1 \end{vmatrix}$
(f) $\begin{vmatrix} 1 & 0 & 0 \\ 0 & 1 & 0 \\ 0 & 0 & 1 \end{vmatrix}$

(g) $\begin{vmatrix} 1 & 0 & 0 & 1 \\ 1 & 1 & 1 & 1 \\ 0 & 1 & 1 & 1 \\ 0 & 0 & 1 & 1 \end{vmatrix}$
(h) $\begin{vmatrix} 1 & 2 & 3 & 1 \\ -1 & 2 & 1 & 1 \\ 0 & 1 & 1 & 0 \\ 1 & 0 & 0 & 1 \end{vmatrix}$.

2. Add the first column of (b) to the second and replace the second column by this sum to obtain

$$\begin{vmatrix} 4 & 10 \\ 1 & 3 \end{vmatrix}.$$

Evaluate and see that these are the same.

3. (a) Expand (h) using the last row.

(b) Get zeroes in (h) in the 2, 1 and 4, 1 positions by replacing the second row with the sum of the first and second rows and by replacing the fourth row with the difference of the fourth and first rows. Evaluate the resulting determinant.

6.12 Inverses of Matrices

Let $A = (a_{ij})_{n \times n}$ be a given square matrix so that $\det A \neq 0$. As in the expansion of determinants, let A_{ij} denote the matrix obtained by deleting the ith row and jth column of A. We call the number $(-1)^{i+j} | A_{ij} |$ the *cofactor of a_{ij}.* For convenience let us denote the cofactor of a_{ij} by a_{ij}^1. Then consider the matrix adj A, called *the adjoint of A,* defined by

$$\text{adj } A = (c_{ij}),$$

where $c_{ij} = a_{ji}^1$.

Thus, the adjoint of A is obtained by placing in the i,j position the cofactor of the element of A in the j,i position.

We recall that, if we have a real number k and any matrix (b_{ij}), the product $k \cdot (b_{ij})$ gives the matrix with every entry in (b_{ij}) multiplied by the number k. That is

$$k \cdot (b_{ij}) = (k \cdot b_{ij}).$$

We state, now, a useful theorem. We feel that the proof for this theorem would be a bit out of place in this text but it provides a useful tool. Hence we include only the statement.

Theorem 6.5. Let A be an $n \times n$ matrix with det $A \neq 0$. Then

$$A^{-1} = \frac{1}{\det A} \cdot \text{adj } A .$$

This theorem gives us a technique for computing the inverse of a matrix. It says that we need only compute the adjoint of A and divide each element of adj A by the determinant of A.

EXAMPLE. Let

$$A = \begin{pmatrix} 1 & 1 & 1 \\ 0 & 1 & 1 \\ 0 & 0 & 1 \end{pmatrix}.$$

In tabular form we find the adjoint of A.

$$a_{11} = 1 \qquad |A_{11}| = \begin{vmatrix} 1 & 1 \\ 0 & 1 \end{vmatrix} = 1 \qquad a_{11}^1 = 1$$

$$a_{12} = 1 \qquad |A_{12}| = \begin{vmatrix} 0 & 1 \\ 0 & 1 \end{vmatrix} = 0 \qquad a_{12}^1 = 0$$

$$a_{13} = 1 \qquad |A_{13}| = \begin{vmatrix} 0 & 1 \\ 0 & 0 \end{vmatrix} = 0 \qquad a_{13}^1 = 0$$

$$a_{21} = 0 \qquad |A_{21}| = \begin{vmatrix} 1 & 1 \\ 0 & 1 \end{vmatrix} = 1 \qquad a_{21}^1 = -1$$

$$a_{22} = 1 \qquad |A_{22}| = \begin{vmatrix} 1 & 1 \\ 0 & 1 \end{vmatrix} = 1 \qquad a_{22}^1 = 1$$

$$a_{23} = 1 \qquad |A_{23}| = \begin{vmatrix} 1 & 1 \\ 0 & 0 \end{vmatrix} = 0 \qquad a_{23}^1 = 0$$

$$a_{31} = 0 \qquad |A_{31}| = \begin{vmatrix} 1 & 1 \\ 1 & 1 \end{vmatrix} = 0 \qquad a_{31}^1 = 0$$

$$a_{32} = 0 \qquad |A_{32}| = \begin{vmatrix} 1 & 1 \\ 0 & 1 \end{vmatrix} = 1 \qquad a_{32}^1 = -1$$

$$a_{33} = 1 \qquad |A_{33}| = \begin{vmatrix} 1 & 1 \\ 0 & 1 \end{vmatrix} = 1 \qquad a_{33}^1 = 1 \, .$$

Now adj $A = (a_{ji}^1)$. So

$$\text{adj } A = \begin{pmatrix} 1 & -1 & 0 \\ 0 & 1 & -1 \\ 0 & 0 & 1 \end{pmatrix}.$$

Now det $A = 1$. So $A^{-1} = \text{adj } A$.

If we check by computation, we get

$$\begin{pmatrix} 1 & 1 & 1 \\ 0 & 1 & 1 \\ 0 & 0 & 1 \end{pmatrix} \cdot \begin{pmatrix} 1 & -1 & 0 \\ 0 & 1 & -1 \\ 0 & 0 & 1 \end{pmatrix} = \begin{pmatrix} 1 & 0 & 0 \\ 0 & 1 & 0 \\ 0 & 0 & 1 \end{pmatrix}.$$

Consider now the system of equations

$$1 \cdot w + 2x + 0 \cdot y + 1 \cdot z = 2$$
$$0 \cdot w + 1 \cdot x + 2 \cdot y + 0 \cdot z = 1$$
$$0 \cdot w + 0 \cdot x + 1 \cdot y + 1 \cdot z = 0$$
$$1 \cdot w + 1 \cdot x + 1 \cdot y + 1 \cdot z = 2 \, .$$

This system is, of course, equivalent to the matrix equation

$$\begin{pmatrix} 1 & 2 & 0 & 1 \\ 0 & 1 & 2 & 0 \\ 0 & 0 & 1 & 1 \\ 1 & 1 & 1 & 1 \end{pmatrix} \cdot \begin{pmatrix} w \\ x \\ y \\ z \end{pmatrix} = \begin{pmatrix} 2 \\ 1 \\ 0 \\ 2 \end{pmatrix}.$$

Let A denote the matrix on the left. If A has an inverse, we can solve our system in matrix form simply by computing

$$A^{-1} \cdot \begin{pmatrix} 2 \\ 1 \\ 0 \\ 2 \end{pmatrix}.$$

Computing det A we get det $A = -3$.

Without showing the computation, we also point out that

$$\text{adj } A = \begin{pmatrix} 2 & 1 & 3 & -5 \\ -2 & -1 & 0 & 2 \\ 1 & -1 & 0 & -1 \\ -1 & 1 & -3 & 1 \end{pmatrix}.$$

So we have A^{-1} computed and, as indicated, the solution to our system of equations is given in matrix form by

$$-\tfrac{1}{3} \cdot \begin{pmatrix} 2 & 1 & 3 & -5 \\ -2 & -1 & 0 & 2 \\ 1 & -1 & 0 & -1 \\ -1 & 1 & -3 & 1 \end{pmatrix} \cdot \begin{pmatrix} 2 \\ 1 \\ 0 \\ 2 \end{pmatrix} = \begin{pmatrix} \tfrac{5}{3} \\ \tfrac{1}{3} \\ \tfrac{1}{3} \\ -\tfrac{1}{3} \end{pmatrix}.$$

We remark, without proof, that, if a matrix A has an inverse, the solution to a system of linear equations which has A as coefficient matrix is unique.

We also remark that a matrix has an inverse if and only if det $A \neq 0$.

As we noted before, this technique for solving systems of linear equations is not necessarily the best computational technique. It is one that will work for n equations in n unknowns, no matter how large n, provided that the coefficient matrix has non-zero determinant.

Exercise 6.15

1. Find the inverses of the following matrices (if they exist.)

(a) $\begin{pmatrix} 1 & 1 \\ 0 & 1 \end{pmatrix}.$

(b) $\begin{pmatrix} 1 & 2 \\ 1 & -1 \end{pmatrix}.$

(c) $\begin{pmatrix} 1 & 1 & 0 \\ 0 & 1 & 1 \\ 1 & 0 & 1 \end{pmatrix}.$

(d) $\begin{pmatrix} 1 & 1 & 0 & 0 \\ 0 & 1 & 1 & 0 \\ 0 & 0 & 1 & 1 \\ 1 & 0 & 0 & 1 \end{pmatrix}.$

(e) $\begin{pmatrix} 1 & 1 & 1 & 1 \\ 0 & 1 & 1 & 1 \\ 0 & 0 & 1 & 1 \\ 0 & 0 & 0 & 1 \end{pmatrix}.$

2. By using the matrix technique of this section, find the solutions for the following systems of equations.

(a) $x + y = 2$
     $x - y = 1.$

(b) $x + y = 2$
     $x + y + z = 1$
     $x - y - z = 0.$

(c) $x + y + z = 1$
     $y + z = 1$
     $z = 1.$

(d) $x + y + z + w = 0$
     $y + z + w = 2$
     $y - z + w = 1$
     $x + y - z - w = 0.$

Trigonometry

Comment. We have considered functions rather extensively thus far. We have treated special properties of functions, such as "one-to-oneness" and "onto-ness," but we have not treated in real depth any particular type of function. In this section, we turn our attention to a class of functions called the *trigonometric functions*. These are the functions traditionally assigning real numbers to angles. They are useful in treating problems in surveying or navigation or geometry. Unfortunately, they have uses in areas not depending on geometric considerations and if we approach our study of these functions in the most intuitive way, we lose some of their power. We deal with them, then, in a way that is general, but we shall point out some of the obvious special applications.

7

7.1 Arc Length and Angles

Consider a plane on which a Cartesian coordinate system has been introduced and consider the point P with coordinates $(1, 0)$. If we treat the origin O as a center of revolution and consider the line segment OP as a rigid bar, on rotating this system, say counterclockwise, about O, the point P traces out a circular arc. In fact, if we stop the rotation at any time, the point P will lie on a point P_1 on the circle with equation $x^2 + y^2 = 1$. From elementary geometry, we can say that if we stop the rotation after one complete revolution (P is back to its original position), the length of the path traveled by P is 2π units. (2π is the circumference of the circle with radius 1.) On the other hand, if we rotate until the path traveled by P has length 2π, we can conclude that P is back to its initial position. Now there is a fine point here concerning the length of the path that we are avoiding. Although we have not defined *length* of a path, we assume that it is defined and will use the notion as if it had been defined.

We would note that, by specifying the length of the path to be generated by our point, P, we, in a sense, prescribe the rotation to take place. To prescribe completely the rotation to take place, we need further specify only its direction (clockwise, counterclockwise). Thus, for example, if one were told to rotate clockwise until our point P traced a path 3π units in length, one could do so (again assuming the ability to measure arc length).

To make things simpler, we agree to denote the length of the circular arc traced by our point P in a counterclockwise rotation by a positive number, and to denote this arc length by a negative number, if the rotation is clockwise.

So, to describe a rotation of our point P we need only to give a real number. The sign of the number denotes the direction of rotation; the absolute value of the number tells us the length of the arc to be traced. We note that any real number whatsoever may be considered as determining a rotation of this sort. It is also true that any rotation of this sort determines a unique real number — the arc length. We now make the following definition.

Definition 7.1. An *angle in standard position* consists of a rotation of the type just described, the positive x axis, the half line from O through the point P_1, and the origin. If s is the real number describing the rotation, we will call the angle an *angle of s radians*. The x axis is called the *initial side* of our angle, the half line OP_1 (Fig. 7.1) is called the *terminal side* of our angle and the origin O is called the *vertex* of the angle.

In general, we can speak simply of an angle. When this occurs we must have two half lines with the same end points, a specification of one of the lines as an initial side and a rotation given. If only the magnitude of the rotation is known, one can arbitrarily choose the initial side. If we are given

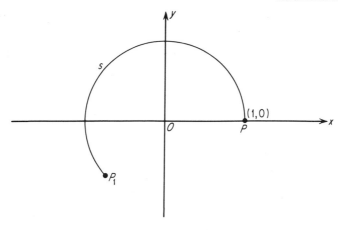

Figure 7.1

an angle, we can specify an initial side and can introduce a coordinate system making this side our positive x axis and thus treat the angle as if it were an angle in standard position.

To clarify one point, suppose α is an angle of θ radians in standard position. Then the length of the arc PP_1 (Fig. 7.2) is θ units. If Q is any point on the positive x axis at a distance r from 0, $r > 0$, and the rotation takes Q onto Q_1, a point on the half line OP_1, then, from geometry, we have that the arc length, s, of the arc QQ_1, the distance, r, and θ satisfy

$$\frac{\theta}{1} = \frac{s}{r} \quad \text{or} \quad \theta = \frac{s}{r} \cdot$$

Thus, to specify the rotation in radians, it is enough to give the quotient s/r, where r is the distance from the vertex of an angle to a point Q on the initial side of the angle and s is the length of the path traced by Q during the rotation.

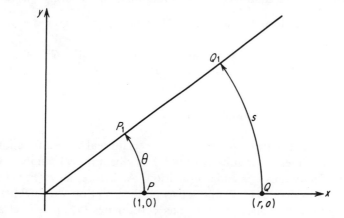

Figure 7.2

Exercise 7.1

1. Draw an angle of 2π radians, π radians, $\dfrac{-\pi}{2}$ radians, 1 radian.

2. Draw an angle of 3π radians, $\dfrac{\pi}{180}$ radians, $\dfrac{-\pi}{3}$ radians, $\dfrac{-\pi}{4}$ radians.

7.2 Degrees and Radians

The reader may not have encountered the concept of radian before this time. The more common measure of angles is in terms of degrees. In terms of Sec. 7.1, the rotation bringing P onto itself is usually referred to as a rotation of 360 degrees or 360°. If the rotation is clockwise, we would have an angle of $-360°$. To reconcile these two systems of measuring angles, we note that 360° and 2π radians are equivalent. Thus 1° and $\pi/180$ radians are equivalent. Hence $k°$ and $k \cdot \pi/180$ radians are equivalent. Concretely, 60° and $60 \cdot \pi/180$ radians or $\pi/3$ radians are equivalent. Conversely, 1 radian and $360/2\pi = 180/\pi$ degrees are equivalent, or k radians and $k \cdot 180/\pi \cdot$ degrees are equivalent. Again, $\pi/4$ radians and $\pi/4 \cdot 180/\pi = 45$ degrees are equivalent.

So, in specifying the rotation, one can use either degrees or radians and we have a translation technique to go from one unit to the other.

Exercise 7.2

1. Give the "radian equivalent" of the following: 30°, 150°, 240°, 270°, 540°, $-45°$, $-180°$.

2. Give the "degree equivalent" of the following: 2 radians, -3.5 radians, $\dfrac{2\pi}{3}$ radians, $\dfrac{-5\pi}{4}$ radians, 9π radians, -231π radians, $\dfrac{\pi}{2}$ radians.

3. Construct a table giving the radian equivalent of 30°, 45°, 60°, 90°, 120°, 135°, 150°, 180°, 210°, 225°, 240°, 270°, 300°, 315°, 330°, 360°.

7.3 The Trigonometric Functions

We now want to turn our attention to certain real-valued functions whose domains are either R^1 or subsets of R^1. Let u be any real number. Consider an angle of u radians in standard position. As before, let P (Fig. 7.3) be the point with coordinates $(1, 0)$ and let P_1 be the point on which P lies after its rotation. We will suppose that P_1 has coordinates (x, y). It is clear that x and y are real numbers and, in fact, satisfy $0 \leq |x| \leq 1$, $0 \leq |y| \leq 1$.

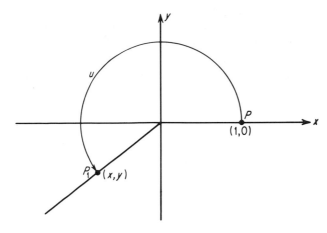

Figure 7.3

Moreover, since P_1 is on the circle with center at the origin and with radius 1, $x^2 + y^2 = 1$.

We define, now, six functions in terms of these numbers x and y. Remember that we are assigning to the number u a real number. The first two functions, s and c, are defined by $s(u) = y$ and $c(u) = x$ for all real numbers u. Now we can make certain observations concerning these functions. Since both x and y are less than 1 in absolute value, we have that $-1 \leq s(u) \leq 1$ and $-1 \leq c(u) \leq 1$, for all real numbers u. This means that the ranges, $R(s)$ and $R(c)$, of s and c are subsets of $[-1, 1]$. On the other hand, if y_0 is any real number in $[-1, 1]$, there exists a point (x, y_0) (in fact, two points) on our unit circle with y coordinate y_0. Thus there exists an angle of u_0

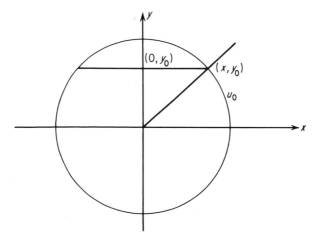

Figure 7.4

(Fig. 7.4) radians so that $s(u_0) = y_0$. Thus, $y_0 \in [-1, 1] \Rightarrow y_0 \in R(s)$. So $[-1, 1] = R(s)$. In a similar fashion, we can show that $R(c) = [-1, 1]$.

Traditionally, given $u \in R^1$, the number $s(u)$ is called the *sine* of u and $c(u)$ is called the *cosine* of u. Further, instead of writing $s(u)$, we write sin u, and, instead of writing $c(u)$, we write cos u. As examples, let $u = \pi/2$. Then the point P_1 has coordinates $(0, 1)$ and we have that $\sin \pi/2 = 1, \cos \pi/2 = 0$. As a further example, let $u = 3\pi/4$. Then, P_1 (Fig. 7.5) has coordinates $(-1/\sqrt{2}, 1/\sqrt{2})$ and $\sin 3\pi/4 = 1/\sqrt{2}$, whereas $\cos 3\pi/4 = -1/\sqrt{2}$.

Before we proceed further, one observation is in order. Recall that, given u, we find our point P_1 with coordinates (x, y). These coordinates satisfy the condition that $x^2 + y^2 = 1$. From the definition of sin u and cos u, we can rewrite this condition as

(J1) $$\sin^2 u + \cos^2 u = 1, \quad \text{for any real number } u.$$

($\sin^2 u$ means $(\sin u)^2$ and $\cos^2 u$ means $(\cos u)^2$).

Because this holds for every real number u, we call this relation an *identity*. It gives us a way of relating these two distinct functions. More will be done with this later, but now we look at other trigonometric functions.

We shall introduce these in their usual notation. The next function we want to consider is the tangent function. Again, given $u \in R^1$, find our point P_1 on the unit circle as before. We define the tangent of u, denoted tan u, by

$$\tan u = \frac{y}{x}; \quad x \neq 0, \quad u \in R^1.$$

This function is *not* defined for those real numbers u which determine points $P_1 : (x, y)$, where $x = 0$. Explicitly, this means that, for those numbers u which are odd integral multiples of $\pi/2$, tan u is not defined. Thus,

$$\left\{ u \mid u = k \cdot \frac{\pi}{2}, k = \pm 1, \pm 3, \pm 5, \ldots \right\}$$

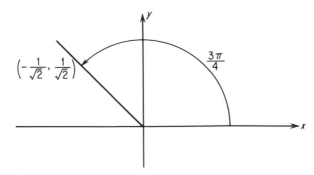

Figure 7.5

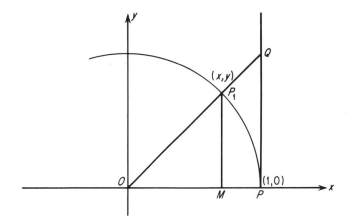

Figure 7.6

is excluded from the domain of the tangent function. All other real numbers are in the domain of this function.

Briefly we turn to the range, $R(\tan)$, of the tangent function. First note that $\tan 0 = 0$. Now let z be any positive real number. In our Cartesian coordinate plane, construct a line segment perpendicular to the x axis at P (Fig. 7.6) above the x axis of length z. Let Q denote the end of this line segment and draw the line OQ. Let P_1 with coordinates (x, y) denote the intersection of this line with our unit circle. Draw the perpendicular P_1M to the x axis. Now the length of P_1M is y and of OM is x. But, $y/x = z/1$ from the similarity of the triangles involved. So, if we choose u so that P_1 is on the terminal side of the angle of u radians in standard position, we have that

$$\tan u = \frac{y}{x} = z \, .$$

This means that every positive real number is in the range of the tangent function. We noted that O is in the range of the function. To show that every negative number is also in the range of this function, proceed as in Fig. 7.6 but draw QP below the x axis. Everything will be the same except that the ratio y/x will be negative. We can conclude, then, that $R^1 = R(\tan)$.

One other observation is in order. From the definitions of the functions involved we have that

(J2) $$\tan u = \frac{\sin u}{\cos u}$$

provided that $\cos u \neq 0$. Again this is referred to as an *identity*. It is *not* a valid relation for all real numbers but only for those real numbers u, where $\cos u$ is not zero. In general, when we speak of an identity, we mean that it is a true statement only when all the functions involved are defined. We automatically exclude from consideration those numbers for which any function is not defined.

We now define the other three trigonometric functions we mentioned earlier. Of course many other functions could be introduced, but the six we present are the ones considered basic. Assume, as before, that the number u has been given, that an angle of u radians has been constructed in standard position and that the point $P_1 : (x, y)$ has been found. We define

$$\cot u = \frac{x}{y} \quad \text{(cotangent of } u\text{)}$$

$$\sec u = \frac{1}{x} \quad \text{(secant of } u\text{)}$$

$$\csc u = \frac{1}{y} \quad \text{(cosecant of } u\text{)}$$

Exercise

Discuss the domains and ranges of these functions.

We note several identities that come directly from these definitions. They are

(J3) $$\cot u = \frac{1}{\tan u}.$$

(J4) $$\sec u = \frac{1}{\cos u}.$$

(J5) $$\csc u = \frac{1}{\sin u}.$$

(Remember these hold only when the functions involved are defined.)

Other identities come fairly directly from our definitions of these functions. For example, from the relation,

$$x^2 + y^2 = 1,$$

satisfied by the coordinates of our point P_1, we see that

$$1 + \frac{y^2}{x^2} = \frac{1}{x^2},$$

when $x \neq 0$. Thus,

(J6) $$1 + \tan^2 u = \sec^2 u.$$

Exercise

Develop the identity

(J7) $1 + \cot^2 u = \csc^2 u$.

For convenience, we list here the several identities that come immediately from the definitions of our six functions. [For any of these functions, for example, tan, we write $\tan^n u$ for $(\tan u)^n$. Clearly we do this to avoid the use of the parentheses. If we mean $\tan (u^n)$ we will write simply $\tan u^n$.]

(1) $\sin u \csc u = 1$

(2) $\cos u \sec u = 1$

(3) $\tan u \cot u = 1$

(4) $\sin^2 u + \cos^2 u = 1$

(5) $1 + \tan^2 u = \sec^2 u$

(6) $1 + \cot^2 u = \csc^2 u$.

7.4   Special Angles

To firm up our notion of these functions, we should look at the functional values for some real numbers. We note first that, if one were asked to give the number sin 231.96, one would be hard-pressed to reply. Fortunately, people have constructed tables that allow us to give an approximate value for this number.

Certain numbers (or angles) are reasonably easy to deal with by simple geometric means. For the sake of examples and because the reader may be expected to know these numbers in other courses, we look at a few of these.

First, observe that, if one were asked to find $\csc \pi/3$, $\pi/3$ would be taken as the measure of an angle in radians. We will agree to allow the angle to be represented in degrees as well as radians. Hence, because $\pi/3$ radians is equivalent to 60°, when faced with finding csc 60°, one understands he is to find the number paired with $\pi/3$, that is $\csc \pi/3$. Because many tables are constructed in terms of degrees, we will use degrees freely.

Let us first look at the values of our functions (Fig. 7.7) for the number 0 (0 radians or 0 degrees). In this case P_1 and P both have coordinates $(1, 0)$ and we can, in tabular form, indicate the values of our functions. (A dash in an entry indicates the function is not defined for that number.)

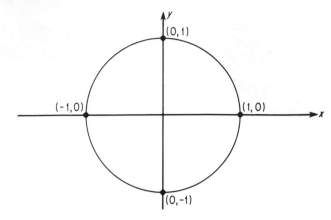

Figure 7.7

Table 7.1 has entries showing the functional values for 0, $\pi/2$, π, $3\pi/2$ for all six of our functions. These were obtained by considering the cases where P_1 had coordinates $(1, 0)$, $(0, 1)$, $(-1, 0)$, and $(0, -1)$. It is easy to obtain the functional values, once the coordinates of our point P_1 are known.

Other angles for which it is simple to obtain these functional values are 45°, 135°, 225°, and 315°. From elementary geometry, we have that, if an isosceles right triangle has a hypotenuse of length 1, the other sides have length $1/\sqrt{2}$ (or $\sqrt{2}/2$).

Placing our angles in standard position and considering the right triangles in heavy lines (Fig. 7.8,) it is easy to see that the points P_1 have the coordinates indicated. The signs of the numbers were adjusted according to the quadrant in which they fell. From Fig. 7.8, it is simple to complete a table for the functional values of the numbers $\pi/4$, $3\pi/4$, $5\pi/4$, $7\pi/4$. We will do this shortly.

Angles related to 30° and 60° also can be handled simply. For, again from elementary geometry, a right triangle with a 30° angle has the property that the hypotenuse has length twice that of the side opposite the 30° angle.

Table 7.1

Degrees	Radians	sin	cos	tan	cot	sec	csc
0°	0	0	1	0	—	1	—
90°	$\dfrac{\pi}{2}$	1	0	—	0	—	1
180°	π	0	−1	0	—	−1	—
270°	$\dfrac{3\pi}{2}$	−1	0	—	0	—	−1

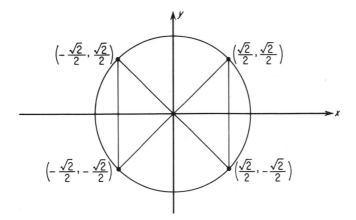

Figure 7.8

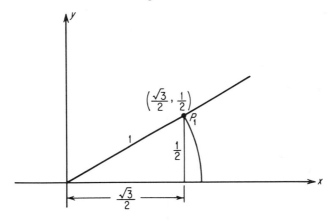

Figure 7.9

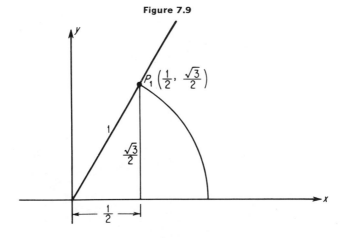

Figure 7.10

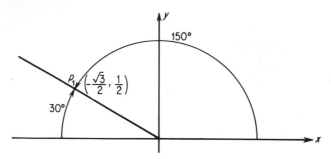

Figure 7.11

So, if the hypotenuse has length 1, one side has length $\frac{1}{2}$ and the other (from the Pythagorean theorem) has length

$$\sqrt{1^2 - \left(\frac{1}{2}\right)^2} = \sqrt{\frac{3}{4}} = \frac{\sqrt{3}}{2}.$$

So, with an angle of 30° in standard position, we see that our point P_1 (Fig. 7.9) has coordinates ($\sqrt{3}/2$, $\frac{1}{2}$). An angle of 60° just reverses the roles of the x and y coordinates (Fig. 7.10). It is not difficult to see that, using this information, we can label angles like 150° (Fig. 7.11).

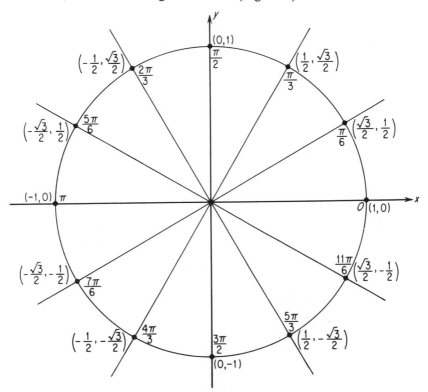

Figure 7.12

We summarize this with Fig. 7.12 which shows the coordinates of the point P_1 for various angles related to 30° or 60°.

From Fig. 7.11 and Fig. 7.12, incorporating Table 7.1, we give a short table of the values of some of the trigonometric functions (Table 7.2).

Table 7.2 *

Degrees	Radians	Sine	Cosine	Tangent
0	0	0	1	0
30	$\dfrac{\pi}{6}$	$\dfrac{1}{2}$	$\dfrac{\sqrt{3}}{2}$	$\dfrac{1}{\sqrt{3}}$
45	$\dfrac{\pi}{4}$	$\dfrac{1}{\sqrt{2}}$	—	1
60	$\dfrac{\pi}{3}$	—	$\dfrac{1}{2}$	$\sqrt{3}$
90	$\dfrac{\pi}{2}$	1	—	—
120	$\dfrac{2\pi}{3}$	$\dfrac{\sqrt{3}}{2}$	$-\dfrac{1}{2}$	—
135	$\dfrac{3\pi}{4}$	$\dfrac{1}{\sqrt{2}}$	$\dfrac{1}{\sqrt{2}}$	-1
150	$\dfrac{5\pi}{6}$	$\dfrac{1}{2}$	—	$-\dfrac{1}{\sqrt{3}}$
180	π	0	-1	0
210	$\dfrac{7\pi}{6}$	$-\dfrac{1}{2}$	$-\dfrac{\sqrt{3}}{2}$	$\dfrac{1}{\sqrt{3}}$
225	$\dfrac{5\pi}{4}$	—	$-\dfrac{1}{\sqrt{2}}$	1
240	$\dfrac{4\pi}{3}$	$-\dfrac{\sqrt{3}}{2}$	$-\dfrac{1}{2}$	$\sqrt{3}$
270	$\dfrac{3\pi}{2}$	-1	0	—
300	$\dfrac{5\pi}{3}$	$-\dfrac{\sqrt{3}}{2}$	$\dfrac{1}{2}$	$-\sqrt{3}$
315	$\dfrac{7\pi}{4}$	—	$\dfrac{1}{\sqrt{2}}$	—
330	$\dfrac{11\pi}{6}$	$-\dfrac{1}{2}$	$\dfrac{\sqrt{3}}{2}$	$-\dfrac{1}{\sqrt{3}}$
360	2π	0		0

* Some of the functional values have not been entered in the proper place. As an exercise, the reader should complete the table.

Now this table gives only the functional values for three of our functions. The fact that $\cot u = 1/\tan u$, $\sec u = 1/\cos u$, and $\csc u = 1/\sin u$ allows us to find the functional values of the other three functions if we know the functional values of the sine, cosine, and tangent functions. For example, since $\sin 240° = -\sqrt{3}/2$, $\csc 240° = -2/\sqrt{3}$.

Exercise 7.3

1. Plot the points $(u, \sin u)$ for the numbers u in the second column of Table 7.2. Connect these points in a "sensible" fashion, thus graphing the sine function for the interval $[0, 2\pi]$.

2. Do the same for the other trigonometric functions we have defined.

7.5 Periodicity of the Trigonometric Functions

It is reasonably clear that if one evaluates the trigonometric functions for a particular number, say, u, that the values of these functions will be the same for the numbers $u + 2k\pi$, $k = 0, \pm1, \pm2, \ldots$. This is true because, if we construct an angle of u radians in standard position, the terminal side of this angle will coincide with the terminal sides of the angles of $(u + 2k\pi)$ radians. In terms of degrees, if we consider $f(\alpha°)$ where f represents any of our trigonometric functions, we have $f(\alpha°) = f((\alpha + k360)°)$, where

$$k = 0, \pm1, \pm2, \ldots$$

We introduce here a concept of which the trigonometric functions are instances:

Definition 7.2. Let $f : A \subset R^1 \to R^1$ be given. Suppose that $k \in R^1$, $k > 0$, satisfies

(1) $f(u + k) = f(u)$ for all $u \in A$,

(2) k is the least positive number with this property.
Then f is periodic of period k.

Our observation that $f(u) = f(u + 2k\pi)$ leads us to ask whether the trigonometric functions are periodic. The fact is that they are periodic of period 2π. It is clear that $f(u) = f(u + 2\pi)$. The proof that 2π is the least positive number with this property is not given but is assumed.

We see, of course, that, if one desires to find $\sin 398°$, it is enough to know $\sin 38°$, because

$$\sin 398° = \sin (360 + 38)° = \sin 38°.$$

In similar fashion,

$$\tan \frac{9\pi}{4} = \tan \left(2\pi + \frac{\pi}{4}\right) = \tan \frac{\pi}{4}.$$

Another example is that

$$\cos \left(-\frac{3\pi}{4}\right) = \cos \left(\frac{5\pi}{4} + 2(-1)\pi\right) = \cos \frac{5\pi}{4}.$$

These remarks tell us that, to evaluate any of the trigonometric functions, it is enough to be able to find their values $f(u)$ where $0 \leq u < 2\pi$.

Exercise 7.4

1. Write the following numbers in the form $u + 2k\pi$ where $0 \leq u < 2\pi$ and $k = 0$, $\pm 1, \pm 2, \ldots$:

$$5\pi, \ 3\pi, \ -6\pi, \ \frac{15\pi}{6}, \ -\frac{98\pi}{3}, \ -\frac{\pi}{2}, \ -\frac{8\pi}{3}, \ \frac{221}{31}\pi, \ -\frac{72}{11}\pi, \ 798\pi, \ -\frac{221}{2}\pi.$$

2. Write the following numbers in the form $u + k \cdot 360$, where $0 \leq u < 360$ and $k = 0, \pm 1, \pm 2, \ldots$:

$$790, \ 540, \ 361, \ -298, \ -2, \ -56, \ 10{,}001, \ 3, \ -926, \ -1125, \ 729, \ 482.$$

3. Using Table 7.2, find $\sin u$, $\cos u$, $\tan u$, where

(a) $u = 540°$.

(b) $u = 3\pi$.

(c) $u = -60°$.

(d) $u = -135°$.

(e) $u = \dfrac{7\pi}{2}$.

(f) $u = -88\pi$.

(g) $u = \dfrac{231}{4\pi}$,

(h) $u = -\dfrac{\pi}{6}$.

(i) 7π.

(j) $-\dfrac{5\pi}{6}$.

(k) $\dfrac{11\pi}{6}$.

(l) $\dfrac{17\pi}{6}$.

(m) $720°$.

(n) $450°$.

(o) $-495°$.

(p) $-210°$.

4. Construct a table similar to Table 7.2 replacing each degree α by $-\alpha$ (and each radian u by $-u$).

7.6 Functional Values of −u

Let f represent any of our trigonometric functions. In this section, we ask the relation (if any) between $f(u)$ and $f(-u)$.

To see the relationships that exist, we note that, if an angle of u radians in standard position has terminal side in the first (second, third, fourth) quadrant, then an angle of $-u$ radians in standard position has terminal side in the fourth (third, second, first) quadrant. Consider the accompanying table showing the coordinates of the points on the terminal sides of the angles of u and $-u$ radians for the various quadrants. Let a and b be positive real numbers. Thus the second line tells us that, if the terminal side of our angle of u radians is in the second quadrant, our angle of $-u$ radians is in the third quadrant. It also tells us that, if the point P_1 for u has coordinates $(-a, b)$, the point P_1 for $-u$ has coordinates $(-a, -b)$.

Quadrant	Coordinates of P_1 for u	Coordinates of P_1 for $-u$	Quadrant
1	(a, b)	$(a, -b)$	4
2	$(-a, b)$	$(-a, -b)$	3
3	$(-a, -b)$	$(-a, b)$	2
4	$(a, -b)$	(a, b)	1

Observe that the second entries in the pairs have opposite signs. Thus $\sin(-u) = -\sin u$. For, if

$$\sin u = b, \sin(-u) = -b = -\sin u,$$

and, if

$$\sin u = -b, \sin(-u) = b = -(-b) = -\sin u.$$

In the same way, we see that $\cos u = \cos(-u)$ for every $u \in R^1$.

Exercise 7.5

1. What is the relation between $\tan u$ and $\tan(-u)$; between $\cot u$ and $\cot(-u)$; between $\sec u$ and $\sec(-u)$; between $\csc u$ and $\csc(-u)$.

2. State the indicated functional values: $\sin(-45°)$, $\cos(-90°)$, $\sec\left(-\dfrac{3\pi}{4}\right)$, $\tan\left(-\dfrac{\pi}{4}\right)$, $\cot(-2\pi)$, $\sec(-\pi)$, $\cos(-\pi)$, $\sin\left(-\dfrac{2\pi}{3}\right)$, $\cos(-7\pi)$, $\sin(-5\pi)$.

3. Find an angle x, $-\dfrac{\pi}{2} \le x \le \dfrac{\pi}{2}$, for which

$$\sin x = -\frac{1}{2}, \sin x = \frac{3}{2}, \tan x = -1.$$

$$\csc x = -2, \cot x = \sqrt{3}, \tan x = -\sqrt{3}.$$

$$\sin x = \frac{\sqrt{2}}{2}, \sin x = -\frac{\sqrt{2}}{2}, \csc x = -\frac{1}{2}.$$

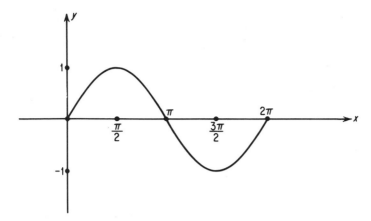

Figure 7.13

7.7   Graphs of the Trigonometric Functions

In earlier sections, we noted the values of $\sin u$ for certain real numbers u. In an exercise, the reader was asked to sketch the graph of the sine function for $0 \leq u \leq 2\pi$. The picture so obtained should look like Fig. 7.13. We further noted that the sine function was periodic of period 2π and we can thus extend this graph to real numbers not in the interval $[0, 2\pi]$, as shown in Fig. 7.14. Similarly, one can sketch the graphs of the other trigonometric functions. The graphs so obtained for the cosine and tangent functions would be as indicated in Figs. 7.15 and 7.16.

To obtain the graphs of the other basic functions, we can use the following technique. The key to the technique is based on the consideration that, if we know the point (x, y), we can find the point $(x, 1/y)$. We observe that if $y = 1, 1/y = 1$; if $0 < y < 1$, then $1 < 1/y$; and if $y > 1$, then $1 > 1/y > 0$. Similar observations can be made concerning negative y's. We further note that, if y is "close to zero," then $|1/y|$ is "large."

As an example of how this is used, consider the points (x_i, y_i) in Fig. 7.17 and their "inversions," $(x_i, 1/y_i)$.

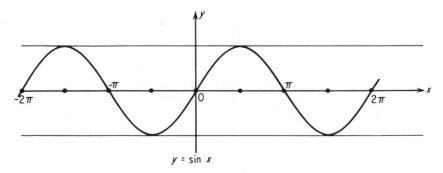

$y = \sin x$

Figure 7.14

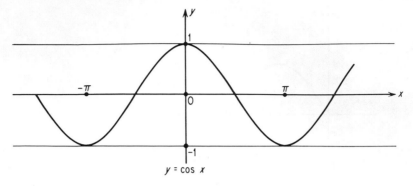

$y = \cos\ x$

Figure 7.15

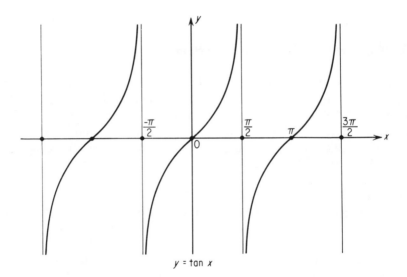

$y = \tan\ x$

Figure 7.16

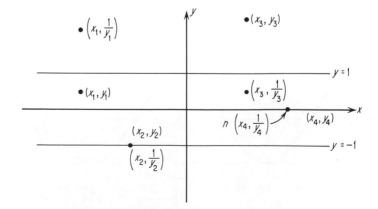

Figure 7.17

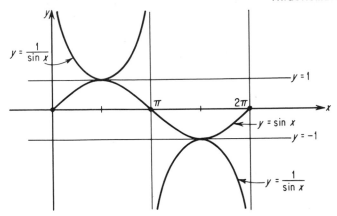

Figure 7.18

Note that, if $y = 0$, $1/y$ is not defined and the point $(x, 0)$ has no "inversion." With this idea in mind, we now "invert" the graph of $y = \sin x$ to obtain the graph of $y = 1/\sin x$ or $y = \csc x$. Notice first that $-1 \leq \sin x \leq 1$. Thus, on inverting, $1/\sin x$, for any x, will either be greater than or equal to 1 or less than or equal to -1. Removing the graph (Fig. 7.18) of $y = \sin x$ and extending our graph, we have the graph (Fig. 7.19) of $y = \csc x$.

Exercise 7.6

1. Sketch the graphs of

   (a) $y = x$.
   (b) $y = x - 1$.
   (c) $y = 2x + 4$.

   (d) $y = x^2$.
   (e) $y = x^2 - 1$.
   (f) $y = \tan x$.

   (g) $y = \cos x$.
   (h) $y = 1 + \sin x$.
   (i) $y = (\cos x) - 1$.

   (j) $y = 2x + 1$.
   (k) $y = 1 + \tan x$.
   (l) $y = \sin^2 x$.

   (m) $y = x^2 + x$.
   (n) $y = x^2 - 2x$.
   (o) $y = x^3$.

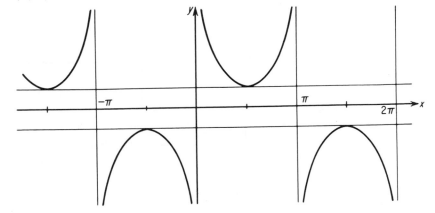

Figure 7.19

2. Use the inversion technique to sketch the graphs of

(a) $y = \dfrac{1}{x}$.

(b) $y = \dfrac{1}{x - 1}$.

(c) $y = \dfrac{1}{2x + 4}$.

(d) $y = \dfrac{1}{x^2}$.

(e) $y = \dfrac{1}{x^2 - 1}$.

(f) $y = \cot x$.

(g) $y = \sec x$.

(h) $y = \dfrac{1}{1 + \sin x}$.

(i) $y = \dfrac{1}{\cos x - 1}$.

(j) $y = \dfrac{1}{2x + 1}$.

(k) $y = \dfrac{1}{1 + \tan x}$.

(l) $y = \dfrac{1}{\sin^2 x}$.

(m) $y = \dfrac{1}{x(x + 1)}$.

(n) $y = \dfrac{1}{x(x - 2)}$.

(o) $y = \dfrac{1}{x^3}$.

7.8   More About Graphs

A few simple observations concerning graphs are in order. First we note that, if we have the graph of a function $y = f(x)$, then we can sketch the graph of a constant multiple of the same function, that is, of $y = k \cdot f(x)$. For, if we have the point (x, y), we can find (x, ky). For example, consider the graph of a function $y = f(x)$. We sketch the graph and the graph of $y = -1 \cdot f(x)$ and $y = 2 \cdot f(x)$. We limit our domain to a finite interval $[a, b]$. (See Fig. 7.20.)

In about the same fashion, we note that we can construct the graph (Fig. 7.21) of $y = f(x) + g(x)$, if we know the graphs of $y = f(x)$ and $y = g(x)$. For "x by x" we add the y values of each of the graphs together. As an example, consider the graph (Fig. 7.22) of $y = x + 2$. We graph $y = x$ and $y = 2$ and "add."

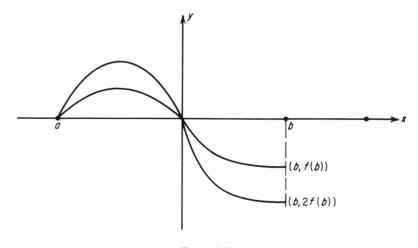

Figure 7.20

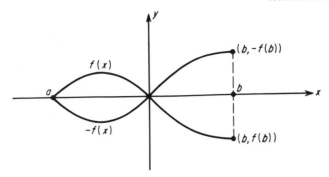

Figure 7.21

As an example of how these techniques are useful, we consider the graph (Fig. 7.23) of $y = 2 \sin x + 1$. We first sketch the graph of $\sin x$, then construct the graph of $y = 2 \sin x$ and, finally, "add" to it the graph of $y = 1$.

Other observations could be made that are helpful in sketching graphs when we know certain other graphs. For our purposes, however, the observations made are the ones most helpful and we make no further observations.

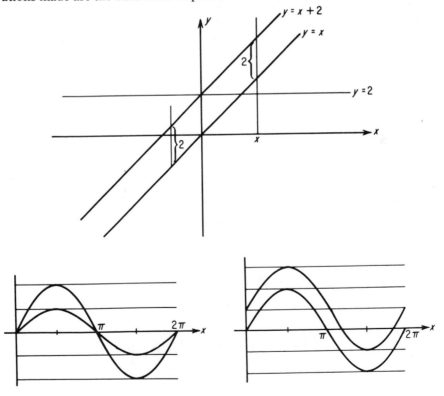

Figure 7.23

Exercise 7.7

Sketch the graphs of

(a) $y = \sin x$.
(b) $y = x$.
(c) $y = \sin x + x$.
(d) $y = \cos x$.
(e) $y = -\cos x$.
(f) $y = 2 \cos x$.
(g) $y = 1 - \cos x$.
(h) $y = 2 + \sin x$.
(i) $y = x^2 + \sin x$.
(j) $y = -\tan x$.
(k) $y = 2 - \tan x$.
(l) $y = \sin (x + \pi)$.

7.9   Identities

Earlier (Sec. 7.3) we noted certain identities relating the trigonometric functions. We now consider certain other identities that are not so immediately consequences of the definitions of these functions.

We would note first that the function $a : R^2 \rightarrow R^2$, defined by

$$a(x, y) = (s, t)$$

where (s, t) is the point obtained by rotating (x, y) u radians about the origin, $(x, y) \in R^2$, is a linear transformation on R^2. For $a[(x_1, y_1) + (x_2, y_2)] = a(x_1, y_1) + a(x_2, y_2)$ and $a(k \cdot (x, y)) = k \cdot a(x, y)$ for $(x_1, y_1), (x_2, y_2), (x, y) \in R^2$ and $k \in R^1$. The reader should verify geometrically that these properties hold.

From our work with matrices and linear transformations, we can write the matrix $A = [a]$ induced by a if we know $a(1, 0)$ and $a(0, 1)$. $a(1, 0)$ is readily seen to be given by

$$a(1, 0) = (\cos u, \sin u) .$$

For this is simply the definition of the sine and cosine functions. To find $a(0, 1)$, we note that $a(1, 0)$, $a(0, 1)$, and $(0, 0)$ are the vertices of a right triangle (Fig. 7.24). If we denote the vertices of $a(0, 1)$ by (x, y), we have the relation $(x - \cos u)^2 + (y - \sin u)^2 = 2$. We also have that $x^2 + y^2 = 1$.

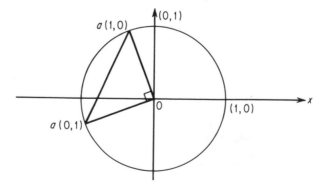

Figure 7.24

On solving this system of equations for x and y, choosing the appropriate solution, we have $x = -\sin u$, $y = \cos u$. Thus,

$$a(0, 1) = (-\sin u, \cos u).$$

We have, then, that

$$A = [a] = \begin{pmatrix} \cos u & \sin u \\ -\sin u & \cos u \end{pmatrix}.$$

Remember that this is the matrix induced by the rotation of a radians about the origin and any rotation of this type induces a matrix with this form.

As a specific example, if a were a rotation of 270°, the matrix $[a]$ is $\begin{pmatrix} 0 & -1 \\ 1 & 0 \end{pmatrix}$. To find the coordinates of the image of any point (x, y) after this rotation, it is enough to compute the matrix product

$$(x, y) \begin{pmatrix} 0 & -1 \\ 1 & 0 \end{pmatrix},$$

obtaining $(y, -x)$.

Suppose that we now have two rotations, a, of u radians and b, of v radians. If we consider the linear transformation of one followed by the other, say $b \circ a$, we know that

$$[b \circ a] = [a] \cdot [b].$$

But this linear transformation is the same as the rotation c, of $u + v$ radians. Thus $[c] = [a] \cdot [b]$. Now we have

$$[a] = \begin{pmatrix} \cos u & \sin u \\ -\sin u & \cos u \end{pmatrix},$$

$$[b] = \begin{pmatrix} \cos v & \sin v \\ -\sin v & \cos v \end{pmatrix},$$

and

$$[c] = \begin{pmatrix} \cos(u + v) & \sin(u + v) \\ -\sin(u + v) & \cos(u + v) \end{pmatrix}.$$

If we compute the product $[a] \cdot [b]$, we have

$$[a] \cdot [b] = \begin{pmatrix} \cos u \cos v - \sin u \sin v & \cos u \sin v + \sin u \cos v \\ -(\cos u \sin v + \sin u \cos v) & \cos u \cos v - \sin u \sin v \end{pmatrix}.$$

But this matrix and the matrix $[c]$ are equal. Thus, equating entries, we have, for any real numbers u and v, that

(J8) $$\cos(u + v) = \cos u \cos v - \sin u \sin v,$$

and

(J9) $$\sin(u + v) = \sin u \cos v + \sin v \cos u.$$

These are important identities, and from this point on, we will assume that they hold. As an immediate consequence of these, we can prove

(J10) $\cos (u - v) = \cos u \cos v + \sin u \sin v$,

and

(J11) $\cos (u - v) = \sin u \cos v - \sin v \cos u$.

To see (J10), consider $\cos (u + (-v))$. From (J8) we have

$$\cos (u + (-v)) = \cos u \cos (-v) - \sin u \sin (-v)$$

$$= \cos u \cos v + \sin u \sin v .$$

(Recall that $\cos (-v) = \cos v$ and $\sin (-v) = -\sin v$.)

Exercise

Prove (J11).

It is simple to obtain a similar formula for the tangent function. For

(5) $\tan (x + y) = \dfrac{\sin (x + y)}{\cos (x + y)} = \dfrac{\sin x \cos y + \sin y \cos x}{\cos x \cos y - \sin x \sin y}$

$$= \dfrac{\tan x + \tan y}{1 - \tan x \tan y} . \overset{*}{}$$

Thus we have the identity,

(J12) $\tan (x + y) = \dfrac{\tan x + \tan y}{1 - \tan x \tan y} .$

To obtain a formula for $\tan (x - y)$, simply replace y by $(-y)$ and simplify. The usual result is

(J13) $\tan (x - y) = \dfrac{\tan x - \tan y}{1 + \tan x \tan y} .$

This uses the fact that $\tan (-u) = -\tan u$. Note that these identities involving the tangent are not valid for certain values of x and y. For the tangent function is not always defined. As an example, consider the case where $x = y = \pi/4$. Then (5) becomes

$$\tan \frac{\pi}{2} = \frac{\tan \pi/4 + \tan \pi/4}{1 - \tan \pi/4 \cdot \tan \pi/4} = \frac{1 + 1}{1 - 1 \cdot 1} = \frac{2}{0} .$$

Moreover, $\tan \pi/2$ is not defined.

* Divide top and bottom by $\cos x \cos y$ to obtain the desired result.

The usefulness of identities is difficult to show except in rather obvious ways. Primarily, they are devices to simplify complicated expressions or to replace unfamiliar expressions by familiar ones. They might be viewed as tricks to use in unexpected situations. The reader who takes a course in calculus will encounter uses for identities in getting the answers the authors of calculus texts furnish to exercises. He will also encounter them in developing certain differentiation formulae.

A very obvious although not a very useful application is in determining certain values of trigonometric functions. For example, if asked to find sin 75° without a table, one can do so if he knows the values of the trigonometric functions for 30° and 45°, because

$$\sin 75° = \sin (45° + 30°)$$
$$= \sin 45° \cos 30° + \sin 30° \cos 45°$$

Thus

$$\sin 75° = \frac{\sqrt{2}}{2} \cdot \frac{\sqrt{3}}{2} + \frac{1}{2} \cdot \frac{\sqrt{2}}{2} = \frac{\sqrt{6} + \sqrt{2}}{4}$$

Exercise 7.8

Without using tables, find

(a) cos 75°.   (b) cos 15°.   (c) tan 15°.   (d) sin 165°.

(e) sec 165°.   (f) sin 105°.   (g) cos 195°.   (h) cot 255°.

We now want to get a little practice in manipulating identities. In practice, one is faced with the problem of reducing a complicated expression or of expanding an unfamiliar expression. For example, consider the expression

$$\sin 2x \cos x + \cos 2x \sin x .$$

The practiced eye would recognize this immediately as sin 3x (sin (2x + x)). On the other hand, one might be asked to express sin 3x in terms of functions of x alone. Then the problem is to expand sin 3x somehow. For example,

$$\sin 3x = \sin (2x + x)$$
$$= \sin 2x \cos x + \cos 2x \sin x$$
$$= \sin (x + x) \cos x + \cos (x + x) \sin x$$
$$= (\sin x \cos x + \sin x \cos x) \cos x$$
$$\qquad\qquad + (\cos x \cos x - \sin x \sin x) \sin x$$
$$= 2 \sin x \cos^2 x + \cos^2 x \sin x - \sin^3 x$$
$$= 3 \sin x \cos^2 x - \sin^3 x .$$

Keep in mind that we have the list of identities that came directly from the definition as well as the sum and difference formulae. The following set of exercises is based on this basic list. As an example, prove the following identity by changing the left-hand side into the right-hand side:

$$\frac{1 - \sin^2 x}{\sin x} = \frac{\cos x}{\tan x}.$$

Now we know $1 - \sin^2 x = \cos^2 x$. So

$$\frac{1 - \sin^2 x}{\sin x} = \frac{\cos^2 x}{\sin x}.$$

But

$$\cos^2 x = \cos x \cdot \cos x,$$

so

$$\frac{\cos^2 x}{\sin x} = \frac{\cos x}{\sin x} \cdot \cos x.$$

But

$$\frac{\cos x}{\sin x} \cdot \cos x = \frac{\cos x}{\sin x / \cos x} = \frac{\cos x}{\tan x}.$$

Normally one would not add these connecting phrases, but would simply string out the equalities.

$$\frac{1 - \sin^2 x}{\sin x} = \frac{\cos^2 x}{\sin x} = \frac{\cos x}{\sin x} \cdot \cos x = \frac{1}{\tan x} \cdot \cos x.$$

As another example, we prove

$$\frac{1 - \tan^2 x}{1 + \tan^2 x} = 1 - 2 \sin^2 x.$$

Again we convert the left side to the right:

$$\frac{1 - \tan^2 x}{1 + \tan^2 x} = \frac{1 - \tan^2 x}{\sec^2 x} = \frac{1}{\sec^2 x} \left(1 - \frac{\sin^2 x}{\cos^2 x} \right)$$

$$= \cos^2 x \left(1 - \frac{\sin^2 x}{\cos^2 x} \right) = \cos^2 x - \sin^2 x$$

$$= (1 - \sin^2 x) - \sin^2 x = 1 - 2 \sin^2 x.$$

Exercise 7.9

Prove the following identities (based on the basic identities) by changing the left side to the right side:

(a) $\sin x \sec x = \tan x.$

(b) $\cos^2 x - \sin^2 x = 2 \cos^2 x - 1.$

(c) $\cot x + \tan x = \sec x \csc x.$

(d) $\dfrac{\cos^2 x}{1 - \sin x} = 1 + \sin x.$

(e) $\dfrac{1 - \cos^2 x}{\cos x} = \sin x \tan x.$

(f) $\dfrac{\tan x - 1}{\tan x + 1} = \dfrac{1 - \cot x}{1 + \cot x}.$

(g) $\dfrac{\tan x - 1}{\tan x + 1} = \dfrac{\sin x - \cos x}{\sin x + \cos x}.$

(h) $\dfrac{1}{\sec x + \tan x} = \dfrac{1 - \sin x}{\cos x}.$

(i) $\dfrac{1}{\csc x - \cot x} - \dfrac{1}{\csc x + \cot x} = 2 \cot x.$

(j) $\dfrac{1 + \sin^2 x}{\cos^2 x} = \sec^4 x - \tan^4 x.$

(k) $\sec^2 x \csc^2 x = \sec^2 x + \csc^2 x.$

(l) $\dfrac{1}{1 + \cos x} = \csc^2 x - \csc x \cot x.$

(m) $\sin^2 x \cot x = \dfrac{1}{\tan x} - \cot x \cos^2 x.$

(n) $\sin^4 x + 2 \sin^2 x \cos^2 x + \cos^4 x = 1.$

(o) $1 + \sin^4 x = \cos^4 x + 2 \sin^2 x.$

7.10   More Identities

We have at our disposal the sum and difference formulae from the last section. These can be used to develop certain other identities that are useful. As a special case of

$$\sin (x + y) = \sin x \cos y + \sin y \cos x ,$$

consider $\sin 2x = \sin (x + x)$. We have, then,

(J14) $\sin 2x = 2 \sin x \cos x$

In a similar fashion, if we consider $\cos 2x$ as $\cos (x + x)$, we get

(J15) $\cos 2x = \cos^2 x - \sin^2 x$

$$= 1 - 2 \sin^2 x$$

$$= 2 \cos^2 x - 1 .$$

Exercise

    (a) Develop a formula for $\tan 2x$.

    (b) Why do the second and third formulae for $\cos 2x$ hold?

If we rewrite (J15) replacing $2x$ by x, and x by $x/2$, we get

$$\cos x = 1 - 2 \sin^2 \frac{x}{2}$$

and

$$\cos x = 2 \cos^2 \frac{x}{2} - 1 .$$

If we solve these for $\sin x/2$ and $\cos x/2$, we get

(J16) $$\sin \frac{x}{2} = \pm \sqrt{\frac{1 - \cos x}{2}} ,$$

and

(J17) $$\cos \frac{x}{2} = \pm \sqrt{\frac{1 + \cos x}{2}} .$$

The sign used will depend on the quadrant in which the terminal side of our angle lies.

    If we divide (J16) by (J17) we get

(J18) $$\tan \frac{x}{2} = \pm \sqrt{\frac{1 - \cos x}{1 + \cos x}}$$

We can reduce the expression on the right by multiplying inside the radical by $(1 + \cos x)/(1 + \cos x)$.

If we do this, we have

$$\frac{1 - \cos x}{1 + \cos x} \cdot \frac{1 + \cos x}{1 + \cos x} = \frac{1 - \cos^2 x}{(1 + \cos x)^2} = \frac{\sin^2 x}{(1 + \cos x)^2} = \frac{\sin x}{1 + \cos x}$$

So, an alternate form of (J18) is

$$\tan \frac{x}{2} = \frac{\sin x}{1 + \cos x} .$$

Exercise

    Show that

$$\tan \frac{x}{2} = \frac{1 - \cos x}{\sin x} .$$

Another type of identity that is useful at times is derived from the sum and difference formulae. As an example,

since
$$\sin (x + y) = \sin x \cos y + \sin y \cos x ,$$
and
$$\sin (x - y) = \sin x \cos y - \sin y \cos x ,$$

on adding, we get that
$$\sin (x + y) + \sin (x - y) = \sin x \cos y .$$

If we make the substitutions, $a = x + y$ and $b = x - y$, we see that
$$x = \frac{a + b}{2} \quad \text{and} \quad y = \frac{a - b}{2}.$$

Thus, for any real numbers a and b,

(J19) $$\sin a + \sin b = 2 \sin \frac{a + b}{2} \cos \frac{a - b}{2}.$$

Exercise 7.10

1. Prove that, for any real numbers a and b,

(J20) $$\sin a - \sin b = 2 \sin \frac{a - b}{2} \cos \frac{a + b}{2}.$$

(J21) $$\cos a - \cos b = -2 \sin \frac{a + b}{2} \sin \frac{a - b}{2}.$$

(J22) $$\cos a + \cos b = 2 \cos \frac{a + b}{2} \cos \frac{a - b}{2}.$$

2. Prove the following identities:

(a) $$\frac{\cos 2x}{\sec x} - \frac{\sin x}{\csc 2x} = \cos 3x.$$

(b) $$\frac{\cos 2x}{1 + \sin 2x} = \frac{\csc x - \sec x}{\sec x + \csc x}.$$

(c) $2 \cos 2x = \csc 2x \sin 4x.$

(d) $$\frac{\sin 5x + \sin 3x}{\sin 5x - \sin 3x} = \frac{\tan 4x}{\tan x}.$$

(e) $$\frac{\cos 3x}{\sec x} - \frac{\sin x}{\csc 3x} = \cos^2 2x - \sin^2 2x.$$

(f) $$\sin 3x = \frac{2 \tan x}{1 + \tan^2 x}.$$

(g) $\sec 2x = \dfrac{\sec^2 x}{2 - \sec^2 x}$.

(h) $\tan 3x = \dfrac{3 \tan x - \tan^3 x}{1 - 3 \tan^2 x}$.

(i) $\cos 3x = 4 \cos^3 x - 3 \cos x$.

(j) $8 \sin^2 3x \cos^2 3x = 1 - \cos 12x$.

3. Evaluate

(a) $\sin 22.5°$.	(b) $\cos 15°$.	(c) $\sin 105°$.
(d) $\sin 165°$.	(e) $\sin 15°$.	(f) $\sin 7.5°$.
(g) $\tan 165°$.	(h) $\tan 15°$.	(i) $\tan 7.5°$.
(j) $\tan 105°$.		

7.11 Inverse Trigonometric Functions

Let us consider the function $s : [-\pi/2, \pi/2] \to [-1, 1]$, defined by $s(x) = \sin x$. We are considering the sine function with a restricted domain. It should be clear that s is a 1–1 onto function. We introduce a new function

$$q : [-1, 1] \to [-\pi/2, \pi/2]$$

as follows:

$$q(x) = y \Leftrightarrow s(y) = x, \quad x \in [-1, 1].$$

We note, then, that $q(-1) = -\pi/2$ because $\sin (-\pi/2) = -1$. Other values might be considered. For example, $q(\tfrac{1}{2}) = \pi/3$ because $\sin \pi/3 = \tfrac{1}{2}$ and $q(1/\sqrt{2}) = \pi/4$, because $\sin \pi/4 = 1/\sqrt{2}$.

Now this function q is called the *inverse* of the sine function and is denoted arc sin (read arc sine). If we had not restricted the domain of the sine function, we would not have a function in q. Because since $\sin \pi/3 = \tfrac{1}{2} = \sin 5\pi/3$, we would not be able to give a unique number arc sin $\tfrac{1}{2}$. (Either $\pi/3$ or $5\pi/3$ would do). Our restricting the domain of the sine function insured that q would be a function. Of course other intervals could have been chosen as the domain of s. For example $[\pi/2, 3\pi/2]$ would have worked.

It is possible to sketch the graph of the arc sin function and the reader should verify that Fig. 7.25 is reasonably accurate.

Actually the graph is the graph of the sine function, restricted to $[-\pi/2, \pi/2]$ reflected through the line $y = x$.

In a similar fashion we define arc cos (the inverse of the cosine function) by:

$$\text{arc cos } x = y \Leftrightarrow \cos y = x,$$

for $x \in [-1, 1]$ and $y \in [0, \pi]$. Here we restrict the domain of the cosine

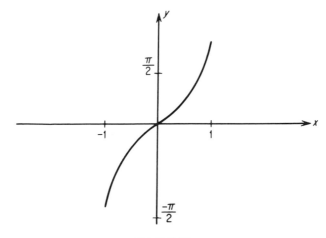

Figure 7.25

function to $[0, \pi]$ in order to obtain a function. We note that arc cos $0 = \pi/2$ because cos $\pi/2 = 0$, that arc cos $1 = 0$ because cos $0 = 1$.

It is possible, of course, to define, in similar fashion, the inverse function of the other trigonometric functions. The reader should, as an exercise, define arc tan, arc cot, arc sec, and arc csc. Care should be taken to restrict the domain of the trigonometric functions in order to insure obtaining functions.

Exercise 7.11

1. Sketch the graphs of y : arc tan x and $y = $ arc cos x.

2. Evaluate

   (a)   arc sin (-1).   (b)   arc cos (-1).   (c)   arc tan (-1).

   (d)   arc tan 3.   (e)   arc cos $\dfrac{\sqrt{2}}{2}$.   (f)   arc sec 1.

   (g)   arc sin (sin π).   (h)   sin (arc cos 1).   (i)   tan $\left(\text{arc sin}\dfrac{1}{2}\right)$.

   (j)   sin $\left(\text{arc tan}\dfrac{y}{x}\right)$.   (k)   cos (arc cos 1).   (l)   cos (arc cos α).

   (m)   arc tan $\dfrac{1}{\sqrt{3}}$.   (n)   cos (arc tan 1).   (o)   cos (arc tan (-1)).

   (p)   tan $\left(\text{arc cos}\dfrac{1}{2}\right)$.   (q)   cot (arc tan x).   (r)   csc (arc sin t).

7.12 Trigonometric Equations

The concept of identity has been introduced and the usual set of basic identities presented. A statement, such as

$$\sin x + \cos x = \frac{1 + \sqrt{3}}{2},$$

is certainly not true for all real numbers x for which the functions are defined. For example, if $x = \pi/2$, this is the obviously false statement

$$1 = \frac{1 + \sqrt{3}}{2}.$$

Our statement, then, is simply an equation and a valid problem would be determining its solution set. Such equations are called *trigonometric equations* and techniques exist for solving some of them. Generally, one would attempt to reduce the equation to the form

$$f(g(x)) = k,$$

where f is one of our trigonometric functions, k is a real number, and g is a function of x. This may be a sticky problem.

The simplest kind of trigonometric equation is of the form $f(x) = k$ where f is one of our basic functions, for example, $\sin x = \frac{1}{2}$. One solution to this equation is arc sin $\frac{1}{2}$ or $\pi/6$. However, other solutions exist — $\pi/6 + n2\pi$, $n = \pm 1, \pm 2, \ldots$. Moreover $5\pi/6$ is a solution as well as the numbers $5\pi/6 + n2\pi$, $n = \pm 1, \pm 2, \ldots$. Usually one is interested in solutions of trigonometric equations in a particular interval, frequently $[0, 2\pi]$.

As another example, let us find all solutions, x, in $[0, 2\pi]$ for the equation

$$\sin 2x = \frac{1}{2}.$$

Here we see that we have solutions when

$$2x = \frac{\pi}{6} \quad \text{or} \quad 2x = \frac{5\pi}{6},$$

or, more generally, when

$$2x = \frac{\pi}{6} + 2n\pi \quad \text{or} \quad 2x = \frac{5\pi}{6} + 2n\pi,$$

with n an integer.

If $2x = \pi/6$, $x = \pi/12$ and if $2x = 5\pi/6$, $x = 5\pi/12$ and these are two of the desired solutions. There are, however, two other solutions satisfying our restriction, namely, those obtained when

$$2x = \frac{\pi}{6} + 2\pi \quad \text{and} \quad 2x = \frac{5\pi}{6} + 2\pi \, ,$$

or

$$x = \frac{\pi}{12} + \pi = \frac{13\pi}{12} \quad \text{and} \quad x = \frac{5\pi}{12} + \pi = \frac{17\pi}{12} \cdot$$

As another example, consider the equation

$$\sin \frac{x}{2} = -\frac{1}{2} \, ,$$

and again let us find all solutions in $[0, 2\pi]$. Now we note that $\sin x/2 = -1/2$ when $x/2 = 7\pi/6$ and when $x/2 = 11\pi/6$. But this means that $x = 7\pi/3$ and $x = 11\pi/3$ are both outside our interval. Thus there are no solutions to our equation in the interval $[0, 2\pi]$.

As a final example, consider the equation

$$\sin x + \cos x = 1$$

and let us find its solution in $[0, 2\pi]$. Certain of these are obvious — $x = 0$ and $x = \pi/2$. Let us first find a way of reducing this equation to one containing only one trigonometric function. We rewrite the equation as

$$\cos x = 1 - \sin x$$

and square both sides, obtaining

$$\cos^2 x = (1 - \sin x)^2$$

or

$$\cos^2 x = 1 - 2 \sin x + \sin^2 x \, .$$

(Remember that every solution of our original equation will satisfy this new equation, but not every solution of this one need be a solution for the original equation.)

We rewrite this as

$$1 - \sin^2 x = 1 - 2 \sin x + \sin^2 x \, , \qquad \text{(How?)}$$

or

$$2 \sin^2 x - 2 \sin x = 0 \, ,$$

or

$$2 \sin x \, (\sin x - 1) = 0 \, .$$

So, if x is a solution to our original equation, either $\sin x = 0$ or $\sin x = 1$.

The possible solutions are, then,

$$x = 0, x = \pi \quad \text{and} \quad x = \frac{\pi}{2}.$$

Trying these in the original equation, we have that $x = 0$ and $x = \pi/2$ are solutions, but $x = \pi$ is not a solution because

$$\sin \pi + \cos \pi = -1 \neq 1.$$

Exercise 7.12

Find the solutions in $[0, 2\pi]$ for the following:

(a) $\sin x = \dfrac{\sqrt{2}}{2}.$ (b) $\sin 2x = \dfrac{\sqrt{2}}{2}.$ (c) $\sin \dfrac{x}{2} = -\dfrac{\sqrt{2}}{2}.$

(d) $\cos x = 2.$ (e) $\sin x + \cos x = \dfrac{1 + \sqrt{3}}{2}.$

(f) $\sin^2 x + \sin x = 0.$ (g) $\tan^2 x + \sin^2 x = 0.$

(h) $(\cos x - 1)^2 - 4 = 0.$ (i) $\dfrac{1 + \cos 2x}{2} = \dfrac{1}{4}.$

(j) $\dfrac{1 - \cos 2x}{2} = \dfrac{1}{4}.$ (k) $\tan^2 x + \sqrt{3} \tan x = 0.$

(l) $\tan^2 x + \sec^2 x = 1.$

7.13 Triangles

We look now at the more traditional type of trigonometry, that dealing with triangles. We do not consider this in great detail but will show briefly how it is not different from what we have done.

Consider a right triangle (Fig. 7.26) with sides of length a, b, c (you pick the units). Suppose that c is the length of the hypotenuse and that the angle opposite the side of length a is of α degrees.

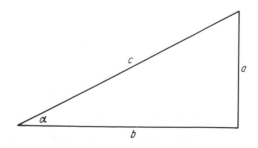

Figure 7.26

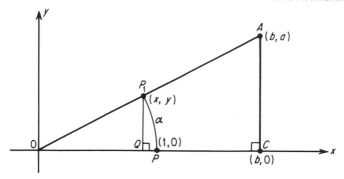

Figure 7.27

Introduce a Cartesian coordinate system in the plane of the triangle (Fig. 7.27) so that α is in standard position and so that the x axis falls along the side adjacent to α. Choose the unit of the triangle as the unit in our coordinate system. Find the point P_1 on the terminal side of α at a distance 1 from 0. Then, if P_1 has coordinates (x, y), we know $y = \sin \alpha$, $x = \cos \alpha$, and $y/x = \tan \alpha$. On drawing the perpendicular, $P_1 Q$ from P_1 to the x axis, we have the triangles OP_1Q and OAC similar. Thus $y = a/c$ and $x = b/c$, or $\sin \alpha = a/c$ and $\cos \alpha = b/c$ ($\tan \alpha = a/b$). That is, the sine of an acute angle in a right triangle is the length of the side opposite the angle divided by the length of the hypotenuse. Similar relations hold for the other trigonometric functions of such an angle.

This is useful in that, given certain information about a right triangle, we can get other information. For example, consider the triangle in Fig. 7.28. Since $\sin 30° = x/100$ and since we know $\sin 30° = \frac{1}{2}$, we can determine x. For $\frac{1}{2} = x/100$ and $x = 50°$ Also, since $\cos 30° = y/100$ and we know $\cos 30° = \sqrt{3}/2$, we find that $y/100 = \sqrt{3}/2$ and $y = 50\sqrt{3}$.

With a table of the trigonometric functions, it is possible to handle problems of this sort for all right triangles. The accuracy of the answer depends on the accuracy of the table. For our purposes, a simple four-place table (Table 7.3) is included in the text and should be used for the problems in Exercise 7-13.

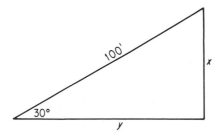

Figure 7.28

Table 7.3. Trigonometric Functions

Degrees	Sine	Cosine	Tangent	Cotan.	Degrees
0	.0000	1.0000	.0000		90
1	.0175	.9998	.0175	57.290	89
2	.0349	.9994	.0349	28.636	88
3	.0523	.9986	.0524	19.081	87
4	.0698	.9976	.0699	14.301	86
5	.0872	.9962	.0875	11.430	85
6	.1045	.9945	.1051	9.5144	84
7	.1219	.9925	.1228	8.1443	83
8	.1392	.9903	.1405	7.1154	82
9	.1564	.9877	.1584	6.3138	81
10	.1736	.9848	.1763	5.6713	80
11	.1908	.9816	.1944	5.1446	79
12	.2079	.9781	.2126	4.7046	78
13	.2250	.9744	.2309	4.3315	77
14	.2419	.9703	.2493	4.0108	76
15	.2588	.9659	.2679	3.7321	75
16	.2756	.9613	.2867	3.4874	74
17	.2924	.9563	.3057	3.2709	73
18	.3090	.9511	.3249	3.0777	72
19	.3256	.9455	.3443	2.9042	71
20	.3420	.9397	.3640	2.7475	70
21	.3584	.9336	.3839	2.6051	69
22	.3746	.9272	.4040	2.4751	68
23	.3907	.9205	.4245	2.3559	67
24	.4067	.9135	.4452	2.2460	66
25	.4226	.9063	.4663	2.1445	65
26	.4384	.8988	.4877	2.0503	64
27	.4540	.8910	.5095	1.9626	63
28	.4695	.8829	.5317	1.8807	62
29	.4848	.8746	.5543	1.8040	61
30	.5000	.8660	.5774	1.7321	60
31	.5150	.8572	.6009	1.6643	59
32	.5299	.8480	.6249	1.6003	58
33	.5446	.8387	.6494	1.5399	57
34	.5592	.8290	.6745	1.4826	56
35	.5736	.8192	.7002	1.4281	55
36	.5878	.8090	.7265	1.3764	54
37	.6018	.7986	.7536	1.3270	53
38	.6157	.7880	.7813	1.2799	52
39	.6293	.7771	.8098	1.2349	51
40	.6428	.7660	.8391	1.1918	50
41	.6561	.7547	.8693	1.1504	49
42	.6691	.7431	.9004	1.1106	48
43	.6820	.7314	.9325	1.0724	47
44	.6947	.7193	.9657	1.0355	46
45	.7071	.7071	1.0000	1.0000	45
Degrees	Cosine	Sine	Cotan.	Tangent	Degrees

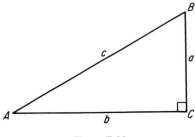

Figure 7.29

Exercise 7.13

For Fig. 7.29, assume we have a right triangle labeled as indicated. Assume all the lengths are in feet. Certain information is given. Find the missing information:

	A	B	a	b	c
(a)	30°		10		
(b)		45°		5	
(c)			5		10
(d)			3	2	
(e)	15°		2		
(f)		60°		3	
(g)	46°		15		
(h)	61°				28
(i)			2	3	
(j)		89°	27		

Without proof, we present certain other relations for general triangles that can be used to find lengths of sides and angles when enough information is given. We assume that the triangles are labeled as in Fig. 7.30; that

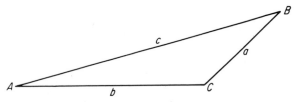

Figure 7.30

is, the angles are A, B, and C and the sides opposite them are of length a, b, and c, respectively.

Law of Sines

$$\frac{\sin A}{a} = \frac{\sin B}{b} = \frac{\sin C}{c}.$$

This is used, when two angles and a side opposite one of them are known, to determine the length of the side opposite the second angle. It is used also to determine the angle opposite a known side when a second side and the angle opposite it are known.

Law of Cosines

$$c^2 = a^2 + b^2 - 2ab \cos C$$

$$b^2 = a^2 + c^2 - 2ac \cos B$$

$$a^2 = b^2 + c^2 - 2bc \cos A .$$

This is used to determine the length of a side opposite an angle when the angle and its adjacent sides are known. The law of cosines is also used to find any angle when all three sides of a triangle are known.

Limits

8.1 Metric Spaces

The next topic we consider is that of limits of functions. This notion is basic to many aspects of mathematics and there are many ways to introduce this concept. We will do it from a fairly general point of view. Basic to our approach is the following definition:

Definition 8.1. Let X be a set. A function $d : X \times X \to R^1$ is a *metric* or *distance function* on X if and only if the following conditions are satisfied.

(a) $d(x, y) \geq 0$ for all $x, y \in X$.

(b) For $x, y \in X$, $d(x, y) = 0 \Leftrightarrow x = y$.

(c) For $x, y \in X$, $d(x, y) = d(y, x)$.

(d) For $x, y, z \in X$, $d(x, y) < d(x, z) + d(z, y)$.

We are familiar to some extent with such functions. We have dealt with distance between points in R^2. In fact, the distance, $d(P, Q)$,

8

between points in R^2, as we defined it, is indeed a metric for the set R^2. In R^1, we defined earlier the distance $d(x, y)$ between the numbers x and y to be $|x - y|$. This is an example of a metric on the set R^1.

So in R^1, the distance between the numbers 5 and -2 relative to this metric is given by

$$d(5, -2) = |5 - (-2)| = 7.$$

In R^2, using the metric with which we are familiar, the distance from $(0, 0)$ to $(3, 4)$ is given by

$$d((0, 0), (3, 4)) = \sqrt{(0 - 3)^2 + (0 - 4)^2} = 5.$$

In general, if we have a set X, a metric on X is a device for measuring distance between points. What is important is that it tells us, in some way, when points are close to each other.

A given set may have many different metrics. For example, let X be any set. Let d_1 be a metric for X defined by

$$d_1(x, y) = \begin{cases} 1 & \text{if } x \neq y \\ 0 & \text{if } x = y, \end{cases} \quad \text{for } x, y \in X.$$

It is not hard to verify that the conditions of the foregoing definition are satisfied. Certainly,

$$d_1(x, y) \geq 0 \quad \text{because} \quad d_1(x, y) = 0 \quad \text{or} \quad 1.$$

From our definition, $x = y \Rightarrow d_1(x, y) = 0$, and

$$x \neq y \Rightarrow d_1(x, y) \neq 0 \quad \text{or} \quad d_1(x, y) = 0 \Leftrightarrow x = y.$$

Because $x \neq y \Rightarrow y \neq x$, we have $d_1(x, y) = d_1(y, x)$. To see that condition (d) holds, we note that $d_1(x, y) \leq 1$. But

$$d_1(x, z) + d_1(z, y) \geq 1,$$

except in the case where $x = z = y$.

In that case, $d_1(x, y) = 0 \leq d_1(x, z) + d_1(z, y)$.

So it is possible, always, to introduce a metric on a set. And it is possible that a given set have more than one metric. For, as we have seen, R^1 and R^2 have the metrics introduced earlier as well as the metric d_1 just defined. Thus, we have two examples of sets on which at least two metrics are defined. For example, we have (R^1, d), where d is defined by

$$d(x, y) = |x - y| \quad \text{for all } x, y \in R^1$$

and (R^1, d_1), where d_1 is defined by

$$d_1(x, y) = 0 \quad \text{if } x = y,$$

$$d_1(x, y) = 1 \quad \text{if } x \neq y,$$

for all $x, y \in R^1$. Here, then, we have the same set R^1 considered with two different metrics. As a metric space (R^1, d) is *not* the same as (R^1, d_1), even though the same set of elements is involved in both.

Definition 8.2. A *metric space* is a set, X, and a metric, d, for X. We use the pair (X, d) to denote a metric space X with metric d.

Remember, then, to have a metric space we need both a set and a metric on that set. If d_1 and d_2 are different metrics for the same set X, the metric space (X, d_1) is not the same metric space as is (X, d_2).

Exercise

Let X be a set and $d : X \times X \to R^1$ be a function (not necessarily a metric). Show that, if d has the properties:

(a) $d(x, x) = 0$ for every $x \in X$.

(b)   For all $x, y \in X$, $d(x, y) = d(y, x)$.

(c)   For all $x, y, z \in X$, $d(x, y) \leq d(x, z) + (z, y)$, then d has the additional property:

(d) $d(x, y) \geq 0$ for all $x, y \in X$.

As another example of a metric space, consider

$$R^3 = \{(x_1, x_2, x_3) \mid x_i \in R^1, \quad i = 1, 2, 3\}.$$

A distance function d is defined on R^3 by

$$d(\bar{x}, \bar{y}) = \sqrt{\sum_{i=1}^{3} (x_i - y_i)^2},$$

where $\bar{x} = (x_1, x_2, x_3)$ and $\bar{y} = (y_1, y_2, y_3)$.

Note that, for all points $\bar{x}, \bar{y} \in R^3$, $d(\bar{x}, \bar{y})$ is defined and is a non-negative number. Also

$$d(\bar{x}, \bar{y}) = 0 \Leftrightarrow x_i = y_i \quad \text{for } i = 1, 2, 3 \Leftrightarrow \bar{x} = \bar{y}.$$

Because $(x_i - y_i)^2 = (y_i - x_i)^2$, we have that

$$d(\bar{x}, \bar{y}) = d(\bar{y}, \bar{x}) \quad \text{for all } \bar{x}, \bar{y} \in R^3.$$

The proof that property (d) of Definition 8.1 holds is a bit complicated and we omit it here. This metric, called the *euclidean metric*, is the ordinary straight-line distance between points in space, as we have seen.

We note that a sphere with radius r and center at $\overline{x}$ is the set of all points whose distance from $\overline{x}$ is r. But if (y_1, y_2, y_3) are the coordinates of a point $\overline{y}$ on the sphere, $\overline{y}$ has distance r from $\overline{x} = (x_1, x_2, x_3)$. That is, $d(\overline{x}, \overline{y}) = r$ and $[d(\overline{x}, \overline{y})]^2 = r^2$.

Thus,

$$(y_1 - x_1)^2 + (y_2 - x_2)^2 + (y_3 - x_3)^2 = r^2 .$$

So, if $\overline{y}$ is a point on this sphere, its coordinates (x, y, z) satisfy the equation:

$$(x - x_1)^2 + (y - x_2)^2 + (z - x_3)^2 = r^2 .$$

It is clear that a point, $\overline{z}$, whose coordinates satisfy this equation is at a distance r from $\overline{x}$. Thus $\overline{z}$ is on the sphere. We have, then, the fact that the equation of a sphere with radius r and center $\overline{x} = (x_1, x_2, x_3)$ is

$$(x - x_1)^2 + (y - x_2)^2 + (z - x_3)^2 = r^2 .$$

The points interior to this sphere have "equation"

$$(x - x_1)^2 + (y - x_2)^2 + (z - x_3)^2 < r^2 .$$

As a matter of fact, in R^3 we have a sphere that agrees with our ordinary concept of sphere. Let (X, d) be any metric space whatsoever. We call

$$\{x \in X \mid d(x, x_0) < r, x_0 \in X, r > 0\}$$

a *solid sphere with radius* r and center x_0. Using this definition, we abandon the boundary or surface of a sphere and keep the interior of the sphere. When we use *sphere* hereafter, we mean it in this sense. As a matter of notation, let $S_r(x_0)$ denote the sphere with radius r and center x_0. (Remember that the appearance of a sphere depends on the metric involved.) With our euclidean metric in R^3 a "sphere" is a sphere. In R^2, however, with

$$d(\overline{x}, \overline{y}) = \sqrt{(x_1 - y_1)^2 + (x_2 - y_2)^2} ,$$

a sphere is flat, a circle. In R^1, with $d(x, y) = |x - y|$ a sphere is an interval.

Let us, more for experience than its importance, look at another metric on R^2. We define it as follows: for $\overline{x}, \overline{y} \in R^2$, let

$$d_2(\overline{x}, \overline{y}) = |x_1 - y_1| + |x_2 - y_2| .$$

Thus, if $\overline{x} = (2, 1)$ and $\overline{y} = (3, 5)$,

$$d_2(\overline{x}, \overline{y}) = |2 - 3| + |1 - 5| = 1 + 4 = 5 .$$

In effect, this says, draw a right-angle path (lines parallel to x and y axes) from one point to the other (Fig. 8.1) and take the sum of the lengths of these paths as the distance between points.

This is not an unnatural way of defining distance. For instance, consider this "map" (Fig. 8.2) of a section of a town. We would say that the

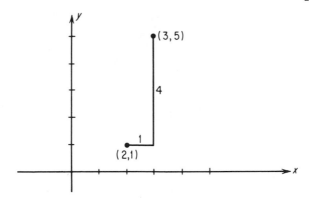

Figure 8.1

distance from point A to point B is 5 blocks and would, in this sense, figure the distance in the way we have just defined it.

We consider the problem of what spheres look like in this metric space. For example, let us consider $\{\bar{x} \mid d_2(\bar{x}, 0) = 1; 0 = (0, 0)\}$. First let us find some points on our sphere. Certainly $(1, 0)$, $(-1, 0)$, $(0, 1)$, $(0, -1)$ are on this sphere. We indicate these on a graph (Fig. 8.3). Because $|PQ| = |QR|$ and $|OQ| + |QR| = 1$ we see that any point, P, on the square satisfies our requirement.   So the boundary of our sphere is the square indicated. The (solid) sphere, $S_1(0)$, without boundary is the interior of this square.

We defined R^n, earlier, as the set of all n-tuples of real numbers; that is, R^n is defined by

$$R^n = \{(x_1, x_2, \ldots, x_n) \mid x_i \in R^1, \quad 1 \leq i \leq n\} .$$

We have pointed out that there are metrics for R^1, R^2, and R^3 that are pretty much the same. If we define a function $d : R^n \times R^n \to R^1$ by

$$d((x_1, x_2, \ldots, x_n), (y_1, y_2, \ldots, y_n)) = \sqrt{\sum_{i=1}^{n} (x_i - y_i)^2}$$

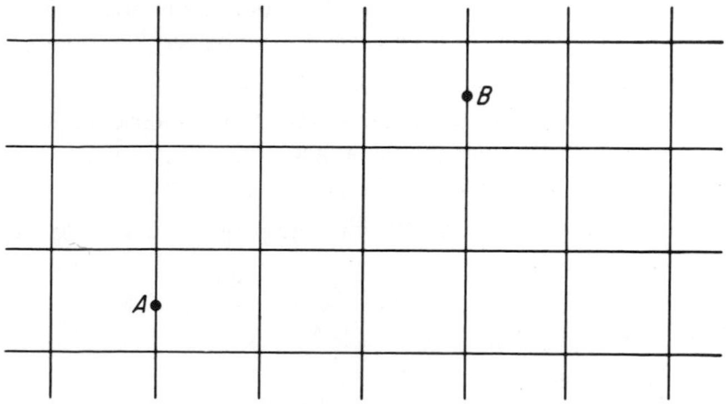

Figure 8.2

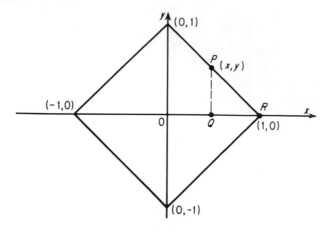

Figure 8.3

we have a metric for R^n called the *euclidean* metric. One can observe that for $n = 1, 2, 3$, this formula gives us the usual metrics for R^1, R^2, and R^3. We will not at this time verify that this is a metric for R^n but simply point out this general euclidean metric.

Exercise 8.1

1. Verify that d_2 as defined earlier is a metric for R^2.

2. Let $J = \{1, 2, 3, \ldots\}$ denote the set of all *positive integers*. For m and n in J, define $d(m, n) = \left| \dfrac{1}{m} - \dfrac{1}{n} \right|$.

   (a) Verify that d is a metric for J.

   (b) Describe the sphere of radius 1 with center at 6 in the metric space (J, d).

   (c) Describe the sphere of radius $1/10$ with center at 5. What if the center is at 20? At 100?

   (d) Explain why, in the metric space (J, d), one might make the paradoxical statement "Some spheres of the same size are bigger than others."

3. Assuming that the function $d : R^2 \times R^2 \to R^1$, defined by $d((x_1, y_1), (x_2, y_2)) = \max(|x_2 - x_1|, |y_2 - y_1|)$ for $(x_1, y_1), (x_2, y_2) \in R$, is a metric for R^2, describe the sphere of radius 1 with center at the origin. ($\max(|x_1 - x_2|, |y_1 - y_2|)$ means the larger of the two numbers.)

4. Using the euclidean metric d for R^n with the proper n, compute the following distances:

   (a) $d(1, -4)$.

   (b) $d((1, 6), (-1, 3))$.

   (c) $d((-2, 0, 3), (1, 4, 3))$.

   (d) $d((6, 2, 3, 4), (7, 6, 1, 4))$.

   (e) $d((0, 0, 0, 0, 0, 0, 0, 0), (1, -1, 1, -1, -1, 1, 1, 1))$.

5. What is the inequality describing the sphere with radius r and center $(z_1, z_2, \ldots, z_n)$ in (R^n, d) where d is the euclidean metric?

6. Describe the following spheres in R^n for the proper n by means of inequalities and, where possible, with a sketch.

(a) $S_1(0)$.   (b) $S_2(0)$.

(c) $S_{1/2}(-1)$.   (d) $S_2(3)$.

(e) $S_1((0, 0))$.   (f) $S_2((0, 0))$.

(g) $S_{1/2}((1/2, 1/2))$.   (h) $S_r((x_0, y_0))$.

(i) $S_1((1, 0, 1, 2))$.   (j) $S_r((a_1, a_2, \ldots, a_n))$.

8.2 Limits

In general, we have dealt with functions $f : X \to Y$ where X and Y were sets. In most of our examples we treated functions where X and Y were the same set, the set of real numbers. We return now to arbitrary sets on which metrics are defined. So let (X, d) and (Y, p) be metric spaces. Suppose now that f is a function from X into Y. For every $x \in X, \exists\, y \in Y$ so that $(x, y) \in f$ or so that $y = f(x)$. In practice, remember that both of these metric spaces might well be R^1 with its usual metric.

We want to consider the concept of the *limit of f at a point* $x_0 \in X$. Intuitively, consider the function $g : R^1 \to R^1$ defined by

$$g(x) = \frac{1}{x^2 + 1}, \quad \text{for } x \in R^1 .$$

If we asked what happens to the functional values $g(x)$ as "x gets close to 1," it would be pretty obvious that the answer should be that the numbers $g(x)$ "get close to $\frac{1}{2}$." If we asked what happens to the numbers $g(x)$ as "x gets close to 0," again the answer would be that the numbers $g(x)$ "get close to 1." In our everyday language, we could answer these questions. The problem that arises is — just what is that "gets close to" business? We might have intuitive notions about this, but it certainly needs to be made more precise before it can be handled mathematically. To indicate the weakness in our intuitive dealings, note that it is also true that $g(x)$ "gets close to 0.50000001" as x gets close to 1. Our notion must be refined to make clear what we mean. One might be inclined to say, why not simply evaluate $g(1)$? Frequently this would tell us what we want to know, but at times this is impossible to evaluate. As an example, what happens to $g(x)$ as x gets larger and larger? Here we cannot "plug in" a number, but it is clear that $g(x)$ gets close to 0. Note that for all x, $g(x) \neq 0$.

To deal with situations, like this we make a definition. It will be in the general setting of metric space described before.

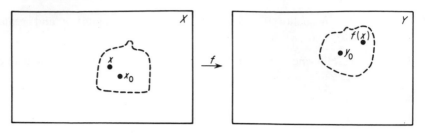

Figure 8.4

Definition 8.3. Let $f(X, d) \to (Y, p)$ be given. Suppose that $y_0 \in Y$ and $x_0 \in X$. The *limit of f at x_0 is y_0* $\Leftrightarrow$ given any sphere $T_r(y_0)$ about y_0, we can find a sphere $S_u(x_0)$ about x_0, so that

$$x \neq x_0 \quad \text{and} \quad x \in S_u(x_0) \Rightarrow f(x) \in T_r(y_0) .$$

Pictorially, we represent our metric spaces as rectangles (Fig. 8.4). Our definition tells us that no matter what sphere we are given about $y_0 \in Y$, we are able to find a sphere about $x_0 \in X$ with the property that, for each x, $x \neq x_0$, in the sphere about x_0, the functional value $f(x)$ lies in the given sphere about y_0.

If y_0 is *not* the limit of f at x_0, there is some sphere about y_0 that has the property that, no matter how we choose a sphere about x_0, there will be at least one point in the sphere about x_0 whose functional value $f(x)$ will be outside the given sphere about y_0.

That is why, in our earlier example, $g(x) = 1/(x^2 + 1)$, the limit of g at 1 is not 0.500001. Because, if we take a sphere (an interval) with radius less than 0.000001 about 0.500001 and, if x is close enough to 1, $g(x)$ will be outside the given sphere (Fig. 8.5).

Instead of using the phrase, "limit of f at x_0," we frequently use the phrase, "limit of $f(x)$ as x approaches x_0." In either case, we use the abbreviations $\lim_{x \to x_0} f(x) = y_0$ to indicate that the limit of f at x_0 is y_0.

As an example of the notion just presented, let us consider the function $f : (R^1, d) \to (R^1, d)$, where d denotes the usual metric $(d(x, y) = |x - y|)$ on R^1 and where f is given by $f(x) = 2x + 1$ for $x \in R^1$.

We claim $\lim_{x \to 2} f(x) = 5$. For, let us consider an arbitrary sphere, $S_r(5)$, about $5 \in R^1$. In the usual metric, $S_r(5) = (5 - r, 5 + r)$, an open interval

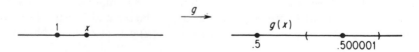

Figure 8.5

centered at 5 with length $2r$. Consider the sphere, $T_{r/2}(2)$, about $2 \in R^1$. Then

$$T_{r/2}(2) = \left(2 - \frac{r}{2}, 2 + \frac{r}{2}\right),$$

an open interval centered at 2 with length $r/2$. Now let $x \in T_{r/2}(2)$ and consider the following argument:

$$x \in T_{r/2}(2) \Rightarrow x \in \left(2 - \frac{r}{2}, 2 + \frac{r}{2}\right)$$

$$\Rightarrow 2 - \frac{r}{2} < x < 2 + \frac{r}{2}$$

$$\Rightarrow 4 - r < 2x < 4 + r$$

$$\Rightarrow 4 - r + 1 < 2x + 1 < 4 + r + 1$$

$$\Rightarrow 5 - r < 2x + 1 < 5 + r$$

$$\Rightarrow 5 - r < f(x) < 5 + r$$

$$\Rightarrow f(x) \in (5 - r, 5 + r) = S_r(5).$$

This tells us that, for any $x \in T_{r/2}(2)$, it is true that $f(x) \in S_r(5)$. But by Definition 8.3, this means $\lim_{x \to 2} f(x) = 5$, because we were given an arbitrary sphere, $S_r(5)$, about 5 and were able to pick a sphere, namely, $T_{r/2}(2)$, about 2, with the property that the functional value of every point in $T_{r/2}(2)$ is in $S_r(5)$.

Exercise 8.2

1. Let $f(x) = 3x + 2$. Show that $\lim_{x \to 1} f(x) = 5$.

   $\left(\text{If } S_r(5) \text{ is an arbitrary sphere about 5, choose } T_u(1) \text{ with } u = \frac{r}{3}.\right)$

2. Let $h(x) = \frac{1}{2}x + 7$. Show that $\lim_{x \to 4} f(x) = 9$. (Choose $u = 2r$.)

3. Let $k(x) = ax + b, a \neq 0$. Show that $\lim_{x \to x_0} k(x) = ax_0 + b$. $\left(\text{Choose } u = \frac{1}{|a|} \cdot r.\right)$

4. For the following linear functions prove that the limit is as indicated.

   (a) $\lim_{x \to 1} (4x + 2) = 6$.

   (b) $\lim_{x \to 3} \left(\frac{3 - x}{6}\right) = 0$.

   (c) $\lim_{x \to -1} (15x + 2) = -13$.

   (d) $\lim_{x \to 2} \left(\frac{x + 2}{2}\right) = 2$.

   (e) $\lim_{x \to 4} \left(\frac{1}{2}x + 5\right) = 7$.

   (f) $\lim_{x \to 0} (2x - 1) = -1$.

8.3 Limits of Real Functions

It is not a trivial matter to prove that $\lim_{x \to x_0} f(x) = L$ for arbitrary functions, even real-valued functions defined on subsets of real numbers. A very simple kind of function is given by $f(x) = x^2$. Even this presents a bit of a problem when we want to prove that $\lim_{x \to 3} f(x) = 9$. A nice rule like that which we can see for linear functions, $f(x) = (ax + b)$, does not hold. Once we choose the right u, however, we should not have much difficulty *showing* we are right. As before, let $S_r(9)$ be an arbitrary sphere about 9 and consider $T_{r/7}(3)$. Assume $r < 7$. Let $x \in T_{r/7}(3)$. Then,

$$x \in T_{r/7}(3) \Rightarrow 3 - \frac{r}{7} < x < 3 + \frac{r}{7} \Rightarrow -\frac{r}{7} < x - 3 < \frac{r}{7}.$$

Now

$$r < 7 \Rightarrow \frac{r}{7} < 1 \quad \text{and} \quad x \in T_{r/7}(3) \Rightarrow 0 < x + 3 < 7.$$

So

$$-\frac{r}{7}(x + 3) < (x + 3)(x - 3) < \frac{r}{7}(x + 3)$$

$$\Rightarrow -r < x^2 - 9 < r$$

$$\Rightarrow 9 - r < x^2 < 9 + r.$$

Thus,

$$x \in T_{r/7}(3) \Rightarrow x^2 = f(x) \in S_r(9).$$

We would now rewrite Definition 8.3 for the special case where (X, d) and (Y, p) are the same metric space, the set R^1 with its usual metric d.

For this case, the definition develops as follows:

$$\lim_{x \to x_0} f(x) = y_0 \Leftrightarrow \text{given any sphere, } T_r(y_0),$$

about the number y_0, we can find a sphere, $S_u(x_0)$, about x_0 so that

$$x \in S_u(x_0), \ x \neq x_0 \Rightarrow f(x) \in T_t(y_0)$$

$$\Leftrightarrow \text{given any sphere, } (y_0 - r, y_0 + r), \text{ about } y_0,$$

we can find a sphere, $(x_0 - u, x_0 + {}_u)$, about x_0 so that

$$x \in (x_0 - u, x_0 + u), \ x \neq x_0 \Leftrightarrow f(x) \in (y_0 - r, y_0 + r).$$

All that is involved in the foregoing reduction of our condition is the spelling out of the nature of "sphere" in R^1. Replacing the word sphere by the word "interval," our condition becomes the following:

Given any interval, $(y_0 - r, y_0 + r)$ about y_0, we can find an interval $(x_0 - u, x_0 + u)$, about x_0 so that

$$x_0 - u < x < x_0 + u, x \neq x_0, \Rightarrow y_0 - r < f(x) < y_0 + r .$$

Realizing we are going to center the spheres about x_0 and y_0, we write our condition in slightly different form.

Given any real number $r > 0$, we can find a real number $u > 0$ so that

$$x_0 - u < x < x_0 + u, x \neq x_0 \Rightarrow y_0 - r < f(x) < y_0 + r .$$

Finally, using the notation of absolute value, we are able to write our condition in another form.

Given any real number $r > 0$, we can find a real number $u > 0$, so that

$$0 < |x - x_0| < u \Rightarrow |f(x) - y_0| < r .$$

This last form is the one usually seen in definitions (with certain modifications) of $\lim_{x \to x_0} f(x) = y_0$, where f is a real-valued function whose domain is a subset of real numbers. For some reason, people, for years, have been using certain Greek letters instead of r and u in the definition. It also happens that, when one is using the notion of limit, the value $f(x_0)$ is frequently not of interest and sometimes is not defined. In view of these remarks, Definition 8.3 is usually seen as follows.

Definition 8.3. Let $f : A \to R^1$ be given, where $A \subset R^1$. For x_0 and $y_0 \in R^1$,

$$\lim_{x \to x_0} f(x) = y_0 \Leftrightarrow \text{given } \epsilon > 0 ,$$

we can find $\delta > 0$ so that,

$$0 < |x - x_0| < \delta \quad \text{and} \quad x \in A \Rightarrow |f(x) - y_0| < \epsilon .$$

8.4 Sequences

We now turn our attention to a slightly less general situation that is of interest in its own right. It might well serve to help the reader's understanding of what has been treated in previous sections. The concept involved is that of *sequence*. For our present purposes let J denote the set of positive integers.

Definition 8.4. Let X be a set. A *sequence* in X is a function from J into X.

This means, then, that a sequence is a function that pairs with each $n \in J$ an element, $f(n)$, in X. As a matter of common notation, when we are dealing with sequences, we write f_n instead of $f(n)$. Thus f_{10} would denote the element of X paired with the integer $10 \in J$.

To know a sequence a in X, we need to know the elements $a_n \in X$ for each $n \in J$. We call a_n the *nth term* of the sequence. The common way of denoting a sequence allows for a bit of confusion with the notation for sets. For, to denote a sequence, we frequently write $\{a_n\}$ or $\{a_1, a_2, \ldots, a_n, \ldots\}$. As an example of a sequence in R^1 consider $\left\{\dfrac{1}{2}, \dfrac{1}{4}, \ldots, \dfrac{1}{2^n}, \ldots\right\}$ or, alternatively, $\left\{\dfrac{1}{2^n}\right\}$. In order to reconcile this notation with that of sets, realize that the set $\{a_1, a_2, \ldots, a_n, \ldots\}$ is the range of the function a.

In what we do we will be dealing much of the time with sequences in R^1.

Definition 8.5. A sequence in R^1 is a *real sequence*.

Now consider the real sequences

(1) $$\{1, 0, 1, 0, \ldots, 1, 0, \ldots\},$$

(here $a_n = 1$ if n is odd and $a_n = 0$ if n is even),

(2) $$\{1, 2, 3, \ldots, n, \ldots\},$$

and

(3) $$\left\{1, \frac{1}{2}, \frac{1}{3}, \ldots, \frac{1}{n}, \ldots\right\}.$$

The sequence (3) has a property not possessed by the other two. It is the fact that, by choosing n "large enough," the nth term of the sequence and the terms "beyond" the nth are very close to the real number 0. The other sequences do not have this property. The sequence (2) in no way gets "close to" any real number. The sequence (1) is a sequence that alternates between two numbers and, in a sense, might be considered as getting close to either 0 or 1. The fact is that the terms of the sequence do not *stay* close to a number, even 0 or 1.

Sequences like the (3) are called *convergent*. We will formally define the concept of a convergent sequence in a metric space. First, one should realize that J, considered under the usual metric d for real numbers, is itself a metric space. Here $d(m, n) = |m - n|$ for $m, n \in J$. This particular metric space has the property that $d(m, n) \geq 1$ if $m \neq n$. In this sense, no distinct elements are close to each other.

Definition 8.6. Let (X, p) be a metric space and let $\{a_n\}$ be a sequence in X. Further let y_0 be an element of X. The *sequence $\{a_n\}$ converges to y_0* (and we write $\lim_{n \to \infty} a_n = y_0$) if and only if, given any sphere $S_r(y_0)$, we can find $N \in J$ with the property that $n \in J$, $n > N$ implies that $a_n \in S_r(y_0)$.

This simply says that, given any sphere about y_0, we can find a term a_n of the sequence so that for *all* the terms "beyond a_n," these terms are in the given sphere. Another way of viewing this is that, for any sphere about y_0, only a finite number of terms of the sequence are outside the sphere. (There might be a great many terms outside a given sphere. For example the first million-billion terms might be outside, but the rest — and there is no way of reaching the end of our count for the terms of a sequence — will be inside the given sphere if the sequence converges to y_0.)

One comment on the notation $\lim_{n \to \infty} a_n$ — we are defining the complete symbolism here and one should not worry about the meaning of $n \to \infty$ except as we have defined the entire concept.

We read $\lim_{n \to \infty} a_n = y_0$, as the limit, as n goes to infinity, of a_n is y_0. The warning just given is intended to avoid the problem of trying to define infinity. Although the word "infinity" is present, we are defining the phrase: the limit of a_n, as n goes to infinity, is y_0.

We should interpret Definition 8.6 for the case of real sequences in order to understand the definitions usually seen of this concept.

Remembering that, if we know where to center a sphere, the only fact we need to know is the radius to know the sphere. Definition 8.6 becomes, for (R^1, d), where d is the usual metric for R^1:

$$\lim_{n \to \infty} a_n = y_0 \in R^1 \Leftrightarrow \text{given any } r \in R^1, r > 0,$$

we can find $N \in J$ with the property that

$$n \in J, n > N \Leftrightarrow a_n \in (y_0 - r, y_0 + r).$$

Remembering that $a_n \in (y_0 - r, y_0 + r)$ is the same as $y_0 - r < a_n < y_0 + r$ and that it is also equivalent to $|a_n - y_0| < r$, we can use any of these conditions on the right of the last implication symbol. Thus, we can rewrite our definition as

Definition 8.6. $\lim_{n \to \infty} a_n = y_0 \Leftrightarrow$ given $r \in R^1, r > 0$, we can find $N \in J$ so that

$$n \in J, n > N \Rightarrow |a_n - y_0| < r.$$

Graphically, if we plot y_0 (Fig. 8.6) and consider the interval $(y_0 - r, y_0 + r)$, r any positive real number, then when we plot $a_1, a_2, \ldots$ we will arrive at a term a_N so that $a_{N+1}, a_{N+2}, \ldots$ will all be plotted inside $(y_0 - r, y_0 + r)$, if the sequence $\{a_n\}$ converges to y_0.

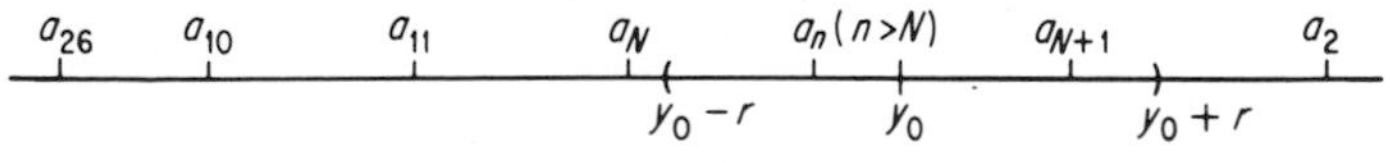

Figure 8.6

As a matter of common terminology, if a sequence converges to y_0 we call y_0 the *limit of the sequence*. Another notation frequently used to denote the fact that $\lim_{n\to\infty} a_n = y_0$ is

$$a_n \to y_0 \quad \text{as} \quad n \to \infty .$$

We look now at some examples of sequences that converge to real numbers.

EXAMPLE 1. Prove

$$\lim_{n\to\infty} \frac{n+1}{n} = 1 .$$

(Here $a_n = (n+1)/n$).

Proof. Let r be any positive real number. By our definition, we must now find a positive integer N so that, for any positive integer n greater than N, it is true that $1 - r < (n+1)/n < 1 + r$. In order that

$$1 - r < \frac{n+1}{n} < 1 + r ,$$

or, what is the same, that

$$1 - r < 1 + \frac{1}{n} < 1 + r ,$$

it is enough that $-r < 1/n < r$. Note that $0 < 1/n$. Thus we need to be sure only that $1/n < r$. But it is sufficient then, to choose N to be any integer greater than the real number $1/r$. (The proof that there exists an integer greater than any given real number is not included in this text. The reader, however, probably is not troubled too much by the use of this fact because it is not against his intuition.) Thus

$$n > N \Rightarrow -r < 0 < \frac{1}{n} < r$$

$$\Rightarrow 1 - r < 1 + \frac{1}{n} < 1 + r .$$

We have shown, then, given any $r < 0$, we can find $n \in J$ so that

$$n \in J, n > N \Rightarrow \frac{n+1}{n} \in (1 - r, 1 + r) .$$

Hence, we have shown that

$$\lim_{n\to\infty} \frac{n+1}{n} = 1 .$$

EXAMPLE 2. Prove

$$\lim_{n\to\infty} \frac{3}{n^2} = 0 .$$

Proof. Again let $r > 0$ be given. Our problem is to choose $N \in J$ so that $n \in J$, $n > N \Rightarrow -r < 3/n^2 < r$ (more properly, $0 - r < 3/n^2 < 0 + r$). Again observe that for $r > 0$, $-r < 0 < 3/n^2$ holds for every $n \in J$. So we need only to be sure that $3/n^2 < r$. But,

$$n > \sqrt{\frac{3}{r}} \Rightarrow n^2 > \frac{3}{r} \Rightarrow r > \frac{3}{n^2}.$$

So, if we select N to be any integer greater than $\sqrt{3/r}$, we have that

$$n > N \Rightarrow \frac{3}{n^2} < r \quad \text{or} \quad -r < \frac{3}{n^2} < r.$$

This means that, for $n > N$, $3/n^2 \in (-r, r)$ and we have proved

$$\lim_{n \to \infty} \frac{3}{n^2} = 0.$$

Let us consider other things that might have happened. The sequence $\{n^2\} = \{1, 4, 9, 16, \ldots\}$ clearly does not converge. Yet it has the property that it gets larger than any given number. Formally, given any real number r, $\exists N \in J$ so that

$$n > N, n \in J \Rightarrow n^2 > r.$$

When this occurs, we traditionally write $\lim_{n \to \infty} n^2 = \infty$, and say that the limit of the sequence is ∞. Realize that this sequence does not converge and that this terminology is introduced to handle this particular kind of lack of convergence.

Exercise 8.3

1. Write out the first five terms of each of the following sequences:

(a) $\left\{\dfrac{1}{2n}\right\}$.

(b) $\left\{\dfrac{1}{n^2}\right\}$.

(c) $\left\{\dfrac{(-1)^n}{n+1}\right\}$.

(d) $\left\{\dfrac{2+n}{n^2}\right\}$.

(e) $\left\{\left(\dfrac{n+1}{n^2+1}\right)^2\right\}$.

2. Prove

(a) $\lim\limits_{n \to \infty} \dfrac{1}{2n} = 0$.

(b) $\lim\limits_{n \to \infty} \dfrac{n}{n+1} = 1$.

(c) $\lim\limits_{n \to \infty} \dfrac{(-1)^n}{n+1} = 0$.

(d) $\lim\limits_{n \to \infty} \dfrac{1}{2^n} = 0$.

(e) $\lim\limits_{n \to \infty} (n-1) = \infty$.

(f) $\lim\limits_{n \to \infty} \dfrac{1 + (-1)^n}{2}$ does not exist.

8.5 Arithmetic and Geometric Sequences

The sequence

$$\{a, a + d, a + 2d, \ldots, a + nd, \ldots\} ,$$

where a and d are real numbers and n is a positive integer, is called an *arithmetic sequence*. The nth term of this sequence is $a + (n - 1)d$. The number a is called the *first term* (obviously) and the number d is called the *difference* (of the terms). It is certainly clear that the difference of any two consecutive terms is d.

If one knows the first term and the difference, it is simple to evaluate the nth term a_n by

$$a_n = a + (n - 1)d .$$

For example, if $a = 2$ and $d = 4$, the tenth term is

$$a_{10} = 2 + (10 - 1) \cdot 4 = 38 ,$$

or the five-hundred-fifty-ninth term is

$$a_{559} = 2 + 558 \cdot 4 = 2{,}234 .$$

With arithmetic sequences, it is reasonably simple to calculate the sum S_n of the first n terms of the sequence. For

$$S_n = a + (a + d) + \ldots + (a + (n - 1)d)$$

$$= n \cdot a + d(1 + 2 + 3 + \ldots + (n - 1))$$

$$= n \cdot a + d \frac{n(n - 1)}{2}$$

$$= n \left[a + \frac{(n - 1)d}{2} \right]$$

$$= \frac{n}{2} [2a + (n - 1)d]$$

$$= \frac{n}{2} [a + a + (n - 1)d]$$

$$= \frac{n}{2} [a + a_n] ,$$

where a_n is the nth term of the sequence.

As an example, let us find the sum S_{50} of the first 50 terms of the arithmetic sequence with $a = 2$ and $d = 4$. Now

$$a_{50} = 2 + 49 \cdot 4 = 198 ,$$

thus,
$$S_{50} = \frac{50}{2} [2 + 198] = 5{,}000 .$$

Another type of sequence, the geometric sequence, yields this same type of information readily.

A geometric sequence is one of the form,

$$\{a, ar, ar^2, ar^3, \ldots, ar^{n-1}, \ldots\}.$$

Here, $a, a \neq 0$, and $r, r \neq 0$ are real numbers and n is a positive integer. The nth term a_n is $a \cdot r^{n-1}$. The ratio $(a_{k+1})/a_n$ of two consecutive terms is the number r. For

$$\frac{a \cdot r^k}{a \cdot r^{k-1}} = r.$$

As an example, consider the geometric sequence where $a = 1$ and $r = \frac{3}{2}$. The fourth term of the sequence is given by

$$a_4 = a \cdot r^{4-1} = 1 \cdot \left(\frac{3}{2}\right)^3 = \frac{27}{8}.$$

To develop a formula for the sum S_n of the first n terms of a geometric sequence, note that

$$S_n = a + ar + ar^2 + \ldots + ar^{n-1},$$

and

$$rS_n = ar + ar^2 + ar^3 + \ldots + ar^n.$$

Subtracting the second of these from the first, we have

$$S_n - rS_n = a - ar^n,$$

or

$$S_n(1 - r) = a(1 - r^n).$$

This relation is not helpful when $r = 1$, but in that case, the problem is simple. For if $r = 1$, each $a_n = a$ and the desired sum S_n is $n \cdot a$.

But, if $r \neq 1$,

$$S_n = \frac{1 - r^n}{1 - r} \cdot a.$$

Earlier, we considered the geometric sequence with $a = 1$ and $r = \frac{3}{2}$. The sum S_4 of the first four terms is

$$S_4 = \frac{1 - (3/2)^4}{1 - 3/2} \cdot 1 = \frac{1 - (81/16)}{-1/2} = \frac{65}{8}.$$

One observation is in order. Let

$$\{a_n\} = \{ar^{n-1}\}$$

be a geometric sequence. Then the sequence

$$\{S_n\} = \left\{a \cdot \frac{1 - r^n}{1 - r}\right\}$$

converges when $|r| < 1$. For, when $|r| < 1$, $\lim\limits_{n \to \infty} r^n = 0$. Thus,

$$\lim_{n \to \infty} S_n = \frac{a}{1 - r}$$

when $|r| < 1$.

Exercise 8.4

1. In this exercise, we are dealing with arithmetic sequences (or progressions). We will give a, the initial term, and d, the difference. For the various sequences:
   (a) Write out the first 6 terms.
   (b) Write the ninety-first term and the five hundred and twenty-fifth term.
   (c) Find the sum S_{100} of the first 100 terms.

	a	d
(1)	1	3
(2)	-5	2
(3)	-98	4
(4)	2	-3
(5)	2	7
(6)	-4	1
(7)	3	-1
(8)	8	10
(9)	1	17
(10)	0	5

2. In this exercise, we deal with geometric sequences. We will give a and r. For the various sequences:
   (a) Write out the first 4 terms.
   (b) Write out the fifth term.
   (c) Find the sum S_5 of the first 5 terms.
   (d) Find $\lim\limits_{n \to \infty} S_n$ if it exists.

	a	r
(1)	1	$\frac{1}{2}$
(2)	1	2
(3)	3	$\frac{1}{4}$
(4)	2	$-\frac{1}{2}$
(5)	8	$\frac{1}{3}$
(6)	2	$\frac{1}{10}$
(7)	-2	$-\frac{1}{2}$
(8)	3	$\frac{1}{4}$
(9)	10	2

8.6 Properties of Limits

We are in a position now to prove certain theorems that are useful in computing limits. First we need the following definition.

Definition 8.7. A real sequence $\{a_n\}$ is *bounded* $\Leftrightarrow \exists$ a positive real number M so that $|a_n| \leq M$ for all $n \in J$.

Recall that $|a_n| < M \Leftrightarrow -M < a_n < M$.

Theorem 8.1. Every real convergent sequence is bounded.

Proof. Suppose that $\{a_n\}$ is a real sequence so that $\lim_{n \to \infty} a_n = y_0$, $y_0 \in R^1$. We must find a real number $M > 0$, so that $|a_n| \leq M$ for all $n \in J$. For every $r > 0, \exists N \in J$ so that, for $n \in J$, $n > N$, it is true that $|a_n - y_0| < r$. In particular, $\exists N_0$, so that, for $n \in J, n > N_0$, it is true that $|a_n - y_0| < 1$. If $|a_n - y_0| < 1$ then $|a_n| - |y_0| < 1$ and $|a_n| < 1 + |y_0|$. Consider now the finite set of numbers

$$\{|a_1|, |a_2|, \ldots, |a_{N_0}|, 1 + |y_0|\} .$$

Let M be the largest of these numbers. Then

$$|a_1| \leq M, |a_2| \leq M, \ldots, |a_N| \leq M .$$

Moreover for

$$n > N_0, |a_n| < 1 + |y_0| \leq M .$$

So, for every $n \in J$, it is true that $|a_n| \leq M$. Thus, $\{a_n\}$ is bounded.

Notice that not every bounded sequence converges. For example, $\{1, 0, 1, 0, \ldots, 1, 0, \ldots\}$ is bounded but does not converge. If $\{a_n\}$ is a real sequence and if k is any real number, we can consider a real sequence $\{ka_n\}$ whose nth term is k times the nth term of $\{a_n\}$. The following theorem relates the convergence of these two sequences:

Theorem 8.2. Suppose $\{a_n\}$ is a real sequence converging to x_0. Let $k \in R^1$. Then $\{ka_n\}$ converges to $k \cdot x_0$.

Proof. We need to show that, given $r > 0$, there exists $N \in J$ so that, for $n \in J$, $n > N$, $|ka_n - kx_0| < r$. So let $r > 0$ be given. If $k = 0$, the new sequence has 0 for each term and clearly converges to 0. If $k \neq 0$, consider the positive number $r/|k|$. Since $\lim_{n \to \infty} a_n = x_0, \exists N \in J$ so that, for $n \in J$,

$$n > N \Rightarrow |a_n - x_0| < \frac{r}{|k|} \Rightarrow |k| \cdot |a_n - x_0| < r$$

$$\Rightarrow |k(a_n - x_0)| \Rightarrow |ka_n - kx_0| < r .$$

So for $n > N$, we have $|ka_n - kx_0| < r$ and, therefore,

$$\lim_{n \to \infty} ka_n = kx_0.$$

Exercise

Prove directly (without using the result of Theorem 8.2) that $\{2a_n\}$ converges to $2x_0$ if $\{a_n\}$ converges to x_0.

We point out that this theorem has an analogue in limits of real-valued functions.

Theorem 8.2 (f). Suppose that $f : R^1 \to R^1$ is given and that $\lim_{x \to x_0} f(x) = y_0$. Let k be a real number. Then $g : R^1 \to R^1$, defined by $g(x) = k \cdot f(x)$ for $x \in R^1$, has the property that $\lim_{x \to x_0} g(x) = ky_0$. This result is frequently stated that,

$$\lim_{x \to x_0} k \cdot f(x) = k \cdot \lim_{x \to x_0} f(x).$$

Proof. If $k = 0$, then $g(x) = 0$ for all $x \in R^1$ and it is clear that

$$\lim_{x \to x_0} g(x) = 0 = k \cdot y_0.$$

Let $k \neq 0$ and suppose that $r > 0$ is given. Then $r/|k|$ is a positive real number. Since $\lim_{x \to x_0} f(x) = y_0, \exists\, u > 0$ so that

$$0 < |x - x_0| < u \Rightarrow |f(x) - y_0| < \frac{r}{|k|}.$$

Then

$$0 < |x - x_0| < u \Rightarrow |k| \cdot |f(x) - y_0| = |k \cdot f(x) - k \cdot y_0| < r.$$
$$\Rightarrow |g(x) - k \cdot y_0| < r.$$

But this insures that $\lim_{x \to x_0} g(x) = k \cdot y_0$.

This duality carries over in other theorems, some of which we now state. (The proofs for some of these will be given.)

Theorem 8.3. Let $\{a_n\}$ and $\{b_n\}$ be real sequences converging to x_0 and y_0, respectively. Then the sequence $\{a_n + b_n\}$, whose nth term is the sum of the nth terms of a_n and b_n, converges to $x_0 + y_0$.

The functional analogue of this theorem is

Theorem 8.3 (f). Let f and g be real-valued functions defined on the same subset A of R^1. Let $x_0 \in A$ and suppose that

$$\lim_{x \to x_0} f(x) = y_1 \quad \text{and} \quad \lim_{x \to x_0} g(x) = y_2.$$

Then the function $h : A \to R^1$, defined by

$$h(x) = f(x) + g(x) \quad \text{for} \quad x \in A,$$

has the property that $\lim_{x \to x_0} h(x) = y_1 + y_2$.

Proof. We first note that the conclusion of Theorem 8.3(f) is that

$$\lim_{x \to x_0} (f(x) + g(x)) = \lim_{x \to x_0} f(x) + \lim_{x \to x_0} g(x).$$

(We frequently state this result, simply, by saying that the limit of a sum of two functions is the sum of their limits.) Let $r > 0$ be given. We find $u > 0$ so that

$$0 < |x - x_0| < u \Longrightarrow |h(x) - (y_1 + y_2)| < r.$$

Now, since $\lim_{x \to x_0} f(x) = y_1, \exists\, u_1 > 0$ so that

$$0 < |x - x_0| < u_1 \Longrightarrow |f(x) - y_1| < \frac{r}{2}.$$

And, since $\lim_{x \to x_0} h(x) = y_2, \exists\, u_2 > 0$ so that

$$0 < |x - x_0| < u_2 \Longrightarrow |g(x) - y_2| < \frac{r}{2}.$$

Let u be the smaller of u_1 and u_2. Then,

$$0 < |x - x_0| < u \Longrightarrow |f(x) - y_1| < \frac{r}{2} \quad \text{and} \quad |g(x) - y_2| < \frac{r}{2}$$

$$\Longrightarrow |f(x) - y_1| + |g(x) - y_2| < \frac{r}{2} + \frac{r}{2}$$

$$\Longrightarrow |(f(x) + g(x)) - (y_1 + y_2)| < r$$

$$\Longrightarrow |h(x) - (y_1 + y_2)| < r.$$

But this is what we needed to prove the theorem.

Exercise

Prove Theorem 8.3.

By Theorem 8.3(f), if we know

$$\lim_{x \to 2} x^2 = 4 \quad \text{and} \quad \lim_{x \to 2} 2x^3 = 16,$$

then we know $\lim_{x \to 2} (x^2 + 2x^3) = 20$.

Other theorems of this sort are as follows:

Theorem 8.4. Let $\{a_n\}$ and $\{b_n\}$ be real sequences converging to x_0 and y_0, respectively. Then

$$\lim_{n \to \infty} a_n b_n = x_0 y_0 .$$

Theorem 8.4 (f). Let f and g be real-valued functions defined on the same subset A of R^1. Let $x_0 \in A$. Then, if

$$\lim_{x \to x_0} f(x) = y_1 \quad \text{and} \quad \lim_{x \to x_0} g(x) = y_2,$$

$$\lim_{x \to x_0} f(x)g(x) = y_1 y_2 .$$

Theorem 8.5. Let $\{a_n\}$ and $\{b_n\}$ be real sequences converging to x_0 and y_0 respectively. Further suppose that $b_n \neq 0$ for $n = 1, 2, \ldots$ and that $y_0 \neq 0$. Then

$$\lim_{n \to \infty} \frac{a_n}{b_n} = \frac{x_0}{y_0} .$$

As one might expect, an analogous theorem holds for functions that says that

$$\lim_{x \to x_0} \frac{f(x)}{g(x)} = \frac{y_1}{y_2}$$

with the proper restrictions on g and y_2.

Remark. The following remark is important and necessary at this time. In some of the theorems that we have stated, we have dealt with functions defined on all of R^1. For we have assumed in each instance that f and g were functions from R^1 into R^1 or from a subset A of R^1 into R^1. We certainly are frequently concerned with functions whose domains are subsets of real numbers.   We treat this general situation:

Let $A \subset R^1$ and let $f : A \to R^1$ be given. Let $x_0 \in A$. We defined (Definition 8.3) what is meant by $\lim_{x \to x_0} f(x) = y_0$. Our definition was

$$\lim_{x \to x_0} f(x) = y_0 \Leftrightarrow \text{given } \epsilon > 0$$

we can find $\delta > 0$ so that, if $x \in A$ and $0 < |x - x_0| < \delta$, then $|f(x) - y_0| < \epsilon$.

Now, we never do let $x = x_0$ (for we require $0 < |x - x_0|$). So we can generalize our concept a bit more. What we do need is the fact that there are $x \in A$ such that $0 < |x - x_0| < \delta$ for whatever δ we happen to have. What is necessary, then, is that every sphere about x_0 contain points of A. When this occurs, we say that x_0 is a *limit point* or *accumulation point* of the set A. So our notion of limit then can be extended to the following:

Let $f : A \to R^1$ be given and suppose x_0 is either a limit point of the set A or $x_0 \in A$. Then,

$$\lim_{x \to x_0} f(x) = y_0 \Leftrightarrow \text{given } \epsilon > 0$$

we can find $\delta > 0$ so that,

$$\text{if } x \in A \quad \text{and} \quad 0 < |x - x_0| < \delta, \text{ then } |f(x) - y_0| < \epsilon.$$

As an example of this situation, consider the function

$$f(x) = \frac{x^2 - 1}{x - 1}.$$

This function is not defined for $x = 1$ but is defined for all other real numbers. So every sphere about 1 contains points of the domain of this function. In view of our preceding comments we can now consider $\lim_{x \to 1} f(x)$. (Note that, if $x \neq 1, f(x) = x + 1$, and it is not hard to prove that $\lim_{x \to 1} f(x) = 2$.)

From now on, when we see the notation $\lim_{x \to x_0} f(x)$, we will assume that f is a real function defined on some subset A of R^1 and that either $x_0 \in A$ or x_0 is a limit point of A.

Remark. The limits of certain functions f at certain points x_0 do not exist. That is, there are no numbers y_0 with the required properties.

As an example consider the following function g on R^1. g is defined by

$$g(x) = n \in I, \quad \text{when } n \leq x < n + 1.$$

That is, $g(x)$ is the largest integer less than, or equal to, x. The common symbol for $g(x)$ is $[x]$. (g is called the *greatest integer function*.) We can graph the function simply (Fig. 8.7).

We would ask about $\lim_{x \to 2} g(x)$. Now in every interval $(2 - r, 2 + r)$ about 2 there are points in the intervals $(1, 2)$ and $(2, 3)$. But for $x \in (1, 2), g(x) = 1$, and for $x \in (2, 3), g(x) = 2$. So, if y_0 is any number whatsoever, consider the interval $U = (y_0 - \frac{1}{4}, y_0 + \frac{1}{4})$. This interval has length $\frac{1}{2}$ and, if $1 \in U$, $2 \notin U$, and vice versa. So, for the choice of $\epsilon = \frac{1}{4}$, it is impossible to find an interval, V, about 2, so that, for x in $V, g(x)$ is in U. Thus, no number y_0 exists so that $\lim_{x \to 2} g(x) = y_0$.

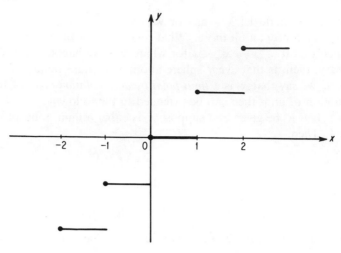

Figure 8.7

On the other hand, although no number might exist which is the limit of a certain function f at a point x_0, one situation occurs frequently enough to warrant a special notation.

Consider, by way of example, $\lim_{x \to 0} 1/x^2$. No number, y_0, exists so that

$$\lim_{x \to 0} \frac{1}{x^2} = y_0 .$$

Because, let y_0 be any number and let $\epsilon = 1$ be given. Now in every interval about 0 there are points x (close to 0) so that $1/x^2 > y_0 + 1$. So it is impossible to find an interval about 0 with the property that, if $x \in U$, $x \neq 0$, $1/x^2 \in (y_0 - 1, y_0 + 1)$, because U contains x so that

$$\frac{1}{x^2} > y_0 + 1 \quad \text{and} \quad \frac{1}{x^2} \notin (y_0 - 1, y_0 + 1) .$$

What *does* happen here is that the functional values get larger than any given number when x gets close to 0. When this happens, we agree to say that the limit of this function is infinity as x goes to 0 and we write

$$\lim_{x \to 0} \frac{1}{x^2} = \infty .$$

Formalizing this, we get the following definition:

Definition 8.8. $\lim_{x \to x_0} f(x) = \infty$ if and only if, given $M \in R^1$, we can find $\delta > 0$ so that, if $0 < |x - x_0| < \delta$ and $f(x)$ is defined, then $f(x) > M$.

In a completely analogous fashion, we make the definition:

Definition 8.8'. $\lim\limits_{x \to x_0} f(x) = -\infty$ if and only if, given $M \in R^1$, we can find $\delta > 0$, so that, if $0 < |x - x_0| < \delta$ and $f(x)$ is defined, then $f(x) < M$.

Remark. A common notation encountered is $\lim\limits_{x \to x_0^+} f(x)$. This means that we consider the limit of the function, dealing only with those x's which satisfy $x_0 < x$. If we see $\lim\limits_{x \to x_0^-} f(x)$, we consider only those x's so that $x < x_0$.

Using this notation, it is true that

$$\lim_{x \to 2^+} [x] = 2 \quad \text{and} \quad \lim_{x \to 2^-} [x] = 1,$$

whereas $\lim\limits_{x \to 2} [x]$ does not exist.

Essentially, when we do this, we change the domain of the function we are dealing with.

Remark. One encounters another bit of notation; the symbols

$$\lim_{x \to \infty} f(x) \quad \text{and} \quad \lim_{x \to \infty} f(x).$$

Here, we are still dealing with functions, f, defined on subsets of R^1 and $\pm \infty$ are not real numbers. To handle these cases, however, we make the following definitions:

Definition 8.9. $\lim\limits_{x \pm \infty} f(x) = y_0 \Leftrightarrow$ given $x > 0$, we can find $M \in R^1$ so that, if $x \lessgtr M$ and $f(x)$ is defined, then $|f(x) - y_0| < \epsilon$.

(Here for $+\infty$ read $>$ and for $-\infty$ read $<$.)

Without a formal definition, we indicate what we would mean by $\lim\limits_{x \to \infty} f(x) = \infty$. This means that, given any $K \in R^1$, we can find $M \in R^1$ so that, $x > M$ and $f(x)$ defined $\Rightarrow f(x) > K$.

As example of these remarks, we point out the following:

$$\lim_{x \to 0^+} \frac{1}{x} = \infty, \quad \lim_{x \to 0^-} \frac{1}{x} = -\infty ,$$

$$\lim_{x \to \infty} \frac{1}{x^2} = 0, \quad \lim_{x \to \infty} x^2 = \infty .$$

The preceding theorems and remarks are useful in the actual evaluation of limits.

For example, if we know that $\lim_{x \to a} x^n = a^n$ for every real number a and any positive integer n, we can evaluate

$$\lim_{x \to z} \frac{2x^3 + 3x + 1}{4x^4 - 2}$$

by the following sequence of steps.

$$\lim_{x \to 2} \frac{2x^3 + 3x + 1}{4x^4 - 2} = \frac{\lim_{x \to 2} (2x^3 + 3x + 1)}{\lim_{x \to 2} (4x^4 - 2)}$$

$$= \frac{\lim_{x \to 2} 2x^3 + \lim_{x \to 2} 3x + \lim_{x \to 2} 1}{\lim_{x \to 2} 4x^4 + \lim_{x \to 2} (-2)}$$

$$= \frac{\lim_{x \to 2} 2 \cdot \lim_{x \to 2} x^3 + \lim_{x \to 2} 3 \cdot \lim_{x \to 2} x + \lim_{x \to 2} 1}{\lim_{x \to 2} 4 \cdot \lim_{x \to 2} x^4 + \lim_{x \to 2} (-2)}$$

$$= \frac{2 \cdot 8 + 3 \cdot 2 + 1}{4 \cdot 16 + (-2)} = \frac{23}{62}.$$

Although it is not necessary to write out these steps in such detail, it is important to be aware that this is the procedure used in evaluating such limits.

Exercise 8.5

1. In the following, assume $\lim_{x \to a} kx^n = ka^n$. Evaluate the following limits:

(a) $\lim_{x \to 1} (3x^4 - 2x)$.

(b) $\lim_{x \to 2} \frac{2}{x^2 + 2}$.

(c) $\lim_{x \to 1} (x^2 + 1)(x + 3)$.

(d) $\lim_{x \to 1} \frac{4 + x^2}{4 + x^3}$.

(e) $\lim_{h \to 0} \frac{(3 + h)^2 - 9}{h}$.

(f) $\lim_{x \to \infty} \frac{1}{(x + 4)}$.

(g) $\lim_{x \to 1} \frac{1}{(x - 1)^2}$.

(h) $\lim_{x \to 0} \frac{1}{x^3}$.

(i) $\lim_{x \to 0^+} \frac{[x + 3] + |x + 2|}{3}$.

(j) $\lim_{x \to \infty} \frac{2x^2 + 4x + 3}{4x^2 - 1}$.

(k) $\lim_{x \to \infty} \frac{x^2 - 4}{x^3 + 2x}$.

(l) $\lim_{x \to \infty} \frac{x^4 + 3x^3 + 1}{x^2 + 2x + 1}$.

[*Hint* for (j) : Since we are dealing with x "large," we can assume that $x \neq 0$ and can divide numerator and denominator by x^2.]

(m) $\lim\limits_{x \to \infty} \dfrac{2x^2 + 4x}{x^2 + 1}$.   (n) $\lim\limits_{x \to 0} \dfrac{x^2 + x}{2x^2 + x}$.

2. In the following consider the given function, hold x as fixed, and consider h as the variable. Then evaluate

$$\lim_{h \to 0} \frac{f(x + h) - f(x)}{h}$$

(a) $f(x) = x^2$.   (b) $f(x) = \dfrac{1}{x}$.

(c) $f(x) = 2x^2 + 3x + 1$.   (d) $f(x) = x + \dfrac{1}{x}$.

(e) $f(x) = x^3 - x$.   (f) $f(x) = \sqrt{x + 1}$.

8.7 Continuity

For our purposes there are several results of immediate use. First we prove

Theorem 8.6. Let $f : R^1 \to R^1$ be defined by

$$f(x) = k \quad \text{for} \quad k \in R^1 \quad \text{and all } x \in R^1 .$$

Then

$$\lim_{x \to x_0} f(x) = k \quad \text{for any } x_0 \in R^1 .$$

Proof. This simply says that the limit of a constant function is that constant. Recall that, for any $x \in R^1, f(x) = k$. Let $r > 0$ be given. We find $u \in R^1$ so that

$$0 < |x - x_0| < u \Rightarrow |f(x) - k| < r .$$

Here choose $u = 1$. Then, for

$$0 < |x - x_0| < 1, |f(x) - k| = |k - k| = 0 < r .$$

(With this theorem, we have Theorem 8.2(f) as a special case of Theorem 8.4(f) that is,

$$\lim_{x \to x_0} k \cdot f(x) = k \cdot \lim_{x \to x_0} f(x)) .$$

Another result of use to us is

Theorem 8.7. Let $f(x) = x^n$ for any $n \in J$ be given. Let $a \in R^1$. Then

$$\lim_{x \to a} f(x) = a^n .$$

The proof of this theorem is omitted here.

As a consequence of the foregoing theorems, we can state

Theorem 8.8. Let
$$f(x) = b_0 + b_1 x + \ldots + b_n x^n$$
and
$$g(x) = c_0 + c_1 x + \ldots + c_m x^m$$

be two polynomials. Then, for any real number a so that $g(a) \neq 0$,

$$\lim_{x \to a} \frac{f(x)}{g(x)} = \frac{f(a)}{g(a)}.$$

This theorem tells us that, for any quotient $Q(x)$ of polynomials, to evaluate $\lim_{x \to a} Q(x)$ we simply "plug in" a for x, provided that the denominator is not 0.

This notion of plugging in the values of interest is not always possible in evaluating limits. For example, if we consider $\lim_{x \to 1} [(x - 1)/(x^2 - 1)]$ and simply "plug in" 1, we get as our answer $0/0$ and this is nothing. Or, if we consider $\lim_{x \to 2} [x]$, we get 2 as answer if we replace x by 2 and this is *not* correct.

Functions for which we get the correct answer by this process are called *continuous* at the point in question. We formalize this by

Definition 8.10. Let $f : A \to R^1$ be given and let $x_0 \in A$. Then f is *continuous at x_0* if and only if

$$\lim_{x \to x_0} f(x) = f(x_0).$$

If f is continuous at every point in A, it is said to be *continuous on A*.

The theorems we have seen before allow us to say that certain functions, e.g., polynomials, are continuous at certain points. Of course, by examples we have seen that there are functions that are not continuous at certain points.

We would remark that our definition implies that we speak of continuity only where a function is defined and that the limit of the function must exist and be the same as the value of the function at the point in question.

In considering the graph of a function that is continuous over an interval, we note that the graph is connected. That is, there are no holes and no jumps. Because, if f is continuous on $[a, b]$ and if $x_0 \in [a, b]$, the fact that

$$f(x_0) = \lim_{x \to x_0} f(x)$$

tells us that, if the functional values approach a number y_0 as x approaches x_0, then the value of the function at x_0 must be the number y_0. Now the graph is not necessarily "smooth" if the function is continuous, but it is connected.*

* There are functions not continuous at enough points where this remark does not apply.

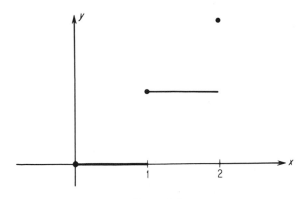

Figure 8.8

As example consider the function $g(x) = [x]$. Now over the interval $[0, 2]$ the function is not continuous and its graph has jumps (Fig. 8.8). But over the interval $[1\frac{1}{4}, 1\frac{3}{4}]$ it is continuous and its graph over this interval is connected.

As another example, consider the function $b(x) = 1/x^2$ as a function over $[-1, 1]$. Now, in fact, this function is not defined at the point $0 \in [-1, 1]$ and is, therefore, not continuous over this interval.

Exercise 8.6

Graph the following functions on the indicated interval and say whether or not they are continuous over the interval:

(a) $f(x) = [x]$ over $[-1, 1]$.

(b) $f(x) = [x]$ over $[1, 2]$.

(c) $f(x) = [x]$ over $[1, 2]$.

(d) $f(x) = \dfrac{1}{x}$ if $x \neq 0$, $f(x) = 0$ if $x = 0$ over $[-1, 1]$.

(e) $f(x) = \dfrac{1}{x}$ over $(0, 1]$.

(f) $f(x) = \dfrac{|x| + x}{2}$ over $(-2, 2)$.

(g) $f(x) = \dfrac{1}{x^2 + 1}$ over $[-2, 2]$.

(h) $f(x) = \dfrac{1}{x}$ over $[0, 2)$.

(i) $f(x) = \dfrac{x^2 + 1}{(x^2 - 1)(x - 2)}$ over R^1.

(j) $f(x) = \dfrac{x}{x - 1}$ over $[0, 2)$.

Applications of the Limit Concept

Comment. The concept of limit has many applications. The concept of derivative of a function is based on it, as is the concept of the integral. Hence, the notion of limit is the heart of calculus.

We now consider some applications of this idea that may be of interest in everyday life. Many applications depend on the nature of the functions involved and therefore on the nature of the graphs of these functions. A useful idea is that of a line tangent to a curve at a point.

9.1 Slope of Tangent Line

9

Consider the graph of a real-valued function f. Suppose that $(x_0, f(x_0))$ is a fixed point of the graph (Fig. 9.1) and let $(x_1, f(x_1))$ be any other point on the graph.

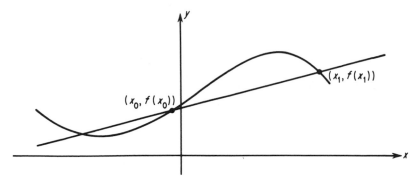

Figure 9.1

These two points determine a line (called a *secant*) with equation

$$y - f(x_0) = \frac{f(x_1) - f(x_0)}{x_1 - x_0} \cdot (x - x_0)$$

and with slope

$$\frac{f(x_1) - f(x_0)}{x_1 - x_0}.$$

Consider the limit

$$\lim_{x_1 \to x_0} \frac{f(x_1) - f(x_0)}{x_1 - x_0} = f'(x_0).$$

This limit may or may not exist (i.e., there is or there is not a real number which is the limit). If $f'(x_0)$ is a real number, we define the line tangent to the graph of f at $(x_0, f(x_0))$ to be the line with slope $f'(x_0)$ passing through $(x_0, f(x_0))$. If this limit is $\pm \infty$, we define the tangent line to be the line $x = x_0$. This is not as mysterious a procedure as it might seem. For all we do is to let $(x_1, f(x_1))$ "get close to $(x_0, f(x_0))$." The secants determined by these points "get close to" the line we defined as the tangent line.

Suppose that we wanted to find the equation of the line tangent to the graph of $f(x) = x^2$ at the point $(2, 4)$. Certainly the line goes through the point $(2, 4)$, so all we need to know in order to get this equation is the slope of the line involved. Thus we apply our definition to find $f'(2)$. Now,

$$f'(2) = \lim_{x_1 \to 2} \frac{f(x_1) - f(2)}{x_1 - 2}$$

$$= \lim_{x_1 \to 2} \frac{x_1^2 - 4}{x_1 - 2}.$$

Now, since $x_1 \neq 2$, we can write $(x_1^2 - 4)/(x_1 - 2)$ as $x_1 + 2$. So

$$f'(2) = \lim_{x_1 \to 2} (x_1 + 2) = 4 .$$

Therefore our tangent line has slope 4 and its equation is

$$y - 4 = 4(x - 2) \quad \text{or} \quad y - 4x + 4 = 0 .$$

A trick we could have used, to make the evaluation of this a bit easier, is that of replacing x_1 by $x_0 + h$. Then $x_1 - x_0 = h$ and

$$f'(x_0) = \lim_{h \to 0} \frac{f(x_0 + h) - f(x_0)}{h} .$$

In the preceding example, we could have asked for the equation of the tangent line at other points than $(2, 4)$, for example, at $(3, 9)$, $(5, 25)$, $(-10, 100)$, or others. In each case, we could go through a procedure just like we used for $(2, 4)$. On the other hand, we might well try to find $f'(x_0)$ for any x_0. Now

$$f'(x_0) = \lim_{h \to 0} \frac{f(x_0 + h) - f(x_0)}{h}$$

$$= \lim_{h \to 0} \frac{(x_0 + h)^2 - x_0^2}{h}$$

$$= \lim_{h \to 0} \frac{x_0^2 + 2x_0 h + h^2 - x_0^2}{h}$$

$$= \lim_{h \to 0} (2x_0 + h) \quad \text{(Remember } h \neq 0.\text{)}$$

$$= 2x_0 .$$

This says that the slope of the line tangent to the graph of $f(x)$ at $(x_0, f(x_0))$ is $2x_0$. Certainly this agrees with our result when $x_0 = 2$.

Exercise

As in the case $x_0 = 2$, compute $f'(3)$, $f'(4)$, $f'(5)$, $f'(-2.5)$, $f'(-10)$ directly and check your answer against the formula $f'(x_0) = 2x_0$.

Now if we know the slope of the tangent line, we know the slope of any line perpendicular to it. If (x_0, y_0) is a point on the graph of a function, we define the *normal* to the graph at this point to be the line perpendicular to the tangent line passing through (x_0, y_0).

Exercise 9.1

1. Compute $f'(x_0)$ for each function f given below.

(a) $f(x) = 1 - 2x$.

(b) $f(x) = \dfrac{x+1}{2}$.

(c) $f(x) = x^2 + x$.

(d) $f(x) = \dfrac{1}{x}$, $x \neq 0$.

(e) $f(x) = x + 1$.

(f) $f(x) = 3x$.

(g) $f(x) = x^3$.

(h) $f(x) = \dfrac{1}{x^2}$.

(i) $f(x) = x + \dfrac{1}{x}$.

(j) $f(x) = \dfrac{1}{\sqrt{x}}$.

2. For each of the preceding functions, find the equation of the tangent line at the point $(3, f(3))$. (In (a), $f(3) = -5$; in (b), $f(3) = 2$, etc.)

3. (a) In (c) find x so that $f'(x) = 3 : f'(x) = 9$.

(b) In (d) find x so that $f'(x) = -\dfrac{1}{4}$.

(c) In (e) find x so that $f'(x) = \dfrac{1}{2}$; $f'(x) = 0$.

9.2 Applications Involving Graphs

Many problems involving limits actually are problems involving the determination of points on graphs where the tangent line must have certain values. In general terms, if a graph of a function f is well behaved, we might be interested in where the function stops rising and where it starts falling when x, the variable of the domain of f, is considered as increasing.

As examples, the graphs in Fig. 9.2 have points, P, on one side of which the slope of a tangent line is positive, whereas, on the other side of P, the slope

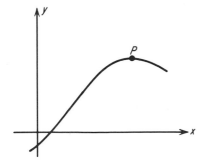
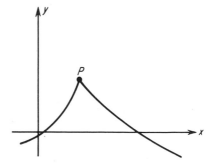

Figure 9.2

of the tangent lines is negative. We consider now an application of the limit concept where we are interested in finding such points.

Assume that a rectangle is to have a perimeter of 20 ft. We would like to choose the lengths of the sides of the rectangle so that its area is as large as possible. (Probably most readers know that we should discover that the area is as large as possible when the rectangle is a square.) Let x be the length of one side of the rectangle. Then the other side will be $10 - x$. Now there are many choices for x, restricted, of course, by the fact that $0 < x < 10$. If we make a choice for x, the area, A, for the resulting rectangle will be

$$A = x(10 - x) = A(x) \quad \text{or} \quad A(x) = 10x - x^2.$$

Now this is a function that we can graph (Fig. 9.3). On this graph there is a point P at which the slope of the tangent line is 0. At this point, the value $A(x)$ is as big as possible. If we can find the coordinates of this point, we will know how to choose x so that $A(x)$ is as large as possible.

Suppose that $(x_0, A(x_0))$ is any point on this graph. The tangent to the curve at this point has slope

$$A'(x_0) = \lim_{x_1 \to x_0} \frac{A(x_1) - A(x_0)}{x_1 - x_0}.$$

We will calculate this limit presently. To help us do this, observe that, if $h = x_1 - x_0 (x_1 = x_0 + h)$, we can rewrite $A'(x_0)$ as

$$A'(x_0) = \lim_{h \to 0} \frac{A(x_0 + h) - A(x_0)}{h}.$$

Now

$$A(x_0 + h) = 10(x_0 + h) - (x_0 + h)^2$$

$$= 10x_0 + 10h - x_0^2 - 2x_0h - h^2,$$

and

$$A(x_0) = 10x_0 - x_0^2.$$

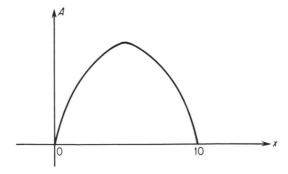

Figure 9.3

Then

$$\frac{A(x_0 + h) - A(x_0)}{h} = \frac{10h - 2x_0h - h^2}{h},$$

and, if $h \neq 0$,

$$\frac{A(x_0 + h) - A(x_0)}{h} = 10 - 2x_0 - h.$$

Thus

$$A'(x_0) = \lim_{h \to 0} \frac{A(x_0 + h) - A(x_0)}{h}$$

$$= 10 - 2x_0.$$

Now, if $x_0 = 2$, $A'(x_0) = 6$; if $x_0 = 7$, $A'(x_0) = -4$. In fact, for any x_0, $0 < x_0 < 10$, we can calculate the slope of the line tangent to our curve at the point $(x_0, A(x_0))$. We are interested in finding the point $(x_0, A(x_0))$ where $A'(x_0) = 0$. It should be clear that this happens when $x_0 = 5$. Realizing that, at this point $A(x)$ is as large as possible, we know that, by choosing $x = 5$ (hence $10 - x = 5$), we have made the area of our rectangle as large as possible. Of course this choice for x makes our rectangle a square.

Other applications might be found in graphing functions. For example, consider the function $y = x^3 - 9x$. It is clear that $y = 0$ when $x = 0$, when $x = 3$, and when $x = -3$. Of course, it is important to note that when $x > 3$, we have $y > 0$ and that $y < 0$ when $x < -3$. Let us now consider the slope of the tangent line at an arbitrary point on the graph. This slope, $m(x_0)$, is given by

$$m(x_0) = \lim_{h \to 0} \frac{(x_0 + h)^3 - 9(x_0 + h) - x_0^3 + 9x_0}{h}.$$

Evaluating this limit (again we insist that $h \neq 0$), we get $m(x_0) = 3x_0^2 - 9 = 3(x_0^2 - 3)$. So $m(x_0) > 0$ when $x_0 < -\sqrt{3}$ and when $x_0 > \sqrt{3}$. Also we have that $m(x_0) < 0$ when $-\sqrt{3} < x_0 < \sqrt{3}$. So it is possible to say that the curve rises from left to right when $x < -\sqrt{3}$ and when $x > \sqrt{3}$, and falls from left to right when $-\sqrt{3} < x < \sqrt{3}$. For when $x > \sqrt{3}$ and when $x < -\sqrt{3}$ the slope of the tangent is a positive number. Thus the rate of change of y, with increasing x, for these values of x is positive. That is, as x increases, y increases. This means the curve is rising from left to right. In a similar fashion, we have the curve falling from left to right when x is between $-\sqrt{3}$ and $\sqrt{3}$.

As a help, then, in graphing the function $y = x^3 - 9x$, we have that the graph rises from left to right when $x < -\sqrt{3}$ and when $x > \sqrt{3}$ because the tangent line has positive slope for these x. The graph falls from left to right when $-\sqrt{3} < x < \sqrt{3}$. And, of course, the tangent line has slope

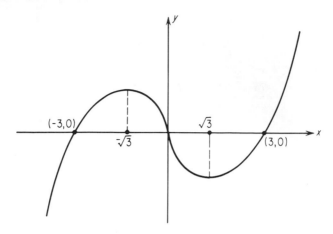

Figure 9.4

0 when $x = \pm\sqrt{3}$. Combining this information with the fact that the graph crosses the x axis at $x = 0$, $x = -3$, and $x = 3$, we see that the graph of the function looks like Fig. 9.4.

Exercise 9.2

1. Sketch the graphs of the following functions: Specifically find the intervals on which $f'(x) > 0$, $f'(x) < 0$ and determine the points where the tangent line is horizontal.

   (a) $y = x^2 - 1$.

   (b) $y = x + \dfrac{1}{x}$.

   (c) $y = x^4 - x^2$.

   (d) $y = x - 1$.

   (e) $y = \dfrac{1}{x}$.

   (f) $y = (x - 1)(x - 2)$.

   (g) $y = \dfrac{1}{x^2}$.

   (h) $y = \dfrac{x^2}{x^2 + 1}$.

   (i) $y = |x|$.

   (j) $y = x + |x|$.

2. A line k is given. A rectangle is to be constructed with a segment from k as one side. The length of the other three sides is to be 60 in. Choose the dimensions of the rectangle so that the area is as large as possible.

3. A closed rectangular box is to have a surface area of 2,400 sq in. and it is to have a square base. Choose its dimensions so that its volume is as large as possible.

4. Two real numbers x and y with sum 16 are chosen so that their product is as large as possible. What are the numbers? (*Hint:* $y = 16 - x$).

5. A box with a square base is to be made from a square piece of tin by cutting squares from each of its corners and bending up the sides. If the piece of tin is 16 in. on each side, what size square should be cut from each corner to obtain the box with maximum volume? What is this maximum volume?

6. A closed box with rectangular base twice as long as wide is to have a fixed surface area of 324 sq in. Find the dimensions of the box if its volume is as large as possible.

9.3 Velocity

Another application of the concept of limit is that of finding "instantaneous velocity." We are pretty well conditioned to thinking in terms of average velocity. So long as velocity is constant over a time interval, this notion is sufficient. But when velocity is always changing, we would, at times, like to speak of the velocity of something at a particular time. Certainly the people riding rockets are interested in how fast they will be traveling at the end of 10 sec of the ride, and the velocity is not constant in this situation.

Our concept of average velocity is defined in terms of displacement from a fixed point of reference at the ends of a time interval. In what we do, we will assume that our motion is on a straight line and that the point of reference is also on that line. For example, if p_0 is the fixed point and if we are y_1 units from p_0 at time t_1 and y_2 units from p_0 at a later time t_2, we take the average velocity over this time interval to be $(y_2 - y_1)/(t_2 - t_1)$ units of distance per unit of time.

Now, in general, the displacement of a point is a function of time and we will write $y = s(t)$. If we write $y_2 = s(t_2)$ and $y_1 = s(t_1)$, the foregoing quotient becomes

$$\frac{s(t_2) - s(t_1)}{t_2 - t_1}.$$

This looks very much like the quotient,

$$\frac{f(x_2) - f(x_1)}{x_2 - x_1},$$

which we were handling in Sec. 9.2, except for the variables involved. Certainly if we wanted to shrink the time interval, we would get a better idea of what the velocity is at a particular time t_1. In fact, we will take as a definition of instantaneous velocity at the time, t_1,

$$v(t_1) = s'(t_1) = \lim_{t_2 \to t_1} \frac{s(t_2) - s(t_1)}{t_2 - t_1}.$$

This definition should pretty well agree with the reader's intuitive idea of what instantaneous velocity should be.

As an example of this, consider the equation,

$$s(t) = s = 256 - 16t^2 .$$

This equation gives the height above the ground at the end of t sec of a ball dropped from a height of 256 ft. (Of course this is idealized and factors, such as air resistance, are ignored.) For example, at the end of 3 sec the height of the ball is

$$s(3) = 256 - 144$$

$$= 112 \text{ ft.}$$

The ball hits the ground at the end of 4 sec because

$$s(4) = 256 - 16 \cdot 4^2 = 0 .$$

Now in terms of what we did before, the velocity at the end of t sec is given by the limit

$$\lim_{h \to 0} \frac{s(t + h) - s(t)}{h} .$$

Evaluating this, we have

$$\lim_{h \to 0} \frac{256 - 16(t + h)^2 - 256 + 16t^2}{h}$$

$$= \lim_{h \to 0} \frac{256 - 16t^2 - 32th - 16h^2 - 256 + 16t^2}{h}$$

$$= \lim_{h \to 0} (32t - 16h)$$

$$= -32t .$$

Thus $v(t) = -32t$. At the end of 3 sec, the velocity of the ball is -96 ft per second. When the ball hits the ground, it does so with a velocity of $-32 \cdot 4 = -128$ ft per second.

The minus sign indicates that, as t increases, the distance from our point of reference decreases.

Exercise 9.3

1. In the following, suppose that s is in feet and t is in seconds. Each formula represents the displacement of a point moving on a line from a fixed point.

(a) $s = t - 1$.

(b) $s = t^2 - 1$.

(c) $s = 32 - t^2$.

(d) $s = t^2 - 2t + 1$.

(e) $s = t^3 - t$.

(f) $s = \dfrac{t}{1 + t^2}$.

In each case, find

　(1)　The initial displacement ($t = 0$).

　(2)　The displacement at the end of 3 sec.

　(3)　The initial velocity (that is, when $t = 0$).

　(4)　The velocity at the end of 2 sec; 4 sec.

2. A ball thrown from the top of a 500-ft building has its height, s, from the ground given by

$$s = 500 + 320t - 16t^2,$$

where s is in feet and t is in seconds.

(a)　When does the ball hit the ground?

(b)　What is its initial velocity?

(c)　What is its velocity when it hits the ground?

(d)　When is its velocity 0?

(e)　How high above the building does it go?

3. A ball thrown from the ground has its height, s, from the ground given by

$$s = 288t - 16t^2,$$

where s is in feet and t is in seconds.
Answer the questions in Problem 2.

4. Replace the equation in Problem 2 by

$$s = 500 + 256t - 16t^2$$

and answer the questions in Problem 2.

9.4　Finding Areas

The application we deal with here is a bit different from those we have seen before and is workable only in very special cases. It is inserted simply because it is a different sort of application.

Consider the triangle (Fig. 9.5) bounded by the lines $y = x$, $x = 2$, and $y = 0$. Its area is clearly 2. Break the interval $[0, 2]$ into n equal parts. Now in Fig. 9.5, we have the interval divided into 6 parts. We have, then, the $n + 1$ points, with x coordinates $0, 2/n, 4/n, \ldots, 2n/n$, on the x axis determining n intervals of length $2/n$. Now on each interval construct a rectangle with height determined by finding the point on the line $y = x$ directly over the right end point of each interval. In this case, if the interval is

$$[[2(i - 1)]/n, (2i/n)]$$

the height of the rectangle is $2i/n$. We are thus able to compute the area of each of the rectangles involved. When $i = 1$, the area of the rectangle is

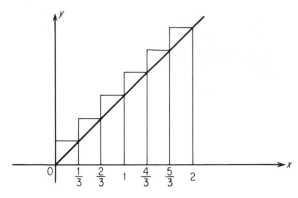

Figure 9.5

$2/n \cdot 2/n = 4/n^2$. When $i = 2$, the area of the rectangle is $2/n \cdot 4/n$. We can do this for each i, $1 \leq i \leq n$, getting the area of the kth rectangle to be $2/n \cdot 2k/n$.

In the particular case we have drawn, where $n = 6$, the areas of the six rectangles are

$$\frac{2}{6} \cdot \frac{2}{6} = \frac{4}{36}, \quad \frac{2}{6} \cdot \frac{4}{6} = \frac{8}{36}, \quad \frac{2}{6} \cdot \frac{6}{6} = \frac{12}{36}, \quad \frac{2}{6} \cdot \frac{8}{6} = \frac{16}{36}, \quad \frac{2}{6} \cdot \frac{10}{6} = \frac{20}{36}$$

$$\text{and} \quad \frac{2}{6} \cdot \frac{12}{6} = \frac{24}{36} \text{ square units .}$$

Now if we add these together, we get $84/36$ square units or $2\frac{1}{3}$ square units. This is an approximation to the area of the triangle in which we are interested. The error of $\frac{1}{3}$ is due to the portion of each rectangle that is outside the area of the triangle. We would expect that, if we had broken our interval into, say, 60 parts instead of 6, the sum of the areas of the rectangles outside the triangle would decrease and the number we would get by adding the areas of the rectangles would be a better approximation to the area of the triangle.

We might ask, what is the sum of the areas of the rectangles when we use n equal subdivisions of the interval $[0, 2]$? We denote this area by A_n. Then

$$A_n = \frac{2}{n} \cdot \frac{2}{n} + \frac{2}{n} \cdot \frac{4}{n} + \frac{2}{n} \cdot \frac{6}{n} + \ldots + \frac{2}{n} \cdot \frac{2n}{n}$$

$$= \frac{4}{n^2}[1 + 2 + \ldots + n].$$

It is well known that the sum of the first n positive integers is $[n(n + 1)]/2$. Thus,

$$A_n = \frac{4}{n^2} \cdot \frac{n(n + 1)}{2} = 2 \cdot \frac{n^2 + n}{n^2} = 2\left(1 + \frac{1}{n}\right).$$

Observe that, when $n = 6$, $A_6 = 2(1 + \frac{1}{6}) = 2 + \frac{1}{3} = 2\frac{1}{3}$. This agrees with our previous calculation.

So for any positive integer n, we have a number A_n which approximates the area of the triangle. For example, $A_{50} = 2 + 1/25$, $A_{500} = 2 + 1/250$, $A_{1,000,000} = 2 + 1/500,000$.

Thus we have a real sequence $\{A_n\}$, and if our intuition is not entirely misleading (and sometimes it is), the area of the triangle should be $\lim_{n\to\infty} A_n$. In this case,

$$\lim_{n\to\infty} A_n = \lim_{n\to\infty} 2\left(1 + \frac{1}{n}\right) = 2,$$

and we have the right answer.

Now at this time, we have no way of saying when this technique will work and when it will not, and we feel it is beyond the scope of this text to resolve this problem. This, however, is a sample of the usefulness of the notion of the limit of a sequence.

Exercise 9.4

1. Use the technique just given to find the area of the triangle bounded by
   (a) $y = 2x$, $x = 1$, $y = 0$.
   (b) $y = \dfrac{x}{2}$, $x = 2$, $y = 0$.
   (c) $y = 4x$, $x = 2.37$, $y = 0$.
   (d) $y = mx$, $x = a$, $y = 0$, $(a > 0, m > 0)$.

2. Use the technique cited to find the area in the first quadrant above the x axis under the curve $y = x^2$ and to the left of $x = 1$.

3. Solve Problem 2 for the curves,
   (a) $y = x + 1$.   (b) $y = 2x + 1$.
   (c) $y = x^2 + 1$.   (d) $y = 1 - x^2$.

   Remark. The applications presented in this chapter are a slight indication of the nature of the problems that can be solved using the notion of limits. We would point out that for a given function f,

$$\lim_{h\to 0} \frac{f(x_0 + h) - f(x_0)}{h},$$

is called the *derivative* of f at x_0. Methods of calculating this limit simply and applications of this concept to various kinds of problems is the subject of differential calculus. The type of application considered in Sec. 9.4 is the sort of material treated in integral calculus. (We do not here imply that these are or should be treated separately.)

Answers
to Exercises

Chapter 1

Exercise 1.1

1. (a) x is an element of set A. (b) Either x is an element of set A or x is an element of set B. (c) y is an element of set B. (d) y is an element of the set of x's such that each x is a positive integer. (e) y is an element of the set of x's such that property P holds for each x.

2. (a) $z \in C$. (b) $x \in B$. (c) $y \in \{x \mid x$ is an integer, $x > 0\}$.

3. (a) True. (b) False. (c) False. (d) True. (e) True.
   (f) True. (g) False. (h) False. (i) True. (j) True.

4. (a) $\{x \mid x$ is an integer, $0 < x < 10\}$.
   (b) $\{x \mid x$ is an integer, $x^2 < 16\}$.
   (c) $\{x \mid x$ is an integer, $x > 9\}$.
   (d) $\{x \mid x$ is an integer, $x < 0\}$.

(e) $\{x \mid x$ is an integer, $0 < x < 101\}$.

(f) $\{x \mid x$ is an integer, $x + 4 = 7\}$.

(g) $\{x \mid x$ is an integer, $x^2 > 9\}$.

(h) $\{x \mid x$ is an integer, $9 < x^2 < 50\}$.

(i) $\{x \mid x$ is an integer, $x^3 < 8, x^3 > 25\}$ NOTE: (This set has no elements in it.)

(j) $\{x \mid x$ is now a teacher in Ohio$\}$.

Exercise 1.2

1. (a) A is a subset of B.   (b) C is a subset of D.   (c)   If x is an element of set A, then x is an element of set C.   (d) A is a subset of B if and only if every x in set A is also in set B.   (e) B is a subset of C if and only if every x in set B is also in set C.

2. (a) $A \subset B$.   (b) $B \subset A$.   (c) $x \in A \Rightarrow x \in B$.   (d) $x \in A \Rightarrow x \in B$.
   (e) $B \subset C \Leftrightarrow (x \in B \Rightarrow x \in C)$.

3. (a)   Yes. (b)   Yes. (c)   No. (d)   No. (e)   Yes, $x \in E \Rightarrow x \in H$.
   (f)   No, 1, 4 $\in H$ but 1, 4 $\notin F$.

4. (a) $C \subset D$.   (b)   No relation.   (c) $C = D$.   (d) $x \in D$.   (e)   No.

5. (b) $\{1, 2, 3, 4\}$ $\{1, 2, 3\}$ $\{1, 2, 4\}$ $\{1, 3, 4\}$ $\{2, 3, 4\}$ $\{1, 2\}$ $\{1, 3\}$
   $\{1, 4\}$ $\{2, 3\}$ $\{2, 4\}$ $\{3, 4\}$ $\{1\}$ $\{2\}$ $\{3\}$ $\{4\}$ $\emptyset$

Exercise 1.3

1. $A \times B = \{(a, 0)(a, 1)(b, 0)(b, 1)(c, 0)(c, 1)(d, 0)(d, 1)\}$.
   $B \times A = \{(0, a)(1, a)(0, b)(1, b)(0, c)(1, c)(0, d)(1, d)\}$.
   $A \times A = \{(a, a)(a, b)(a, c)(a, d)(b, a)(b, b)(b, c)(b, d)$
   $\qquad\qquad\qquad\qquad (c, a)(c, b)(c, c)(c, d)(d, a)(d, b)(d, c)(d, d)\}$.
   $B \times B = \{(0, 0)(0, 1)(1, 0)(1, 1)\}$.

2. (a) $K' = \{(a, 1)(b, 2)(c, 3)(d, 4)\}$.
   (b) $K'' = \{(a, 4)(b, 3)(c, 2)(d, 1)\}$.
   (c)   (1)   Once in K'; once in K''; (2) once in K'; once in K''; (3) K' satisfies it; K'' satisfies it.
   (d) $\{(n, 2n) \mid n \in N\}$.   (e) $\{(n, 2n - 1) \mid n \in N\} = K'$.

3. (b) $K' = \{(n, n + 9) \mid n \in N\}$.

Exercise 1.4

1. (a) $A \cup B = \{1, 3, 5, 7, 8\}$. $A \cap B = \{3, 5\}$.
   (b) $A \cup B = \{1, 2, 3, 4, 5, 6, 8\}$. $A \cap B = \emptyset$.

3. (a) $x \in (A \cap B) \Rightarrow x \in A$ and $x \in B$.
   (b) $(x \in A$ or $x \in B) \Rightarrow x \in (A \cup B)$.
   (c) $(x \in A$ and $x \in B) \Rightarrow x \in (A \cap B)$.
   (d) $x \in (A \cup B) \Rightarrow x \in A$ or $x \in B$.

4. (a) $E \cup F = \{1, 2, 3, 4, 5, 6\}$. $E \subset (E \cup F)$.

(b) $E \cap F = \{2, 5\}$; $(E \cap F) \subset E$; $(E \cap F) \subset F$; $(E \cap F) \subset (E \cup F)$.

(c) $E \cup F = \{1, 2, 3, 4, 5, 6\}$ $G = \{4, 5, 6, 7\}$
$(E \cup F) \cup G = \{1, 2, 3, 4, 5, 6, 7\}$.

(d) $E = \{1, 2, 4, 5\}$ $F \cup G = \{2, 3, 4, 5, 6, 7\}$
$E \cup (F \cup G) = \{1, 2, 3, 4, 5, 6, 7\}$ $E \cup (F \cup G) = (E \cup F) \cup G$.

(e) $\{2\}$ $(1, 4]$. (f) $\varnothing$ $(1, 6]$. (g) $[3, 7][1, 8]$.

Exercise 1.6

1. (a) (1) $E' = \{3, 6, 7, 8\}$; (2) $F' = \{1, 4, 7, 8\}$; (3) $G' = \{1, 2, 3, 8\}$.

(b) $E' \cap F' = \{7, 8\}$.

(c) $(E \cup F)' = \{7, 8\}$, $E' \cap F' = (E \cup F)'$.

(d) $(E \cap F)' = \{1, 3, 4, 6, 7, 8\}$.

(e) $E' \cup F' = \{1, 3, 4, 6, 7, 8\}$ $E' \cup F' = (E \cap F)'$.

Exercise 1.7

1. (a) f_1 and f_5.

(b) (1) domain of $f_1 = \{1, 2, 3\}$, domain of $f_5 = \{1, 2, 3\}$;

(2) $R(f_1) = \{a\}$; $R(f_5) = \{a, b, c\}$; (3) image space of f_1
$= \{a, b, c\}$; image space of $f_5 = \{a, b, c\}$.

(c) f_5 is 1–1. (d) f_5 is onto.

2. (a) $f_1, f_3,$ and f_5.

(b) (1) domain of $f_1 = \{1, 2, 3\}$; domain of $f_3 = \{1, 2, 3\}$;
domain of $f_5 = \{1, 2, 3\}$.

(2) $R(f_1) = \{a\}$; $R(f_3) = \{a, b, d\}$; $R(f_5) = \{a, b, c\}$.

(3) Image space of $f_1 = \{a, b, c, d\}$; image space of $f_3 = \{a, b, c, d\}$;
image space of $f_5 = \{a, b, c, d\}$.

(c) f_3 and f_5 are 1–1. (d) None are onto.

3. (a) Not 1–1 since the pairs $(1, 2)$ and $(-1, 2)$ are both in the function.

(b) Not onto because $0 \notin R(h)$ although $0 \in$ image space.

Exercise 1.8

1. (a) $\{x \mid x \in R^1\}$. (b) $\{x \mid x \in R^1\}$. (c) $\{x \mid x \in R^1, x \neq 1\}$.

(d) $\{x \mid x \in R^1, x > 1\}$. (e) $\{x \mid x \in R^1, x \leq 1\}$.

(f) $\{x \mid x \in R^1, x \neq \pm 1\}$.

2. (a) $\{x \mid x \in R^1\}$. (b) $\{x \mid x \in R^1, x \neq 0\}$.

(c) $\{t \mid t \in R^1, t \neq 0\}$.

(d) $\{z \mid z \in R^1, z \neq 0\}$. (e) $\{T \mid T \in R^1, T \neq 0\}$.

(f) $\{y \mid y \in R^1, y \neq 0\}$. (g) $\{x \mid x \in R^1\}$.

(h) $\{h \mid h \in R^1, h \neq 0\}$.

3. (1) $f(x)$; $g(x)$; $u(x)$.

(2) $f(x)$; $f(t)$; $f(z)$; $u(T)$; $r(x)$; $w(h)$.

4. $R(f) = \{x \mid x \in R^1\}$;
$R(g) = \{y \mid y \in R^1, y \neq 0\}$;

$R(h) = \{y \mid y \in R^1, y \geq 1\}$;
$R(u) = \{y \mid y \in R^1, y > 0\}$.

Exercise 1.9

1. (a) $\{(x, y) \mid x \in R^1, y = 1 - x\}$.

(b) $\left\{(x, y) \mid x \in R^1, x \neq 0, y = \dfrac{1}{x}\right\}$.

(c) $\{(x, y) \mid x \in R^1, y = x^2 - 1\}$.

(d) $\left\{(x, y) \mid x \in R^1, x \neq 0, x \neq 1, y = \dfrac{x}{x} - 1\right\}$.

(e) $\{(x, y) \mid x \in R^1, x \neq 0, x = y\}$.

(f) $\left\{(x, y) \mid x \in R^1, x > \dfrac{1}{3} \text{ or } x < 0, y = \sqrt{\dfrac{x}{(3x - 1)}}\right\}$.

(g) $\left\{(x, y) \mid x = \dfrac{1}{3}, y \in R^1\right\}$.   (h) $\{(x, y) \mid x \in R^1, y = \pm x\}$.

(i) $\{(x, y) \mid x \in R^1, y = -3x\}$.   (j) $\{(x, y) \mid x \in R^1, y = 4x^2 + x + 1\}$.

(k) $\left\{(x, y) \mid x \in R^1, x \neq 0, y = -\dfrac{1}{x}\right\}$.   (l) $\{(x, y) \mid x \in R^1, y = x + 2\}$.

3. (a) $\{(u, v) \mid v = \sqrt{1 - u}\}$ for any $u > 1 \not\exists v \in R^1 \in (u, v)$ of the solution set.

(b) There are no numbers $u, v \in R^1$ that make this a true statement.

(c) $\{(u, \pm 2) \mid u \in R^1\}$ thus $(x, 2)(x, -2)$ are elements of the solution set, but this contradicts the definition of a function.

(d) $\{(u, \pm u) \mid u \in R^1, u \neq 0\}$ thus, as above (u, u), $(u, -u)$ contradicts the definition of a function.

Exercise 1.10

(a) Reflexive, symmetric, transitive. (b) Symmetric. (c) (Reflexive: under certain definitions of parallel), symmetric, transitive. (d) Reflexive, transitive. (e) Symmetric. (f) Symmetric. (g) Reflexive. (h) Reflexive, symmetric, transitive. (i) Reflexive, symmetric, transitive. (j) Reflexive, symmetric, transitive.

Exercise 1.11

1. (b) $[(a, b)] = \{(c, d) \mid (c, d) \in X, a - c = b - d\}$.

2. (b) $[(a, b)] = \{(x, y) \mid (x, y) \in X, a - x = y - b\}$.

3. (b) $[(a, b)] = \{(f, g) \mid (f, g) \in K, a \cdot g = b \cdot f\}$.

Chapter 2

Exercise 2.1

1. (a) Yes. (b) Yes. (c) No. (d) No. (e) Yes. (f) Yes.

Exercise 2.3

1. (a) Commutative, associative. (b) Commutative, associative. (c) Associative. (d) Neither. (e) Neither. (f) Commutative. (g) Commutative. (h) Neither.

Exercise 2.4

1. (a) $\{-3\}$. (b) $\emptyset$. (c) $\{2\}$. (d) $\{0, 4\}$. (e) $\{2, -1\}$.

   (f) $\left\{\dfrac{7}{2}, -\dfrac{1}{3}\right\}$. (g) $\left\{0, \dfrac{1}{8}\right\}$. (h) $\{2\}$. (i) $\{-3, -2\}$.

   (j) $\left\{\dfrac{1}{3}\right\}$. (k) $\{+1, -1\}$. (l) $\{+4, -4\}$. (m) $\{-2, -1\}$.

Exercise 2.5

   (a) $\dfrac{19}{15}$. (c) $\dfrac{7}{12}$. (e) $\dfrac{3 + xy}{3x}$. (g) $\dfrac{2x}{x^2 - 4}$.

   (i) $\dfrac{x^2 + 4}{2x}$. (k) $\dfrac{5x^2 - 6x^4 - 6}{6x^2}$. (m) $\dfrac{x^2 + 4x}{2x + 4}$. (o) $\dfrac{yz + xy + xz}{xyz}$.

Exercise 2.7

1. (a) $\{3\}$. (b) $\emptyset$. (c) $\{-2\}$. (d) $\{4, 2\}$. (e) $\emptyset$.
   (f) $\emptyset$. (g) $\{+2, -2\}$. (h) $\emptyset$.

2. (1) (a) $\{3\}$. (b) $\emptyset$. (c) $\{-2\}$. (d) $\{4, 2\}$. (e) $\left\{-\dfrac{2}{5}\right\}$.

   (f) $\left\{\dfrac{3}{2}\right\}$. (g) $\{+2, -2\}$. (h) $\emptyset$.

   (2) Same as part 2 Sec. (1).

Exercise 2.9

1. (a) $\{x \mid x \in R^1, x < -4\}$. (c) $\{x \mid x \in R^1, x < 2\}$.

   (e) $\{x \mid x \in R^1, x > -22\}$. (g) $\left\{x \mid x \in R^1, x > -\dfrac{1}{2}\right\}$.

   (i) $\{x \mid x \in R^1, 0 < x < 1\}$. (k) $\{x \mid x \in R^1, x < 1 \ \ \text{or} \ \ x > 2\}$.
   (m) $\{x \mid x \in R^1, x < -2 \ \ \text{or} \ \ x > 2\}$. (o) $\emptyset$.

   (q) $\left\{x \mid x \in R^1, x < \dfrac{5}{4}\right\}$. (s) $\left\{x \mid x \in R^1, x < -\dfrac{3}{2}\right\}$.

   (u) $\{x \mid x \in R^1\}$. (w) $\{x \mid x \in R^1, x > 0, \ \ \text{or} \ \ x < -2\}$.

2. (a)   Reflexive, transitive.   (b)   O2, O3, O4.

3. (a) $\{x \mid x \in R^1, x \leq -4\}$.   (c) $\{x \mid x \in R^1, x \leq 2\}$.

   (e) $\{x \mid x \in R^1, x \geq -22\}$.   (g) $\{x \mid x \in R', x \geq -\frac{1}{2}\}$.

   (i) $\{x \mid x \in R^1, 0 \leq x < 1\}$.   (k) $\{x \mid x \in R^1, x \leq 1$ or $x \geq 2\}$.

   (m) $\{x \mid x \in R^1, x \leq -2$ or $x \geq 2\}$.   (o) $\{x \mid x \in R^1, x = -2\}$.

   (q) $\{x \mid x \in R^1, x \leq \frac{5}{4}\}$.   (s) $\{x \mid x \in R^1, x \leq -\frac{3}{2}\}$.

   (u) $\{x \mid x \in R^1\}$.   (w) $\{x \mid x \in R^1, x \geq 0$ or $x \leq -2\}$.

Exercise 2.10

3. (a) $\{x \mid x \in R^1, -4 < x < 10\}$.   (b) $\{x \mid x \in R^1, x = -4$ or $x = 10\}$.

   (c) $\{x \mid x \in R^1, x < -4$ or $x > 10\}$.

   (d) $\{x \mid x \in R^1, x = -1$ or $x = -2\}$.

   (e) $\{x \mid x \in R^1, -2 < x < -1\}$.

   (f) $\{x \mid x \in R^1, -3 \leq x \leq 3\}$.

   (g) $\emptyset$.   (h) $\{x \mid x \in R^1, -4 < x < 4\}$.

   (i) $\{x \mid x \in R^1, -\frac{1}{2} \leq x \leq \frac{7}{2}\}$.   (j) $\{x \mid x \in R^1, -3 \leq x \leq 1\}$.

4. (a) $\emptyset$.   (b) $\{x \mid x \in R^1, x = \frac{5}{2}$ or $x = -\frac{5}{2}\}$.

   (c) $\{x \mid x \in R^1, -\frac{11}{7} < x < \frac{3}{7}\}$.

   (d) $\{x \mid x \in R^1, x = \frac{7}{2}$ or $x = -\frac{7}{2}\}$.

   (e) $\{x \mid x \in R^1, x < 5\}$.   (f) $\{x \mid x \in R^1, x < 0\}$.

   (g) $\{x \mid x \in R^1\}$.   (h) $\{x \mid x \in R^1, x = \frac{4}{3}$ or $x = -\frac{4}{3}\}$.

   (i) $\emptyset$.   (j) $\{x \mid x \in R^1, x > 0\}$.

Exercise 2.11

   (a) $\{x \mid x \in R^1, x = 3$ or $x = -1\}$.

   (c) $\{x \mid x \in R^1, x = -3$ or $x = 1\}$.

   (e) $\{x \mid x \in R^1, x = 2\}$.

   (g) $\{x \mid x \in R^1, x = \frac{-3 + \sqrt{6}}{3}$ or $x = \frac{-3 - \sqrt{6}}{3}\}$.

   (i) $\{x \mid x \in R', x = \frac{-\pi + \sqrt{\pi^2 + 20/\pi}}{10}$ or $x = \frac{-\pi - \sqrt{\pi^2 + 20/\pi}}{10}\}$.

Chapter 3

Exercise 3.1

1. On x axis; first; second; third; fourth; fourth; first.

Exercise 3.2

1. 2; 3; 3; 4; 4; 0.

Exercise 3.3

1. (a) 2. (c) 5. (e) 5. (g) $\sqrt{x^2 + y^2}$. (i) $\sqrt{(x - h)^2 + (y - k)^2}$.
   (k) $b\sqrt{10}$.

3. $3\sqrt{10} + 5\sqrt{2}$.

4. $6\sqrt{5} + 4\sqrt{2}$.

5. $d(P, Q) = \sqrt{5};\quad d(Q, R) = 2\sqrt{5}; d(P, R) = 3\sqrt{5}$.

9. (b) 28.

10. (a) $(2, -2)$. (b) Inscribing the triangle in a circle.

Exercise 3.5

1. (a) $(3, 3)$. (c) $(3, \frac{1}{2})$. (e) $(\frac{1}{2}, \frac{5}{2})$. (g) $\left(\dfrac{h}{2}, \dfrac{k}{2}\right)$.

   (i) $\left(\dfrac{a + b}{2}, \dfrac{c}{2}\right)$. (k) $(1, \frac{1}{2})$.

2. (a) $\left(\dfrac{7}{3}, \dfrac{7}{3}\right)$. (c) $\left(2, \dfrac{1}{3}\right)$. (e) $\left(0, \dfrac{8}{3}\right)$. (g) $\left(\dfrac{2h}{3}, \dfrac{k}{3}\right)$.

3. (a) $\left(\dfrac{13}{5}, \dfrac{13}{5}\right)$. (c) $\left(\dfrac{12}{5}, \dfrac{2}{5}\right)$. (e) $\left(\dfrac{1}{5}, 3\right)$. (g) $\left(\dfrac{3h}{5}, \dfrac{2k}{5}\right)$.

4. $2\sqrt{2}$; $\sqrt{41}$; $\sqrt{53}$.

5. $\sqrt{5} + \sqrt{13} + \sqrt{10}$.

Exercise 3.6

1. 10.

2. $\dfrac{1}{2}[(x_1y_3 + y_1x_2 + x_3y_2) - (x_2y_3 + x_3y_1 + x_1y_2)]$.

Exercise 3.7

   (a) b, c, e, g are functions. (b) b, c, e are 1–1; b, c are onto.

Chapter 4

Exercise 4.1

1. (a) $(6, 4)$. (c) $(3, 2)$. (e) (x, y). (g) $(0, t + 1)$. (h) $(0, 0)$.
   (j) $(0, 0)$. (l) $(3, 2b)$.
3. (a) $(-1, 3)$. (c) $(5, 9)$. (e) $(0, 0)$. (g) $(a - c, b - d)$.

Exercise 4.2

3. The points lie on a line.

4. (a) $(-5, 6)$. (c) $\left(\dfrac{a_1}{2} + \dfrac{a_2}{2}, \dfrac{b_1}{2} + \dfrac{b_2}{2} \right)$. (e) (h, b).

5. (a) $s = 1, t = -1$. (b) $s = \dfrac{1}{2}, t = \dfrac{1}{2}$. (c) $s = 2, t = -3$.

   (d) $s = \dfrac{1}{2}, t = 0$. (e) $s = -3, t = -\dfrac{1}{2}$.

Exercise 4.3

1. (a) $(3, 6)$. (b) $(0, -1)$. (c) $(-7, -9)$. (d) $(-2, 4)$.
   (e) $(0, 9)$. (f) $(-3, 2)$. (g) $\left(\dfrac{3}{2}, -\dfrac{3}{2} \right)$.

2. (a) $\sqrt{10}$. (b) 5. (c) $2\sqrt{5}$. (d) $\sqrt{2}$. (e) $2\sqrt{29}$.
   (f) $\sqrt{58}$. (g) $3\sqrt{29}$. (h) 0.

3. $(1, 1)$ and $(3, 2)$.
4. $(-1, 4)$.
5. $(2, 1)$.

6. $\left(\dfrac{5}{2}, -2 \right)$.

7. $\dfrac{5}{2}$.

Exercise 4.4

(a) $x - y = 0$. (b) $x + y = 0$. (c) $x - 2 = 0$. (d) $x - y = -1$.
(e) $6x + 7y = 46$. (f) $x - y = 1$. (g) $x - 2y = -6$.
(h) $691x + 2y = 889$. (i) $y - 6 = 0$. (j) $x - y = 11$.

Exercise 4.5

1. (b) Parallel to, or coincides with, the x axis. (c) Parallel to, or coincides with, the y axis. (d) $y = 0$: $x = 0$.

2. (a) $2x - y = 0.$ (b) $x - y = 0.$ (c) $x - y = 1.$ (d) $3x + 2y = 5.$

(e) $x - 2y = -4.$ (f) $x - 10y = 95.$ (g) $3x + 4y = 16.$

(h) $5y - 2 = 0.$ (i) $x + 8 = 0.$ (j) $ax - y = ax_1 - y_1.$

4. $y = 2.$

5. $(10, 5).$

6. (a) $3x - 2y = 1.$ (b) $y = 28.$

Exercise 4.7

(a) $\dfrac{3}{4}.$ (b) $-9.$ (c) $0.$ (d) No slope.   (e) $2.$ (f) $\dfrac{1}{6}.$

(g) $-\dfrac{1}{2}.$ (h) $\dfrac{3}{8}.$ (i) $\dfrac{1}{9}.$ (j) $\dfrac{5}{2}.$ (k) $4.$ (l) $-2.$

Exercise 4.8

1. (a) $x - y = 0.$ (b) $x + y = 0.$

2. (a) $3x - y + 1 = 0.$ (b) $x + 3y - 13 = 0.$

3. (a) $x + 1 = 0.$ (b) $y - 3 = 0.$

4. (a) $y + 1 = 0.$ (b) $x - 1 = 0.$

5. $2x - y = 5.$

8. $\dfrac{4\sqrt{5}}{5}.$

Exercise 4.9

(a) $(1, 8).$ (c) $(4, -1).$ (e) $(a, b).$ (g) $(10, 0).$ (i) $(a^2 + b^2, 0).$

(k) $(1, 0).$ (m) $(-1, 0).$ (o) $(-b, a).$ (p) $(-12, -7).$ (r) $(0, 0).$

Exercise 4.10

1. (a) $2 - i.$ (b) $0 - i.$ (c) $1 + 0i.$ (d) $0 + i.$ (e) $0 + i.$

(f) $0 - i.$ (g) $0 + i.$ (h) $14 - 2i.$ (i) $-10 + 0 \cdot i.$

(j) $-1 + \dfrac{1}{2}i.$ (k) $-\dfrac{1}{2} - \dfrac{1}{2}i.$ (l) $2 - 3i.$

(m) $-\dfrac{4}{25} - \dfrac{3}{25}i.$ (n) $\dfrac{1}{2} + \dfrac{1}{2}i.$ (o) $0 - i.$

(p) $\dfrac{1}{5} - \dfrac{3}{5}i.$ (q) $\dfrac{13}{4} - \dfrac{9}{4}i.$ (r) $\dfrac{13}{4} + \dfrac{9}{4}i.$

2. (a) $x = \pm i.$ (b) $x = \dfrac{4i - 3}{2}.$ (c) $x = 2i - 6.$

(d) $x = \dfrac{-1 \pm i\sqrt{3}}{2}.$ (e) $x = 0; x = -i.$ (f) $x = \dfrac{-1 \pm \sqrt{11}}{2}.$

Exercise 4.12

2. (a) $x = z, y = 1.$ (b) $-x + 1 = y = z - 1.$

(c) $\dfrac{x - 1}{-1} = \dfrac{y - 1}{1} = \dfrac{z + 2}{6}.$ (d) $x = y = z - 3.$

(e) $\dfrac{x + 2}{6} = \dfrac{y - 3}{3} = \dfrac{z + 3}{1}.$

Exercise 4.13

1. (a) $\sqrt{3}.$ (c) $\sqrt{41}.$ (e) $\sqrt{30}.$ (g) $3\sqrt{2}.$

(i) $\sqrt{a^2 + b^2 + c^2 - 2a - 2b + 2}.$ (k) $2t + 1.$

3. (a) $x + y + z = 6.$ (c) $x + y + z = 15.$ (e) $x = 1.$

4. (a) $x^2 + y^2 + z^2 - 2x - 2y - 2z = 6.$

(b) $x^2 + y^2 + z^2 - 2y - 2z = 2.$

5. (a) $x = y = z.$ (b) $\dfrac{x + 1}{3} = \dfrac{y + 1}{4} = \dfrac{z}{4}.$

(c) $\dfrac{x + 2}{2} = \dfrac{y + 4}{5} = \dfrac{z - 1}{-1}.$ (d) $\dfrac{x}{1} = \dfrac{y - 3}{-1} = \dfrac{z + 3}{4}.$

(e) $\dfrac{x - 1}{a - 1} = \dfrac{y - 1}{b - 1} = \dfrac{z}{c}.$ (f) $\dfrac{x + t - 1}{2t} = \dfrac{y - t + 1}{2} = \dfrac{z - 1}{-1}.$

Chapter 5

Exercise 5.1

1. (a) $(5, -1).$ (c) $\left(-\dfrac{1}{17}, -\dfrac{19}{17}\right).$ (e) $\left\{(x, y) \mid y = \dfrac{1 - x}{3}\right\}.$

(g) $\left(\dfrac{47}{13}, -\dfrac{1}{13}\right).$ (j) There is no pair (x, y) of real numbers such that $x + y = 7$ and $2x + 2y = 9.$

Exercise 5.3

1. (a) Maximum $(5, 10)$; minimum $(2, 0).$ (b) Maximum $(12, 15)$; minimum $(10, 5).$ (c) Maximum $(10, 10)$; minimum $\left(\dfrac{7}{2}, 0\right).$

(d) Maximum $(7, 5)$; minimum $(1, 1).$ (e) Not a polygon.

2. (a) Maximum $(5, 0)$; minimum $(0, 10).$ (b) Maximum $(10, 5)$; minimum $(10, 15).$ (c) Maximum $(6, 10)$; minimum $(10, 10).$

(d) Maximum $(4, 2)$; minimum $(2, 4).$ (e) Not a polygon.

3. (a) Fifteen min for the comic; 5 min for the band; 10 min for the commercials.
   (b) Yes; 10 min for the comic; 10 min for the band; 10 min for the commercials.
   (c) 10 min for the comic; 17 min for the band; 3 min for the commercials.

4. (a) history   6 hr   82 points
   English   6 hr   76 points
   mathematics   12 hr   78 points
   chemistry   6 hr   68 points

   (b) history $4\frac{1}{2}$ hr $71\frac{1}{2}$ points
   English $7\frac{1}{2}$ hr   85 points
   mathematics   9 hr   66 points
   chemistry   9 hr   77 points

   (c) history   5 hr   75 points
   English   6 hr   76 points
   mathematics   10 hr   70 points
   chemistry   9 hr   77 points

   (d) He is not wrong.
   history   5 hr   75 points
   English $8\frac{1}{3}$ hr   90 points
   mathematics   10 hr   70 points
   chemistry $6\frac{2}{3}$ hr   70 points

5. (a) Ship 400 to A, 800 to B, none local.

   (b) Ship 700 to A, 500 to B, none local.

Chapter 6

Exercise 6.1

1. (a) $\left\{1, \frac{1}{2}, \frac{1}{3}, \frac{1}{4}, \frac{1}{5}\right\}$. (b) $\left\{\frac{1}{3}, \frac{2}{9}, \frac{4}{27}\right\}$. (c) $\{1, 3, 5, 7\}$.

   (d) $\left\{-\frac{1}{3}, \frac{1}{5}, -\frac{1}{7}, \frac{1}{9}\right\}$. (e) $\{2, 4, 6, 8\}$. (f) $\left\{\frac{1}{2}, \frac{1}{6}, \frac{1}{12}\right\}$.

   (g) $\{2, 4, 8, 16\}$. (h) $\left\{-1, \frac{1}{2}, -\frac{1}{5}, \frac{1}{10}, -\frac{1}{17}\right\}$.

   (i) $\left\{\frac{1}{4}, \frac{1}{8}, \frac{1}{16}, \frac{1}{32}, \frac{1}{64}\right\}$. (j) $\{1, x, x^2, x^3, x^4\}$.

   (k) $\{1, 2, 6\}$. (l) $\left\{1, -\frac{1}{2}, \frac{1}{6}, -\frac{1}{24}, \frac{1}{120}\right\}$.

   (m) $\left\{0, \frac{1}{2}, 1, \frac{3}{2}, 2, \frac{5}{2}, 3\right\}$. (n) $\{9, -27, 81, -243\}$.

2. (a) 15. (b) $\frac{15}{8}$. (c) 36. (d) 36. (e) 0. (f) 13.

   (g) 50. (h) $\frac{37}{24}$. (i) 255. (j) $\frac{5,171}{400}$.

3. (a) $\left\{\frac{1}{2^k}\right\}^4_{k=1}$. (b) $\{k\}^3_{k=0}$.

   (c) $\{(-1)^{k+1}(k^2 + 1)\}^4_{k=1}$ or $\{(-1)^k[(k + 1)^2 + 1]\}^3_{k=0}$.

   (d) $\left\{\frac{k}{k^2 - 1}\right\}^5_{k=2}$.

(e) $\left\{\dfrac{k}{k(k-1)+1}\right\}_{k=1}^{5}$ or $\left\{\dfrac{k+1}{k(k+1)+1}\right\}_{k=0}^{4}$.

(f) $\displaystyle\sum_{i=1}^{5}\frac{1}{i}$. (g) $\displaystyle\sum_{i=1}^{100} i$. (h) $\displaystyle\sum_{i=1}^{5} i(i+1)$.

Exercise 6.2

1. (a) $\{1, 2, 4, 3, 9\}$. (b) $\left\{1, 2, 3, \dfrac{1}{2}, \dfrac{3}{2}, \dfrac{1}{4}, \dfrac{3}{4}\right\}$.

(c) $\{2, 3, 4, 5, 6\}$. (d) $\{1, 2, 4, 8\}$. (e) $\{0, 1, 2, 3\}$.

(f) $\left\{\dfrac{1}{2}, 1, 2, 4, \dfrac{1}{3}, \dfrac{2}{3}, \dfrac{4}{3}, \dfrac{8}{3}, \dfrac{1}{4}\right\}$. (g) $\{-2, -3, -4, 2, 3, 4\}$.

(h) $\{1, 2, 4, 8, 16, 32, 64, 256, 1024\}$.

2. (a) $\dfrac{11}{2}$. (b) 18. (c) $\dfrac{7}{6}$. (d) 19. (e) $\dfrac{13}{4}$.

3. (a) $\{j+k\}_{j=1,\,k=1}^{3,\,2}$. (b) $\{j^k\}_{j=1,\,k=1}^{4,\,2}$.

(c) $\{j^k\}_{j=2,\,k=1}^{4,\,3}$. (d) $\left\{\dfrac{a^k}{j}\right\}_{j=1,\,k=1}^{2,\,3}$.

(e) $\left\{\dfrac{k}{j}\right\}_{j=2,\,k=1}^{4,\,3}$.

Exercise 6.3

1. (a) 2. (b) 99. (c) 0. (d) 10.

2. (a) $\begin{pmatrix} 2 & 3 & 4 & 5 \\ 3 & 4 & 5 & 6 \end{pmatrix}$. (b) $\begin{pmatrix} 1 & 2 & 3 & 4 \\ 2 & 4 & 6 & 8 \end{pmatrix}$.

3. $\begin{pmatrix} -1 \\ 1 \\ -1 \\ 1 \\ -1 \\ 1 \\ -1 \\ 1 \\ -1 \\ 1 \end{pmatrix}$.

4. (a) $\begin{pmatrix} 0 & -1 & -2 & -3 & -4 \\ 1 & 0 & -1 & -2 & -3 \\ 2 & 1 & 0 & -1 & -2 \\ 3 & 2 & 1 & 0 & -1 \\ 4 & 3 & 2 & 1 & 0 \end{pmatrix}$. (b) $\begin{pmatrix} 2 & 5 & 10 & 17 & 26 \\ 5 & 8 & 13 & 20 & 29 \\ 10 & 13 & 18 & 25 & 34 \\ 17 & 20 & 25 & 32 & 41 \\ 26 & 29 & 34 & 41 & 50 \end{pmatrix}$.

(c)
$$\begin{pmatrix} 1 & 2 & 3 & 4 & 5 \\ 5 & 4 & 5 & 6 & 7 \\ 11 & 10 & 9 & 10 & 11 \\ 19 & 18 & 17 & 16 & 17 \\ 29 & 28 & 27 & 26 & 25 \end{pmatrix}.$$

(d)
$$\begin{pmatrix} 1 & \frac{1}{2} & \frac{1}{3} & \frac{1}{4} & \frac{1}{5} \\ 2 & 1 & \frac{2}{3} & \frac{1}{2} & \frac{2}{5} \\ 3 & \frac{3}{2} & 1 & \frac{3}{4} & \frac{3}{5} \\ 4 & 2 & \frac{4}{3} & 1 & \frac{4}{5} \\ 5 & \frac{5}{2} & \frac{5}{3} & \frac{5}{4} & 1 \end{pmatrix}.$$

(e)
$$\begin{pmatrix} 2 & 3 & 4 & 5 & 6 \\ 3 & 4 & 5 & 6 & 7 \\ 4 & 5 & 6 & 7 & 8 \\ 5 & 6 & 7 & 8 & 9 \\ 6 & 7 & 8 & 9 & 10 \end{pmatrix}.$$

(f)
$$\begin{pmatrix} 0 & 1 & 2 & 3 & 4 \\ 0 & 2 & 4 & 6 & 8 \\ 0 & 3 & 6 & 9 & 12 \\ 0 & 4 & 8 & 12 & 16 \\ 0 & 5 & 10 & 15 & 20 \end{pmatrix}.$$

(g)
$$\begin{pmatrix} 1 & 4 & 9 & 16 & 25 \\ 4 & 16 & 36 & 64 & 100 \\ 9 & 36 & 81 & 144 & 225 \\ 16 & 64 & 144 & 256 & 400 \\ 25 & 100 & 225 & 400 & 625 \end{pmatrix}$$

(h)
$$\begin{pmatrix} 5 & 6 & 7 & 8 & 9 \\ 6 & 7 & 8 & 9 & 10 \\ 7 & 8 & 9 & 10 & 11 \\ 8 & 9 & 10 & 11 & 12 \\ 9 & 10 & 11 & 12 & 13 \end{pmatrix}.$$

Exercise 6.4

(a)
$$\begin{pmatrix} 1 & 0 & 2 & 1 \\ 0 & 2 & 1 & 1 \\ 2 & 1 & 1 & 0 \end{pmatrix}.$$

(b)
$$\begin{pmatrix} 4 & 5 \\ 6 & 6 \\ 4 & 0 \end{pmatrix}.$$

(c) $(0 \ 0 \ 0)$.

(d)
$$\begin{pmatrix} 1 & 0 & 0 & -1 \\ 0 & 2 & -1 & 1 \\ 0 & -1 & 1 & 0 \end{pmatrix}.$$

(e)
$$\begin{pmatrix} 0 & 0 \\ 0 & 0 \end{pmatrix}.$$

(f) $(4 \ 4 \ 4)$.

(g) Undefined.

(h)
$$\begin{pmatrix} 1 \\ 2 \\ 1 \end{pmatrix}.$$

Exercise 6.5

1. (a) Both equal $\begin{pmatrix} 3 & 2 & 3 \\ 0 & 2 & -1 \end{pmatrix}$.

(b) Both equal $\begin{pmatrix} 2 & 2 & 4 \\ 0 & 1 & -1 \end{pmatrix}$.

2. (a) (1) $\begin{pmatrix} 2 & 4 & 6 \\ -2 & 0 & -2 \end{pmatrix}$.

(2) $\begin{pmatrix} 4 & 4 & 8 \\ 0 & 2 & -2 \end{pmatrix}$.

(3) $\begin{pmatrix} 4 & 4 & 8 \\ 0 & 2 & -2 \end{pmatrix}$.

(4) $\begin{pmatrix} 0 & 2 & 8 \\ 1 & -1 & -1 \end{pmatrix}$.

Exercise 6.6

1. (a) $\begin{pmatrix} -2 & 2 \\ 2 & -2 \\ 13 & -13 \end{pmatrix}$.

(b) $\begin{pmatrix} 0 & 0 \\ 0 & 0 \end{pmatrix}$.

(c) $\begin{pmatrix} 1 & 0 & 0 \\ 0 & 1 & 0 \\ 0 & 0 & 1 \end{pmatrix}$.

(d) $\begin{pmatrix} 1 & 1 & 1 \\ 1 & 1 & 1 \\ 1 & 1 & 1 \end{pmatrix}$.

(e) (14).

(f) Not defined.

(g) $\begin{pmatrix} c & d \\ 0 & 0 \end{pmatrix}$.

(h) $\begin{pmatrix} 1 & 0 & 0 & 0 \\ 2 & 1 & 0 & 0 \\ 3 & 2 & 1 & 0 \\ 4 & 3 & 2 & 1 \end{pmatrix}$.

(i) Not defined.

(j) $\begin{pmatrix} 0 & 0 \\ 0 & 0 \end{pmatrix}$.

(k) $\begin{pmatrix} a + 4b + c & 2a + 6b + c \\ d + 4e + f & 2d + 6e + f \end{pmatrix}$.

(l) $\begin{pmatrix} ae + bg & af + bh \\ ce + dg & cf + dh \end{pmatrix}$.

(m) $\begin{pmatrix} a_{11}b_{11} + a_{12}b_{21} & a_{11}b_{12} + a_{12}b_{22} \\ a_{21}b_{11} + a_{22}b_{21} & a_{21}b_{12} + a_{22}b_{22} \end{pmatrix}$.

2. (a) $\sum\limits_{k=1}^{3} a_{2k}b_{k3}$.

(b) $\sum\limits_{k=1}^{3} a_{1k}b_{k2}$.

(c) $\sum\limits_{k=1}^{3} b_{2k}a_{k3}$.

Exercise 6.7

1. $A \cdot B = \begin{pmatrix} -3 & 1 \\ -6 & 2 \end{pmatrix}$.

$A \cdot C = \begin{pmatrix} -3 & 1 \\ -6 & 2 \end{pmatrix}$.

$A \cdot B = A \cdot C \not\Rightarrow B = C$.

2. (a) $(k \cdot A) \cdot J = k \cdot A$ for any real number k.

(b) No. Consider $X = \begin{pmatrix} 0 & 3 & 0 \\ 0 & 0 & 0 \\ 0 & 0 & 0 \end{pmatrix}$, then $X \cdot J = \begin{pmatrix} -3 & -3 & -3 \\ 0 & 0 & 0 \\ 0 & 0 & 0 \end{pmatrix}$.

(c) No. $J \cdot A = \begin{pmatrix} 3 & 3 & 3 \\ -3 & -3 & -3 \\ 3 & 3 & 3 \end{pmatrix} = 3 \cdot J$.

(d) Yes. $J \cdot \begin{pmatrix} 0 & 0 & 0 \\ 0 & 0 & 0 \\ 0 & 0 & 0 \end{pmatrix} = \begin{pmatrix} 0 & 0 & 0 \\ 0 & 0 & 0 \\ 0 & 0 & 0 \end{pmatrix}$.

3. $I \cdot J = I$ by identity property of J.
$I \cdot J = J$ by identity property of I.
$\therefore I = J$.

4. (a) (1) Both equal. $\begin{pmatrix} 0 & 2 & 6 \\ 1 & 0 & -3 \\ 2 & 6 & 3 \end{pmatrix}$.

(2) Both equal. $\begin{pmatrix} 2 & 3 & 2 \\ 0 & 0 & 2 \\ 3 & 9 & 7 \end{pmatrix}$.

(b) (1) Both equal. $\begin{pmatrix} 0 & 0 \\ 0 & 0 \end{pmatrix}$.

(b) Both equal. $\begin{pmatrix} 0 & 0 \\ 0 & 0 \end{pmatrix}$.

Exercise 6.8

1. Consider
$$C^{-1}B^{-1}A^{-1} : (ABC)(C^{-1}B^{-1}A^{-1}) = (AB)I(B^{-1}A^{-1}) = ABB^{-1}A = AIA^{-1}$$
$$= AA^{-1} = I \Rightarrow (C^{-1}B^{-1}A^{-1}) = (ABC)^{-1}.$$

2. Consider $(BA)C = I_nC = C \Rightarrow C = B$
$$B(AC) = BI_n = B.$$

Exercise 6.9

1. (a) $\begin{pmatrix} 3 & 5 \\ -1 & -2 \end{pmatrix}.$ (b) Does not exist.

(c) $\begin{pmatrix} 5 & -\dfrac{1}{2} \\ 2 & \\ -\dfrac{13}{2} & \dfrac{3}{2} \end{pmatrix}.$ (d) $\begin{pmatrix} 0 & -1 \\ -1 & 0 \end{pmatrix}.$

2. (a) The inverse of A is C, or $A^{-1} = C$.

(b) $\begin{pmatrix} x \\ y \\ z \end{pmatrix} = \begin{pmatrix} 8 \\ -25 \\ 10 \end{pmatrix}.$

3. (a) The inverse of A is D, or $A^{-1} = D$.

(b) $\begin{pmatrix} x \\ y \\ z \end{pmatrix} = \begin{pmatrix} -2 \\ -1 \\ 7 \end{pmatrix}.$

4. $\begin{pmatrix} 2 & -1 & 1 & -1 \\ 1 & 0 & 1 & 1 \\ 3 & 3 & 0 & 0 \\ 0 & 1 & 0 & 1 \end{pmatrix} \begin{pmatrix} x \\ y \\ z \\ u \end{pmatrix} = \begin{pmatrix} 3 \\ 2 \\ 4 \\ -2 \end{pmatrix}.$

5. S is the matrix of coefficients for the system with rows interchanged. If S^{-1} existed then
$$\begin{pmatrix} x \\ y \\ z \end{pmatrix} = S^{-1} \begin{pmatrix} 2 \\ 0 \\ -4 \end{pmatrix}$$
but there is no solution to the system since the equations are inconsistent. That is, $x + y + z = 2$ and $x + y + z = -4$.

6. $\begin{pmatrix} x \\ y \\ z \end{pmatrix} = \begin{pmatrix} 2 \\ 3 \\ -2 \end{pmatrix}.$

Exercise 6.10

(a) (1)

	A	B	C	D	E	
	0	1	1	1	1	A
	1	0	0	0	0	B
	1	0	0	1	0	C
	1	0	1	0	1	D
	1	0	0	1	0	E

One-stage Routes

(2)

	A	B	C	D	E	
	4	0	1	2	1	A
	0	1	1	1	1	B
	1	1	2	1	2	C
	2	1	1	3	1	D
	1	1	2	1	2	E

Two-stage Routes

(3)
$$
\begin{array}{c}
\begin{array}{ccccc} \text{A} & \text{B} & \text{C} & \text{D} & \text{E} \end{array} \\
\left(\begin{array}{ccccc}
4 & 4 & 6 & 6 & 6 \\
4 & 0 & 1 & 2 & 1 \\
6 & 1 & 2 & 5 & 2 \\
6 & 2 & 5 & 4 & 5 \\
6 & 1 & 2 & 5 & 2
\end{array}\right)
\begin{array}{c} \text{A} \\ \text{B} \\ \text{C} \\ \text{D} \\ \text{E} \end{array}
\end{array}
$$
Three-stage Routes

(4)
$$
\begin{array}{c}
\begin{array}{ccccc} \text{A} & \text{B} & \text{C} & \text{D} & \text{E} \end{array} \\
\left(\begin{array}{ccccc}
4 & 1 & 2 & 3 & 2 \\
1 & 1 & 1 & 1 & 1 \\
2 & 1 & 2 & 2 & 2 \\
3 & 1 & 2 & 3 & 2 \\
2 & 1 & 2 & 2 & 2
\end{array}\right)
\begin{array}{c} \text{A} \\ \text{B} \\ \text{C} \\ \text{D} \\ \text{E} \end{array}
\end{array}
$$
One- or Two-stage Routes

(b) (1)
$$
\begin{array}{c}
\begin{array}{cccc} \text{A} & \text{B} & \text{C} & \text{D} \end{array} \\
\left(\begin{array}{cccc}
0 & 1 & 1 & 1 \\
1 & 0 & 1 & 0 \\
1 & 1 & 0 & 1 \\
1 & 0 & 1 & 0
\end{array}\right)
\begin{array}{c} \text{A} \\ \text{B} \\ \text{C} \\ \text{D} \end{array}
\end{array}
$$
One-stage Routes

(2)
$$
\begin{array}{c}
\begin{array}{cccc} \text{A} & \text{B} & \text{C} & \text{D} \end{array} \\
\left(\begin{array}{cccc}
3 & 1 & 2 & 1 \\
1 & 2 & 1 & 2 \\
2 & 1 & 3 & 1 \\
1 & 2 & 1 & 2
\end{array}\right)
\begin{array}{c} \text{A} \\ \text{B} \\ \text{C} \\ \text{D} \end{array}
\end{array}
$$
Two-stage Routes

(3)
$$
\begin{array}{c}
\begin{array}{cccc} \text{A} & \text{B} & \text{C} & \text{D} \end{array} \\
\left(\begin{array}{cccc}
4 & 5 & 5 & 5 \\
5 & 2 & 5 & 2 \\
5 & 5 & 4 & 5 \\
5 & 2 & 5 & 2
\end{array}\right)
\begin{array}{c} \text{A} \\ \text{B} \\ \text{C} \\ \text{D} \end{array}
\end{array}
$$
Three-stage Routes

(4)
$$
\begin{array}{c}
\begin{array}{cccc} \text{A} & \text{B} & \text{C} & \text{D} \end{array} \\
\left(\begin{array}{cccc}
3 & 2 & 3 & 2 \\
2 & 2 & 2 & 2 \\
3 & 2 & 3 & 2 \\
2 & 2 & 2 & 2
\end{array}\right)
\begin{array}{c} \text{A} \\ \text{B} \\ \text{C} \\ \text{D} \end{array}
\end{array}
$$
One- or Two-stage Routes

(c) (1)
$$
\begin{array}{c}
\begin{array}{cccc} \text{A} & \text{B} & \text{C} & \text{D} \end{array} \\
\left(\begin{array}{cccc}
0 & 1 & 1 & 1 \\
1 & 0 & 1 & 3 \\
1 & 1 & 0 & 2 \\
1 & 3 & 2 & 0
\end{array}\right)
\begin{array}{c} \text{A} \\ \text{B} \\ \text{C} \\ \text{D} \end{array}
\end{array}
$$
One-stage Routes

(2)
$$
\begin{array}{c}
\begin{array}{cccc} \text{A} & \text{B} & \text{C} & \text{D} \end{array} \\
\left(\begin{array}{cccc}
3 & 4 & 3 & 5 \\
4 & 11 & 7 & 3 \\
3 & 7 & 6 & 4 \\
5 & 3 & 4 & 14
\end{array}\right)
\begin{array}{c} \text{A} \\ \text{B} \\ \text{C} \\ \text{D} \end{array}
\end{array}
$$
Two-stage Routes

(3)
$$
\begin{array}{c}
\begin{array}{cccc} \text{A} & \text{B} & \text{C} & \text{D} \end{array} \\
\left(\begin{array}{cccc}
12 & 21 & 17 & 21 \\
21 & 20 & 21 & 51 \\
17 & 21 & 18 & 36 \\
21 & 51 & 36 & 22
\end{array}\right)
\begin{array}{c} \text{A} \\ \text{B} \\ \text{C} \\ \text{D} \end{array}
\end{array}
$$
Three-stage Routes

(4)
$$
\begin{array}{c}
\begin{array}{cccc} \text{A} & \text{B} & \text{C} & \text{D} \end{array} \\
\left(\begin{array}{cccc}
3 & 5 & 4 & 6 \\
5 & 11 & 8 & 6 \\
4 & 8 & 6 & 6 \\
6 & 6 & 6 & 14
\end{array}\right)
\begin{array}{c} \text{A} \\ \text{B} \\ \text{C} \\ \text{D} \end{array}
\end{array}
$$
One- or Two-stage Routes

Exercise 6.11

1. (a) $a[k(x_1, y_1) + m(x_2, y_2)] = [k(x_1, y_1) + m(x_2, y_2)] \cdot A$
   $= [(kx_1, ky_1) + (mx_2, my_2)] \cdot A = (kx_1 + mx_2, ky_1 + my_2) \cdot A$
   $= (kx_1 + mx_2, ky_1 + my_2)\begin{pmatrix} 0 & 1 \\ 1 & 0 \end{pmatrix} = (ky_1 + my_2, kx_1 + mx_2)$
   $= (ky_1, kx_1) + (my_2, mx_2) = (kx_1, ky_1) \cdot A + (mx_2, my_2) \cdot A$
   $= k(x_1, y_1) \cdot A + m(x_2, y_2) \cdot A = ka(x_1, y_1) + ma(x_2, y_2).$

   (b) This function reflects the point (x_a, y_a) about the line $x = y$.

Exercise 6.12

(a) (1) $[a] = \begin{pmatrix} 1 & 0 \\ 0 & 1 \end{pmatrix}.$ (2) $(2, 0).$

(3) $(-2, 0).$ (4) $(7, 0).$

(b) (1) $[a] = \begin{pmatrix} 1 & -1 \\ 0 & 0 \end{pmatrix}.$ (2) $(2, -2).$

(3) $(-2, 2).$ (4) $(7, -7).$

(c) (1) $[a] = \begin{pmatrix} 1 & 2 \\ 0 & 0 \end{pmatrix}.$ (2) $(2, 8).$

(3) $(-2, -4).$ (4) $(7, 14).$

(d) (1) $[a] = \begin{pmatrix} \dfrac{\sqrt{2}}{2} & -\dfrac{\sqrt{2}}{2} \\ \dfrac{\sqrt{2}}{2} & \dfrac{\sqrt{2}}{2} \end{pmatrix}.$ (2) $(3\sqrt{2}, \sqrt{2}).$

(3) $\left(\dfrac{\sqrt{2}}{2}, \dfrac{5\sqrt{2}}{2}\right)$ (4) $(\sqrt{2}, -6\sqrt{2}).$

(e) (1) $[a] = \begin{pmatrix} \dfrac{3}{2} & 0 \\ 0 & \dfrac{3}{2} \end{pmatrix}.$ (2) $(3, 6).$

(3) $\left(-3, \dfrac{9}{2}\right).$ (4) $\left(\dfrac{21}{2}, \dfrac{-15}{2}\right).$

Exercise 6.13

1. (a) $a \cdot b$ projects all points into the y axis.

(b) $[a] = \begin{pmatrix} 0 & 0 & 0 \\ 0 & 1 & 0 \\ 0 & 0 & 1 \end{pmatrix}.$ $[b] = \begin{pmatrix} 1 & 0 & 0 \\ 0 & 1 & 0 \\ 0 & 0 & 0 \end{pmatrix}.$

$[a \cdot b] = \begin{pmatrix} 0 & 0 & 0 \\ 0 & 1 & 0 \\ 0 & 0 & 0 \end{pmatrix}.$

2. (a) $[a] = \begin{pmatrix} 0 & 1 \\ 1 & 0 \end{pmatrix}.$ $[b] = \begin{pmatrix} 2 & 0 \\ 0 & 2 \end{pmatrix}.$

(b) $[a \cdot b] = \begin{pmatrix} 0 & 2 \\ 2 & 0 \end{pmatrix}.$

3. (a) $[a] = \begin{pmatrix} 0 & 1 \\ 1 & 0 \end{pmatrix}.$ $[b] = \begin{pmatrix} -1 & 0 \\ 0 & -1 \end{pmatrix}.$

$[a \cdot b] = \begin{pmatrix} 0 & -1 \\ -1 & 0 \end{pmatrix}.$

Exercise 6.14

(a) 0. (b) 2. (c) 0. (d) 0. (e) 2. (f) 1. (g) −1. (h) −2.

Exercise 6.15

1. (b) $\begin{pmatrix} 1 & -1 \\ 0 & 1 \end{pmatrix}.$ (b) $\begin{pmatrix} \dfrac{1}{3} & \dfrac{2}{3} \\ \dfrac{1}{3} & -\dfrac{1}{3} \end{pmatrix}.$ (c) $\begin{pmatrix} 0 & 0 & 1 \\ 1 & 0 & -1 \\ -1 & 1 & 1 \end{pmatrix}.$

(d) Does not exist.

(e) $\begin{pmatrix} 1 & -1 & 0 & 0 \\ 0 & 1 & -1 & 0 \\ 0 & 0 & 1 & -1 \\ 0 & 0 & 0 & 1 \end{pmatrix}.$

2. (a) $\begin{pmatrix} x \\ y \end{pmatrix} = \begin{pmatrix} \frac{3}{2} \\ \frac{1}{2} \end{pmatrix}.$

(b) $\begin{pmatrix} x \\ y \\ z \end{pmatrix} = \begin{pmatrix} \frac{1}{2} \\ 3 \\ 2 \\ -1 \end{pmatrix}.$

(c) $\begin{pmatrix} x \\ y \\ z \end{pmatrix} = \begin{pmatrix} 0 \\ 0 \\ 1 \end{pmatrix}.$

(d) $\begin{pmatrix} x \\ y \\ z \\ w \end{pmatrix} = \begin{pmatrix} -2 \\ 2 \\ -\frac{1}{2} \\ 1 \\ \frac{1}{2} \end{pmatrix}.$

Chapter 7

Exercise 7.2

1. $\dfrac{\pi}{6}$; $\dfrac{5\pi}{6}$; $\dfrac{4\pi}{3}$; $\dfrac{3\pi}{2}$; 3π; $-\dfrac{\pi}{4}$; $-\pi$.

2. $\left(\dfrac{360}{\pi}\right)^{\circ}$; $\left(\dfrac{-630}{\pi}\right)^{\circ}$; $120°$; $-225°$; $1{,}620°$; $41{,}580°$; $90°$.

3. See Table 7.2.

Exercise 7.4

1. $5\pi = \pi + 2\cdot 2\pi,\ -6\pi = 0 + (-3)\cdot 2\pi,\ -\dfrac{98}{3}\pi = \dfrac{4\pi}{3} + (-17)\cdot 2\pi,$

$-\dfrac{8\pi}{3} = \dfrac{4\pi}{3} + (-2)\cdot 2\pi,\ -\dfrac{72}{11}\pi = \dfrac{16}{11}\pi + (2)\cdot 2\pi,$

$-\dfrac{221}{2}\pi = \dfrac{3\pi}{2} + (-56)\cdot 2\pi.$

2. $790 = 70 + (2)(360),\qquad 361 = 1 + (1)(360).$
   $-2 = 358 + (-1)(360),\qquad 10{,}001 = 281 + (27)(360).$
   $-926 = 154 + (-3)(360),\qquad 729 = 9 + (2)(360).$

Exercise 7.5

3. $\sin\left(-\dfrac{\pi}{6}\right) = -\dfrac{1}{2}$, $\sin x \neq 3$, $\tan\left(-\dfrac{\pi}{4}\right) = -1.$

$\csc\left(-\dfrac{\pi}{6}\right) = -2$, $\cot\dfrac{\pi}{6} = \sqrt{3}$, $\tan\left(-\dfrac{\pi}{3}\right) = \sqrt{3}.$

$\sin\dfrac{\pi}{4} = \dfrac{\sqrt{2}}{2}$, $\sin\left(-\dfrac{\pi}{4}\right) = -\dfrac{\sqrt{2}}{2}$, $\csc x \neq -\dfrac{1}{2}.$

Exercise 7.8

1. (a) $\cos 75° = \dfrac{\sqrt{2}}{4}(\sqrt{3} - 1)$.   (b) $\tan 15° = 2 - \sqrt{3}$.

   (c) $\sec 165° = \sqrt{2}(\sqrt{3} - 1)$.   (g) $\cos 195° = -\dfrac{\sqrt{2}}{4}(\sqrt{3} + 1)$.

Exercise 7.11

2. (a) $-\dfrac{\pi}{2}$.   (c) $-\dfrac{\pi}{4}$.   (e) $\dfrac{\pi}{4}$.   (g) 0.   (i) $\dfrac{1}{\sqrt{3}}$.   (k) 1.   (m) $\dfrac{\pi}{6}$.

   (o) $\dfrac{\sqrt{2}}{2}$.   (q) $\dfrac{1}{x}$.

Exercise 7.12

   (a) $\dfrac{\pi}{4}, \dfrac{3\pi}{4}$.   (c) $270°$.   (e) $30°, 60°, 210°, 240°$.

   (g) $0, \pi$.   (i) $120°, 240°$.   (k) $0, \pi, \dfrac{2\pi}{3}, \dfrac{5\pi}{3}$.

Exercise 7.13

	A	B	a	b	c
(a)	30°	60°	10	$10\sqrt{3}$	20.
(c)	45°	45°	5	5	$5\sqrt{2}$.
(e)	15°	75°	2	7.48	7.74.
(g)	46°	44°	15	15.5	21.6.
(i)	33°40′	56°20′	2	3	$\sqrt{13}$.

Chapter 8

Exercise 8.1

1. (b) $S = \{x \mid x \in J\}$.   (c) (1) $S = \{x \mid x \in J \text{ and } 4 \le x \le 9\}$.
   (2) $S = \{x \mid x \in J \text{ and } x \ge 7\}$.   (3) $S = \{x \mid x \in J \text{ and } x \ge 10\}$.
3. $S = \{(x, y) \mid -1 < x < 1 \quad \text{and} \quad -1 < y < 1\}$.
4. (a) 5.   (b) $\sqrt{13}$.   (c) 5.   (d) $\sqrt{21}$.   (e) $\sqrt{7}$.
   (In 5, 6, all $x_i, y_i \in R^1$)
5. $S = \{(x_1, x_2, \ldots x_n) \mid \displaystyle\sum_{i=1}^{n} (z_i - x_i)^2 < r^2\}$.
6. (a) $S_1(0) = \{x \mid x \in (-1, 1)\}$.   (b) $S_2(0) = \{x \mid x \in (-2, 2)\}$.
   (c) $S_{1/2}(-1) = \left\{x \mid x \in \left(-\dfrac{3}{2}, -\dfrac{1}{2}\right)\right\}$.   (d) $S_2(3) = \{x \mid x \in (1, 5)\}$.
   (e) $S_1(0, 0) = \{(x, y) \mid x^2 + y^2 < 1\}$.
   (f) $S_2(0, 0) = \{(x, y) \mid x^2 + y^2 < 4\}$.

(g) $S_{1/2}\left(\dfrac{1}{2},\dfrac{1}{2}\right) = \left\{(x, y) \mid \left(x - \dfrac{1}{2}\right)^2 + \left(y - \dfrac{1}{2}\right)^2 < \dfrac{1}{4}\right\}.$

(h) $S_r(x_0, y_0) = \{(x, y) \mid (x - x_0)^2 + (y - y_0)^2 < r^2\}.$

(i) $S_1(1, 0, 1, 2) = \{(x_1, x_2, x_3, x_4) \mid (x_1 - 1)^2 + x_2^2$
$$+ (x_3 - 1)^2 + (x_4 - 2)^2 < 1\}.$$

(j) $S_r(a_1, a_2, \ldots a_n) = \{(x_1, x_2, \ldots x_n) \mid \sum_{i=1}^{n} (x_i - a_i)^2 < r^2\}.$

Exercise 8.3

1. (a) $\left\{\dfrac{1}{2}, \dfrac{1}{4}, \dfrac{1}{6}, \dfrac{1}{8}, \dfrac{1}{10}, \ldots\right\}.$ (b) $\left\{\dfrac{1}{2}, \dfrac{1}{4}, \dfrac{1}{9}, \dfrac{1}{16}, \dfrac{1}{25}, \ldots\right\}.$

(c) $\left\{-\dfrac{1}{2}, \dfrac{1}{3}, -\dfrac{1}{4}, \dfrac{1}{5}, -\dfrac{1}{6}, \ldots\right\}.$ (d) $\left\{\dfrac{3}{1}, \dfrac{4}{4}, \dfrac{5}{9}, \dfrac{6}{16}, \dfrac{7}{25}, \ldots\right\}.$

(e) $\left\{\dfrac{4}{4}, \dfrac{9}{25}, \dfrac{16}{100}, \dfrac{25}{289}, \dfrac{36}{676}, \ldots\right\}.$

Exercise 8.5

1. (a) 1. (b) $\dfrac{1}{3}.$ (c) 8. (d) 1. (e) 6. (f) 0. (i) $\dfrac{5}{3}.$ (j) $\dfrac{1}{2}.$ (k) 0.

(m) 2. (n) $\dfrac{1}{2}.$

2. (a) $2x.$ (b) $4x + 3.$ (c) $3x^2 - 1.$ (d) $-\dfrac{1}{x^2}.$

(e) $1 - \dfrac{1}{x^2}.$ (f) $\dfrac{1}{2\sqrt{x+1}}.$

Exercise 8.6

(a) Discontinuous. (b) Discontinuous. (c) Continuous.
(d) Discontinuous. (e) Continuous. (f) Continuous.
(g) Continuous. (h) Discontinuous (undefined at $x = 0$).
(i) Discontinuous (undefined at $x = \pm 1, 2$). (j) Discontinuous (undefined at $x = 1$).

Chapter 9

Exercise 9.1

1. (a) $-2.$ (b) $\dfrac{1}{2}.$ (c) $2x + 1.$ (d) $-\dfrac{1}{x^2}.$ (e) 1.

(f) 3. (g) $3x^2.$ (h) $-\dfrac{2}{x^3}.$ (i) $1 - \dfrac{1}{x^2}.$ (j) $-\dfrac{1}{2x\sqrt{x}}.$

2. (a) $y = -2x + 1$. (b) $y = \dfrac{1}{2x} + \dfrac{1}{2}$. (c) $y = 7x - 9$.

(d) $y = -\dfrac{1}{9x} + \dfrac{2}{3}$. (e) $y = x + 1$. (f) $y = 3x$.

(g) $y = 27x - 54$. (h) $y = -\dfrac{2}{27}x + \dfrac{1}{3}$. (i) $y = \dfrac{8}{9x} + \dfrac{2}{3}$.

(j) $y = \dfrac{-\sqrt{3}}{18}x + \dfrac{\sqrt{3}}{2}$.

3. (1) $x = 1$. (2) $x = \pm 2$. (3) Does not exist.

Exercise 9.2

1. (a) $x > 0 \Rightarrow f'(x) > 0$,
$x < 0 \Rightarrow f'(x) < 0$,
$x = 0 \Rightarrow f'(x) = 0$.

(b) $x \in (\leftarrow, -1)$ or $x \in (1, \rightarrow) \Rightarrow f'(x) > 0$,
$x \in (-1, 0)$ or $x \in (0, 1) \Rightarrow f'(x) < 0$,
$x \in \{1, -1\} \Rightarrow f'(x) = 0$. Undefined for $x = 0$.

(c) $x \in \left(-\dfrac{\sqrt{2}}{2}, 0\right)$ or $x \in \left(\dfrac{\sqrt{2}}{2}, \rightarrow\right) \Rightarrow f'(x) > 0$,

$x \in \left(\leftarrow, \dfrac{-\sqrt{2}}{2}\right)$ or $x \in \left(0, \dfrac{\sqrt{2}}{2}\right) \Rightarrow f'(x) < 0$,

$x \in \left\{\dfrac{-\sqrt{2}}{2}, 0, \dfrac{\sqrt{2}}{2}\right\} \Rightarrow f'(x) = 0$.

(d) $f'(x) > 0$ for all $x \in R^1$.

(e) $f'(x) < 0$ for all $x \in R'$ where $x \neq 0$. Undefined for $x = 0$.

(f) $x \in \left(\dfrac{3}{2}, \rightarrow\right) \Rightarrow f'(x) > 0$.

$x \in \left(\leftarrow, \dfrac{3}{2}\right) \Rightarrow f'(x) < 0$.

$x = \dfrac{3}{2} \Rightarrow f'(x) = 0$.

(g) $x \in (\leftarrow, 0) \Rightarrow f'(x) > 0$,
$x \in (0, \rightarrow) \Rightarrow f'(x) < 0$. Undefined for $x = 0$.

(h) $x \in (0, \rightarrow) \Rightarrow f'(x) > 0$
$x \in (\leftarrow, 0) \Rightarrow f'(x) < 0$. Undefined for $x = 0$.

(i) $x \in (0, \rightarrow) \Rightarrow f'(x) > 0$
$x \in (\leftarrow, 0) \Rightarrow f'(x) < 0$. Undefined for $x = 0$.

(j) $x \in (0, \rightarrow) \Rightarrow f'(x) > 0$
$x \in (\leftarrow, 0) \Rightarrow f'(x) < 0$. Undefined for $x = 0$.

2. 15×15.

3. $20 \times 20 \times 20$.

4. $8, 8$.

5. $\dfrac{16}{3}$, $V = 151 \dfrac{19}{27}$ cubic units.

6. $3 \sqrt{3} \times 6 \sqrt{3} \times 4 \sqrt{3}$.

Exercise 9.3

1. (a.1) $S_0 = -1$.   (b.1) $S_0 = -1$.   (c.1) $S_0 = 32$.
   (a.2) $S_3 = 2$.   (b.2) $S_3 = 8$.   (c.2) $S_3 = 23$.
   (a.3) $V_0 = 1$.   (b.3) $V_0 = 0$.   (c.3) $V_0 = 0$.
   (a.4) $V_2 = 1$.   (b.4) $V_2 = 4$.   (c.4) $V_2 = -4$.
   (a.5) $V_4 = 1$.   (b.5) $V_4 = 8$.   (c.5) $V_4 = -8$.
   (d.1) $S_0 = 1$.   (e.1) $S_0 = 0$.   (f.1) $S_0 = 0$.

   (d.2) $S_3 = 4$.   (e.2) $S_3 = 24$.   (f.2) $S_3 = \dfrac{3}{10}$.

   (d.3) $V_0 = -2$.   (e.3) $V_0 = -1$.   (f.3) $V_0 = 1$.

   (d.4) $V_2 = 2$.   (e.4) $V_2 = 11$.   (f.4) $V_2 = -\dfrac{3}{25}$.

   (d.5) $V_4 = 6$.   (e.5) $V_4 = 47$.   (f.5) $V_4 = \dfrac{17}{289} = -\dfrac{1}{17}$.

2. (a) $\dfrac{20 + 5 \sqrt{21}}{2}$ sec after thrown.

   (b) 320 ft/sec. (c) $-80 \sqrt{21}$ ft/sec. (d) After 10 sec. (e) 2100 ft.

3. (a) After 18 sec. (b) $V_0 = 288$ ft/sec.
   (c) $V_{18} = -288$ ft/sec. (d) After 9 sec.
   (e) 1296 ft.

4. (a) After $\dfrac{16 + \sqrt{381}}{2}$ sec. (b) $V_0 = 256$ ft/sec.

   (c) $-16 \sqrt{381}$ ft/sec. (d) After 8 sec. (e) 1524 ft.

Exercise 9.4

1. (a) 1. (b) 1. (c) 11.2338. (d) $\dfrac{ma^2}{2}$.

2. $\dfrac{1}{3}$.

3. (a) $\dfrac{3}{2}$. (b) $\dfrac{4}{3}$. (c) 2. (d) $\dfrac{2}{3}$.

Index

Index
of Symbols